To D

wit

Noel

Jan '98

YOUNG MEN AT WAR

NOEL CURRER-BRIGGS

YOUNG MEN AT WAR

THE GAY MEN'S PRESS

First published 1996 by GMP Publishers Ltd,
P O Box 247, Swaffham, Norfolk PE37 8PA, England

British Library Cataloguing in Publication Data
        Currer-Briggs, Noel
        Young men at war
        1. English fiction — 20th century
        I. Title
        823.9'14[F]
        ISBN 0 85449 236 4

Distributed in Europe by Central Books,
99 Wallis Rd, London E9 5LN

Distributed in North America by InBook/LPC Group,
1436 West Randolph Street, Chicago, IL 60607

Distributed in Australia by Bulldog Books,
P O Box 300, Beaconsfield, NSW 2014

Printed and bound in the EU by The Cromwell Press,
Melksham, Wilts, England

In Memoriam P. A. L.

Ask me no more, for fear I should reply;
Others have held their tongues, and so can I:
Hundreds have died, and told no tale before:
Ask me no more, for fear I should reply —

How one was true and one was clean of stain
And one was braver than the heavens are high,
And one was fond of me: and all are slain.
Ask me no more, for fear I should reply.

A. E. Housman

Author's Note

This book is not, strictly, an autobiography, for I have taken a novelist's liberty with persons, places, institutions and the wartime events in Périgord. Only three or four of the characters are entirely fictitious; on the other hand none attempts to be a truthful portrait. The narrator himself, like the rest, is a composite character. At the same time, certain historical persons play small parts in the story, and their actions and motives have been recorded as accurately as possible. Finally, I owe a debt of gratitude to the late Robert Musil, whose work went some way to inspire me to write this story.

Dedicatory Letter

Dear Tim,

You were only eighteen when you came to live with Peter and me in 1975. I recall how often we used to sit over Peter's excellent dinners with a bottle or two of wine, when one or other of you would ask me what it was like to be gay in the '30s and '40s. Although I was then well into middle age, and had lived with Peter for eight years, I didn't feel old, though I suppose I seemed old to both of you, who were young enough respectively to have been my son and grandson. Those three years were such fun; there was something flattering at that period of my life to live in the company of two men so much younger than I was. But I do not recall that you were tactless enough to ask, 'What did you do in the war, grandad?' though the war must seem as remote to you as the Battle of Waterloo does to me.

I never did tell you everything about myself — few people ever do tell *everything*. Although I mentioned Manfred von Schrade, Michel Loreau and Jack Cuttlance (who died the year before I met Peter) from time to time, I have never told you the full story of my relationship with them. Peter would have been jealous of Manfred; he would have distrusted Michel and disliked Jack, because Peter saw his role in life as my guardian, though it was Jack who brought me out of the closet and was a father-figure to me for many years, until I, in turn, became a father-figure to Peter.

But I have outlived Manfred, Michel, Jack and Peter. War, age and Aids have taken their toll, leaving me to get along as best I can, to grieve their loss. You alone survive, so I want to tell you how it was with the four of us. In their different ways, Manfred, Michel and Jack were three of the bravest men I ever met. Historians cannot write an account of the tragedy of 1939-1945, or draw a true picture of France and Germany, without listening to the confidences of those who gave their lives for their country.

I met Manfred and Michel when we were all about sixteen,

and Jack when I was twenty-one and he was forty. In order that you may fully understand my relationship with them, I must take you back to the very beginning, for until you know how our paths crossed — Manfred a German, Michel a Frenchman, and I an Englishman — three years before the outbreak of the war, you won't be able fully to grasp why we acted as we did.

You must also understand that by today's standards we were as green as grass — at least Manfred and I were. Michel, being French, was more streetwise, as we'd say today, than either of us, and Jack had lived with Stanley, his lover, for more than twenty years when we first met in 1940, at a time when they risked prison if the true nature of their relationship had been discovered. We were also romantic idealists, which most young men still are. We saw how much was wrong with the world, and we thought we knew how to make it better. I'm not sure whether we were successful or not.

I am not going to preach; I shall just tell you how we came to do what we did without seeking praise or blame. Today's problems are so different from those we had to face, but thanks to the tv we are able to see over our national boundary fences into the gardens of our neighbours, so it won't be easy for a Hitler or a Stalin to hoodwink you quite as well as they hoodwinked us. The war in which we fought did not end in 1945. Those of us who survived had to wait till 1989 when Russia and East Germany shook themselves free of communism. So we are today at the beginning of a new era. I hope it will be a more tolerant age than the one that is now dying.

With love from
Noel

Prologue

I became very fond of the Salisbury. In those days it was crammed with servicemen on leave in London in addition to its usual clientele. Jack Cuttlance had taken me there soon after I'd finished my basic training in the autumn of 1941. 'I've been coming here for years,' he'd told me, but he hadn't added that it was then the best-known gay bar in town. He probably thought that if he took me there, I'd soon enough discover this for myself, but on that first occasion I think I admired the engraved, Victorian glass as much as the clientele, which struck me as friendly, but not more friendly than that of any other pub. On this occasion, as on the previous one, I was in the uniform of a private in the Queen's Infantry Regiment, so it wasn't in any way extraordinary to be offered a drink by a stranger. The man who offered me one now was middle-aged, probably a clerk or junior civil servant, pleasant enough, with a warm, open smile. He was standing a few feet away from me at the bar, while I was trying to catch the eye of the overworked barman. I'd been waiting a couple of minutes when I turned in his direction, looking towards the door, expecting Jack's arrival, and as I did, I saw him smile and beckon me towards a pint of beer on the bar in front of him.

'Have this one,' he said. 'Have it on me.'

'That's very kind of you,' I replied, 'but I'm expecting a friend any minute.'

A shadow crossed the man's face — disappointment? resentment? annoyance? It was hard to say. He shrugged and said: 'On leave?'

'Sort of. Between postings.'

Perhaps it was my public-school accent that surprised him, but I couldn't think why it should. There were, after all, plenty of public-school Other Ranks about then. Yet there was no doubt about the subtle change in his attitude. I took a sip of the beer he'd bought me, not quite knowing how to move away without seeming rude or

9

hurting his feelings, for just at that moment the blackout curtains in front of the door parted and Jack came in, blinking in the bright lights after the darkness outside.

'My friend's just come in,' I said to the man, 'I must go and join him. Sorry I can't stay. Thanks so much for the drink.'

I smiled and held out my hand: 'It was kind of you.'

He seemed surprised by such formality, but smiled back. 'Sorry about that. I'd've liked to get to know you better,' he said. 'Maybe I'll see you here again one day while you're in town.'

'I'll buy you a drink next time,' I said. 'Cheers.'

I went over to Jack, who had been watching this little exchange with an amused expression on his handsome face. He was dressed in the uniform of a major in a smart infantry regiment: 'Who's your friend?' he asked.

'No idea. He just bought me a drink, that's all. What can I get you?'

'Gin and It if they have any; if not, a pint of bitter.'

'I'll see what I can do,' I said.

Jack made his way towards the back of the bar, where there were a couple of empty places on the curved sofa-benches that lined the wall beneath the elaborately cut-glass mirrors.

'I'll bag that table,' he said. 'We'll be able to talk there out of the way of people.'

This time I caught the barman's eye, ordered another pint for myself, and a gin and Italian for Jack. Astonishingly they were still able to find some Vermouth here. I took the drinks over, and sat down on the bench next to Jack.

'So what's this all about?' I asked as soon as I was settled. 'I want to hear all about your new job, and about Stanley, and about IVAC, and everything.'

Jack smiled and put his hand on my leg. 'Steady on; a bit at a time. I can only stay a few minutes, but I wanted to see you tonight to find out how *you've* got on since you joined up. I may have a job that would interest you. Let's talk about that.'

'Would I be working with you?' I asked.

'Only up to a point. I'm recruiting officer for a new organisa-tion that's just been set up. It's a crazy sort of outfit; the kind of thing Randolph Rassendyll might have gone in for. It seems a bit odd at the moment, but I'm sure it'll turn out to be eminently sen-sible in the long run.'

'Okay. Tell me about it.'

'Not here. I'm on my way home; are you free for dinner? If so, come back now and I'll tell you there.'

'I've got to catch the night train to Wraysby,' I said. 'It doesn't leave till after eleven, so I think I've got time.'

'Oh, plenty. I'll order a taxi for ten-fifteen. That should give you enough time provided there isn't an air raid. If there is, you'll have to walk; that'll take longer. I see you've got your tin hat with you, so you'll be okay.

Half an hour later, when we sat down to our meal, Jack began. 'The Outfit's a bit like a club. Membership is by invitation only: it's not what you know, but whom you know that matters. We've not got a regular recruiting system, though there's enough of one to prevent people from inviting themselves to join and simply walking in. At home,' he went on, 'every potential member gets carefully vetted. We've got to prevent enemy penetration. A fair number of us, I dare say, are neurotic, or've been crossed in love — much the same thing, I suppose — but we try to avoid taking people like that if we can, because what we need are level heads and steady nerves.'

He looked at me with a penetrating eye as if to determine which of these characteristics I might possess.

'Swift, intelligent, brutal types who make good saboteurs,' he continued, 'are seldom patient, careful or methodical enough to undertake the grinding job of organising and training an underground resistance circuit, and not at all suited for the dull and dangerous work of a wireless operator in the field. The people we need at home are different again. We want people who can produce in three days a virtually indistinguishable copy of a document part printed and part written, after having manufactured and water-marked the paper to do it on, and cutting the type to print it with. We need people who can design and make portable explosive charges with silent time-fuses capable of destroying any given piece of industrial equipment. We need people who can invent ciphers that are for all practical purposes unbreakable, or who can make sense of messages from frightened agents, who've done their enciphering badly and in a hurry. And what's more,' he added as an afterthought, 'we want people who can do this without endangering the agent any more by asking him to repeat his message. These are not the sort of jobs we can advertise in the Situations Vacant columns of *The Times*, are they?'

'Hardly,' I said laughing. 'So where do I come in?'

'You're not unintelligent,' he replied with a smile; 'you think for yourself. You speak good French and German; you have an enquiring mind; I think you are capable of taking risks without being foolhardy. I hesitate to tell you you're brave, for that's something only time and circumstances will tell, but you reacted well to that emergency last winter when we were in IVAC. We'll know better how to use you when you've been through the course.'

He went on to tell me that the work I would be doing, if they accepted me, would be extremely secret, and on no account must I tell anyone about it. This wouldn't be difficult, since my family and friends already knew that although I had been doing my basic training in the Queen's Regiment, I'd been accepted by the Intelligence Corps, so they assumed that whatever it might be, my work was bound to be very hush-hush.

'You'll be called to the Students' Assessment Board if you get through the first interview. It lasts several days, and you'll be subject to a lot of psychological tests,' Jack went on. 'They'll ask you a lot about your family, your education, your motivation and your private life. They'll be particularly interested to find out why, having registered as a conscientious objector, you have now decided to join up. If you pass the SAB, you'll be put through a stiff paramilitary course lasting about five weeks, where they'll teach you "silent killing".'

'What's that?' I asked in some alarm, which I hoped my expression didn't betray.

'It's the most savage form of unarmed combat. It consists of knife work, rope work, boat work, pistol and submachine-gun training in British and enemy weapons, plus field craft, some map and paper work, elementary morse, and advanced raiding tactics. You'll probably be taught how to poach salmon and game, how to break safes and pick locks as well,' he said laughing. 'And you'll get plenty of practice with explosives. In fact when they've done with you, you'll probably be able to live the rest of your life from crime, I wouldn't wonder!'

I laughed. 'Sounds a very useful course, I must say.'

'If you get on okay,' Jack continued 'you'll be trained in parachute jumping. They'll give you four or five daytime drops, and at least one nighttime one. After that, *if* you survive,' he grinned, 'you'll be taught the elements of clandestine techniques and security.'

'How d'you mean?'

'They'll teach you how to look natural and ordinary while doing unnatural and extraordinary things.'

'Such as?' I queried.

12

'Such as how to spot when you're being followed; when to change your address; how to conceal your personality. They'll put you through a gruelling interrogation, and it won't seem all that "mock" either, I can assure you. You'll be surprised by how much they'll know about you,' he warned, 'so don't lie to them. They'll know if you're telling the truth or not. It's here that you'll be trained in coding and ciphering, and on German armed forces, particularly their counter-espionage services. At the end of the course, you'll be put through a four-day scheme, which'll include reconnaissance of a target, contact by pre-arranged password with other agents, and how to secure explosives and take them to such targets. Once there, you'll be required to lay them on the target, and throughout you'll be carefully watched, often by people you don't know and have never met. They may include pretty girls who will try to seduce you to see whether you're boastful or conceited, or just a plain chatterbox. You may even be arrested by the police and grilled.'

'On what grounds?'

'Oh, they'll think of something. But don't do anything silly; you won't know whether your arrest is genuine or just part of the scheme. Not until afterwards, at any rate,' he added. 'Either way, you may find yourself in prison,' he laughed, 'but the point to remember is that you must have your cover story pat. Oh! and another thing — you'll learn how to run a reception committee, and I don't mean a vicarage tea-party.

'No!' he went on more seriously, 'The whole course is aimed to make you think aggressively and securely. Security, you will find, is an attitude of mind, and most of us have to be taught it. I can guarantee that at the end of the course you'll feel more self-reliant than you do now, and I hope it'll teach you patience. It's asking a lot of you, and the course is all too short, but time isn't on our side. If you pass, you'll have achieved a lot. If you don't pass, you'll still have learnt a lot that'll stand you in good stead later on, so don't think you're a failure if you don't get through. If they don't think you'll be suitable for the job, you can rest assured we'll find something else more fitted to your talents and abilities. So good luck.'

The doorbell rang. 'That'll be the taxi,' said Jack. 'I'll come down with you. It's been great seeing you again. I'll be in touch. Where will you be during the next ten days?'

'I'm going to my father's tonight, and I'll be there about five days, and then to my mother's till my posting comes through.'

I tore a sheet of paper from the back of my diary, scribbled two phone numbers on it and handed it to Jack.

'Here, take this. I can be contacted on either number. I'll hope to hear from you again very soon.'

'You will if they decide to call you for an interview, but I'm guaranteeing nothing.'

He led the way downstairs, and we parted on the pavement.

'King's Cross, please,' I told the taxi driver. I leant out of the cab window and waved to Jack. He smiled and blew me a kiss. Laughing, I shouted 'Goodbye.'

It was early in December 1941, shortly after my twenty-second birthday.

I had before me a five-hour journey in a blacked-out carriage, with not enough light to read by and nothing else to do but ponder what Jack had told me. It certainly sounded interesting work, but I wondered whether I would be up to what was clearly going to be a very rigorous training. The train, of course, was packed, but I had got to the station in plenty of time, and having stacked my kitbag on the rack and wrapped myself up in my greatcoat, I sank into a corner seat, closed my eyes and pretended to go to sleep. I felt disinclined to talk, and, in any case, there was no need, for the compartment soon filled up with a family of six, who chattered and bickered among themselves.

There was much Jack had told me that made me pause for thought. I would be questioned about my family, my education, my motives and the events that had brought me to this point of volunteering for what was certainly dangerous work. This set me thinking about the path that led from my childhood in Wraysby, through school and my friendships there, to Cambridge, pacifism and finally the army. I would be interviewed in French and German, but that wouldn't be a problem, for I was fluent in both languages. This, in turn, led me to think of Michel and Manfred; where were they now? I wondered. Was Michel a prisoner-of-war in Germany, or had he managed to escape and join the Free French forces? And Manfred, where was he? Somewhere in Russia, no doubt. I'd had a telegram from Clara Edelstedt in Sweden about six months ago telling me he had phoned her from Norway and told her, in the code we had arranged before we parted at Jeven just before the war, that he'd been playing the Schubert String Quintet. By this, I knew that he was fit and well then.

What should I say about Manfred at my interview? I'd told Jack about our friendship: how we'd been at school together; how

I'd visited his home in Germany just before the war, but not much else. I think that Jack was a bit surprised when I told him Manfred had been a member of the Hitler Jugend, only because he knew that I was then a pacifist, and he had found it strange that I should have had a friend with such different loyalties. I hadn't told him how much else we shared in common.

And then I asked myself if I wanted to do the kind of work Jack had described. It would certainly be very dangerous, but that didn't worry me particularly. He had made it clear that if I were not happy about the work I might be offered, I would have a perfect right to draw back. But I didn't want to do that for fear of appearing cowardly. By the same token, if they were unhappy with me, they had an equal right to get rid of me, or give me something different to do. I couldn't tell whether I would be suitable for the work — I'd find that out soon enough — so all I could do for the moment was parade before my mind's eye, like a drowning man, the course of events that had brought me to this strange, but not uninteresting, situation.

Part One: A Boy's Story

I

The year 1919 was not a good one. It was the year of the Versailles Treaty which sowed the seeds of that future conflict which broke out just when I was ripe enough to take part in it. So, although it was the year of my birth, which I suppose I must reckon a *Good Thing*, it wasn't, in retrospect, much of a year for those of my contemporaries who were destined to be maimed or slaughtered in the next holocaust. But for those, like my parents, who had just survived the last one, it must have seemed like the return of spring after a winter of death.

In my family a lively spring it certainly was, for my mother and both my aunts were pregnant. My cousin Peggy was the first to arrive, followed fairly rapidly by my cousin Jean, and finally by me. We were privileged children, and I the most privileged of us all because I was the eldest son of my father who, in turn, was the eldest son of Sir Arthur Kildwick, JP, sometime Lord Mayor of the Yorkshire city of Wraysby, a man widely acknowledged by his family and friends to have been Good and Great. As the firstborn son of my generation, the circumstances of my arrival in this world and the first weeks of my life were lovingly chronicled by my mother in embarrassing detail. Given the name, Arthur, there is no doubt that my parents saw in me the hopeful successor of my mayoral grandsire, who, in his way, had lived up to the high moral standards of the great, knightly king. My mother was consequently determined that posterity should know all there was to know about my birth and progress.

The Times on the day of my birth recorded that a plane had flown at the amazing speed of 170 mph; that the Red Army was advancing on General Denikin's front near Kiev; that eight thousand ex-officers were out of work; that in Vienna there was a shortage of coal and food, and that in Birmingham a 'skilled abortionist' was given seven years penal servitude. There were no fewer than thirty-five theatrical performances in London that night, among them such masterpieces as *Lord Richard's in the Pantry, The Wild Widow,* and *Baby Hunting.* With a welcome such as this it is hard to imagine how much more privileged one could be.

Unhappily, the shock to the system of my arrival that cold November day caused me immediately to lose seven ounces, showing as clearly as possible that I much preferred the cosiness of my mother's womb to the chill of a Yorkshire autumn. But this was only a temporary setback, for by January 20th, 1920, when my infant biography ends, I had achieved eleven pounds three ounces 'before feed, without shawl, but in binder'. In binder? Could it be that I was in what the Bible calls 'swaddling clothes'? Because if so, I find this, if not blasphemous, at least presumptuous. But whatever my binder was, I'm sure I was in it for my own good, for when I look back I realise that everything constricting was then thought to be beneficial, and I expect that my mother and nanny were quite right, and that I am the better for my binder to this day.

On the third page of the album my mother had bought to record my history, she pasted photographs of my paternal grand-parents. There were two of my mayoral grandfather, one robed and chained, the other in profile. In one he bears a striking resemblance to King George V, and in the other to the king's cousin, Czar Nicholas II, to neither of whom was he in any way related. Between these two pictures was one of his wife, my grandmother, Naomi Grover (née Grossbaum), always known to me as Damdam. On the next page she pasted photographs of my maternal grand-parents, Michael Hinmers de Vergy, ninth Baron Tynron and his wife, Florence Anne Rudgeley. Granny (to distinguish her from Damdam) is wearing a magnificent sable coat and a stunning fur hat shaped like a bird's wing, the very height of Edwardian fashion in stark contrast to the sensible frumpishness of Lady Kildwick. Beneath these photographs of her parents my mother pasted one of her brother, a strikingly handsome young officer in the uniform of the 27th King's Own Galloway Light Infantry, beneath which she wrote:

'Anthony Michael Hinmers de Vergy, tenth Baron Tynron, their son. Born Dec. 16th, 1892. Killed at Loos Sep. 25th, 1915.'

It was in his memory that I was given the name Anthony, for he was the only man, my father not excepted, my mother ever really loved.

It appears from my mother's careful account of my early life that I was apt to suffer from constipation and from wind; that I needed 'artificial help most days', that I was fed on mother's milk, which didn't suit me, on Virolax, which caused wind, but that I became more regular in *all* my habits on a diet of oatmeal water and a little oil. It is hard to imagine why. December 29th, 1919 was a great day: I had my first bath. A month later I was taken out of my binder and put into long clothes for the first time, and on that comforting note my infant biography ends.

On Boxing Day 1919 my mother noted: 'Nurse Walker left and Nanny Prowte came to help me with him.' I cannot help feeling sorry for Nurse Walker. To be booted out on Boxing Day because I was windy and constipated seems unfair. I feel sure that my first Christmas on earth was more to blame, for it must have been one of unadulterated adulation on the part of my parents and Damdam. With three newly born grandchildren, Damdam would have been in her element, and since her idea of pleasure was to stuff people with rich food, I have no doubt that both I and my parents were by Boxing Day suffering from acute dyspepsia, which is why they took it out on Nurse Walker.

My mother was two years older than my father. I have a photograph of her at the age of three which shows a curly-headed, round-faced, extremely pretty child, but the set of her jaw and her look of determination prophesied a character of stubborn strength coupled with a certain naivety and great impetuosity. She talked very little about her family, largely because she feared and disliked her mother and idolised her father, who had died at the early age of forty-seven when mother was still in her teens. Although a peer, my grandfather was by profession a doctor, and the younger son of a younger son, who had inherited his title, but no money to go with it, from a slightly dotty uncle who had fallen overboard from a yacht during Cowes Week and drowned.

My parents didn't share many common interests; father had little liking for music apart from the noisier bits of Wagner, and hardly read any books other than *Huckleberry Finn* and *Hiawatha*. Mother, on the other hand, loved music and literature. Father was an excellent shot and a keen fisherman; mother was bored to death by field sports. She loved France and the French: he thought of them as unreliable froggies. The only thing that bound them together initially were their good looks, for both were very handsome, the love they bore for their respective fathers (both of whom had died when they were young), and their equally passionate dislike of their mothers.

Though ravishingly pretty and a peer's daughter, my mother did not become engaged during her Coming Out season in 1908, nor in 1909, nor in 1910. By 1911 my grandmother was becoming desperate; she had abandoned all hope of her marrying an elder son, and was beginning to resign herself to the prospect of having to accept a younger one. As winter sports were coming into fashion, she decided to try Adelboden to see what the ice rink might produce in the way of eligible young men. It didn't; but it did produce my father's recently married sister, Margaret. My mother and Margaret became fast friends, and since the latter had married a baronet's son, my grandmother was content to let my mother visit her at Wraysby, a town she did not much approve of, since it was in the industrial north. Mother's visits became longer and more frequent as her friendship for Margaret grew more passionate.

Neither of my parents told me anything about their courtship. I gained the impression that it proceeded slowly, and that there was no question of marriage until after the outbreak of the Great War. The Kildwicks were in trade, and no matter how many of them might have been Lord Mayors, a mere knighthood counted for nothing with my grandmother. From Damdam's point of view, the de Vergys may have been an ancient family with dozens of titles, but when it came down to brass tacks they hadn't enough brass.

My father and my uncle, Anthony Tynron, were almost the same age, and they joined up about the same time in September 1914. Father was commissioned in the Royal Artillery but, unlike my uncle, who was sent to France almost at once and was killed within a year, he didn't go until September 1915. He was at the front for about five months, when he was invalided home severely shell-shocked. Nowadays, when so much is known about mental stress, a more charitable view is taken of those who are unable to stand up to the horror of prolonged bombardment and shelling. At that time, shell-shock victims were regarded as cowards, while those who lost limbs were heroes. The thought that he was a weakling haunted my father all his life, and people's cruel ignorance caused him immense suffering. It was doubly hard for him, because his younger brother went through the war unscathed and with distinction, but then he was not in the front line for more than a very short period. Damdam with stupendous insensitivity used to make invidious comparisons between her two sons to father's disadvantage.

When he returned from France, my father was sent first to a hospital near Sheffield and then, when he was beginning to recover, to Damdam's convalescent Home for Officers in the Lake District, where mother and Margaret were working as VADs. His mental condition was still deplorable; he was unable to go out alone and never in daylight; he spoke with a severe stammer, and was prone to fits of weeping and to frightening nightmares.

As if this were not bad enough for my mother, who was already attracted to him, the news of her brother Tony's death had been a crushing blow. Her sense of loss was overwhelming. She felt it was mean and cruel, even for a moment, to feel glad to be alive. By degrees, however, she began to see in my father's gradual recovery a means to her own salvation. Her innate generosity, and that capacity for tenderness and care she had inherited from her father, found full expression in her fight for father's sanity. This, of course, was love of a very real kind, but my mother was never in love with my father in the usually accepted sense. She was tending him as her father would have tended a patient, and furthermore, she was tending him in memory of her brother, Tony. Her love for my father was like her love for my brother and for me — warm, maternal and protective — and thus an entirely false basis upon which to contemplate a marriage.

My father, of course, saw things very differently. Deeply sensitive and highly emotional, he was as warm-hearted as she, whom he looked upon not just as an extremely beautiful young woman to whom he was much indebted, but also as the means whereby his shattered self-confidence was being restored. Alas! it is impossible to make a successful marriage with one's guardian angel.

None of this was either apparent or understood at the time, and so with the wholehearted blessing of Margaret, and the somewhat less enthusiastic approval of Lady Kildwick, my father proposed and was accepted.

It was not a festive wedding. Owing to wartime restrictions and the difficulty of travel, it was decided to hold it at Bletchley, a compromise between the Lake District and London, where conveniently grandmother Tynron's sister-in-law happened to have a house. Both Lady Kildwick and the former Baroness Tynron objected to this arrangement for reasons that neither my father nor mother could understand, but accept it they eventually did. It was the first and only time my formidable grandmothers met, and they took an instant dislike to each other. Lady Tynron pronounced Lady Kildwick vulgar and common. Lady Kildwick considered Lady Tynron an outrageous snob. Both were undeniably right. Father, being in no condition to take a strong line in the matter, left all the arrangements to my mother and her aunt. In view of all this, it is hardly surprising that it was more than three years before I put in an appearance, but what, perhaps, is more surprising is that the marriage lasted as long as it did.

* * *

Tolstoy says in *War and Peace* that reminiscences are not the melancholy memories of old age, but the romantic memories of youth, those impressions of one's remotest past in which dreamland melts into reality. On that train journey to see my father in 1941, I found it hard to distinguish clearly between dream and reality where my earliest childhood was concerned. But I have never forgotten certain events from my early youth, for they have returned time and time again, not so much to haunt as to puzzle me. There were memories recorded on film in mother's album of my childhood, but there were many more that were not. There was no record, for example, of me sneaking off to play with Bob, the boy next door, our neighbour's gardener's son, who because of his broad Yorkshire accent was not considered a suitable playmate for the grandson of a Lord Mayor and a baron. It was not that my parents were any greater snobs than others of a similar background, only that, in those days, even children were segregated into social classes. There was nothing in the album of the dark-haired boy, a few years older than me, whom I once saw standing at the entrance to Olderton Park, where we lived. We were on our way — Nanny, my younger brother, Michael, and I — to tea with our cousins Peggy and Bingo. He was raggedly dressed with grubby knees and socks down round his ankles. To me he looked heroic. I wanted desperately to grow up like him; to be tough and rough, not soft and clean like everyone was trying to make me. I stopped and stared at him from across the road.

'Come along, dear; don't dawdle,' said Nanny.

I took no notice, and continued to stare. Why couldn't I be allowed to play with boys like him and Bob, instead of with what Nanny called 'nicely brought-up children' like Peggy and Bingo? As I stood and stared I felt a strange tightening of the throat and my tongue cleaving to the roof of my mouth, which felt dry. The dark-haired boy stared back at me scowling and contemptuous.

'Come *along*, dear. It's rude to stare at people like that. What's the matter with you today?'

If only I'd known! If I'd known then what the term 'macho' meant, I might have been able to explain. As it was, I felt unlike I'd ever felt before.

Reluctantly, as Nanny took my hand, I let myself be pulled along behind her, looking back over my shoulder at the boy, my mouth getting drier and drier, and the pain (was it really a pain?), the sensation of something welling up inside me getting stronger and stronger. The boy stood his ground returning my gaze impassive, expressionless, contemptuous; and then he put his tongue out as we rounded the corner of Church Lane out of his sight.

Soldiers, especially those who had lost limbs, haunted me. In those days it was still not unusual to see men in uniform and wounded ex-servicemen in hospital blue limping round Olderton Park, usually in pairs, the halt leading the blind. That I owed my very existence to such as these was something my parents and Nanny instilled into me from birth. Talk about the horrors of the late war went on all around me, and a consciousness of its frightfulness was planted in my mind from infancy. When General Furze, my father's late commanding officer, came to stay, I remember as vividly as if it were yesterday being carried downstairs to meet him. The image of this huge, red-faced, moustachioed, khaki-clad and bemedalled man had the most disturbing effect on me, for I screamed and screamed until I had to be taken back to the nursery in disgrace, where I was scolded for my bad manners, which made me scream all the louder. From that time my nightmares were peopled with khaki-clad, booted and breeched ogres, and when I was told that I would soon be going to boarding school (I was then nearly eight) the picture that formed in my mind was of a barracks, in which I would be drilled and beaten by schoolmasters who all looked like General Furze.

Though chronicling my life proved to be beyond my mother's literary capacity, she was nevertheless a keen operator of the Box Brownie, which enabled her to leave for posterity a pictorial record of my progress. In this album I can be seen cooing in my pram, gurgling in my pedal-car, held aloft by doting parents and aunts, with Nanny always hovering anxiously in the background lest harm befall the Lord Mayoral heir. But why is she 'Mouse' and not Nanny or Nurse Prowte? And why was she dressed in fashionable coats and skirts, fur tippets and smart hats, and not in uniform. Those with a mental image of Nanny Hawkins sitting by her fireside in the upper storey of Brideshead should forget it. Nanny Prowte did have her own room upstairs near the day and night nurseries, but she spent her evenings in the drawing room, and ate in the dining room. It was more than fifty years before I learnt from a cousin that she and my mother had been lovers, and that this was why my parents got divorced.

Another unrecorded memory was of crawling into my father's bed on Sunday mornings before church. He and mother were sleeping in separate rooms by then, and I used to curl up beside him to have my back scratched. My father liked having his back scratched too, and we used to play a game about it. He had a snake tattooed on his chest, which fascinated me, and the first thing I did when getting into bed with him was ask to see it. The game was for him to pretend it had vanished, but that if I scratched his back first it might come back, so in I got and scratched away like mad for a second or two. 'Not enough,' he would say, 'scratch some more,' and I would give another furious scratch, and eventually he would say, 'I think the snake's come back,' and turn over, open his pyjama jacket and reveal it in all its blue-green glory. Then I'd ask, 'If you scratch my back will the snake grow on my chest?' to which he would reply, 'Not until you grow up, but I'll give your back just a little scratch to start it off,' but this always seemed unfair because I got much less scratching than he did, and I suspected that he didn't really want me to have a snake on my chest at all. But I never complained because it was a bargain between us, and I loved him dearly.

He must have been a very unhappy man, my father. He had done his best to establish some kind of relationship with me after the divorce, but we had become strangers. When, as I was obliged to do every holiday under the terms of the settlement, I visited him in Wraysby, it wasn't him I wanted to see but Nanny, for she was without doubt the person I then loved best. I had assumed that she and my father were having an affair, for it had never occurred to me that it might have been with my mother. But looking back now, it was all quite clear. The fact that Mouse, unlike other nannies, was treated as a member of the family and not as a servant, or even as other nannies were treated, was extraordinary. It explained why my grandmother Tynron refused to allow her to come to London with us when it was our turn to spend Christmas there; and it explained why father never came on holidays with us, but always went fishing with his brother and brother-in-law. It explained Mouse's violent dislike of Lady Tynron, and mother's assertion that she had been disloyal in some never defined fashion.

That my mother never saw anything wrong in her friendship for Mouse was evident from something that occurred when I was about fourteen. She had just got hold of a copy of *The Well of Loneliness*, which had recently been put on trial as obscene. In the eyes of the magistrate, the book's great offence resided in its failure to suggest that anyone with the horrible tendencies described in it was in the least degree blameworthy. Mother had said when she handed it to me, 'This may help you to understand how important it is to love people for what they are, and not to condemn them for what they do. It doesn't mean that people are wicked because society disapproves of their love for each other. Love between two people is beautiful no matter what form it takes.'

Father, on the other hand was quite unable to understand what had happened to him, or why mother seemed to prefer Mouse to him. One evening when I was staying with him, he came up to say goodnight before turning in. He sat down on the bed, and suddenly putting his head in his hands burst into tears. 'I don't know what it is I've done to lose you,' he sobbed. 'I've tried to be a good father to you. I just don't understand why they've taken you away from me. I've done everything I could for your mother; it's so cruel when I love you so much.'

It was the first time I'd seen a grown-up cry. I didn't know what to do or say. It seemed all wrong; it was the business of grown-ups to comfort children when *they* cried. I began to cry myself, not quite knowing why. At last he pulled himself together, kissed me goodnight and went out of the room. I lay awake between tears and anger, and from that time until I found out the truth, I felt as if he had let me down, and that, after all, he was a coward and a weakling. May God forgive me! Children inflict great cruelty on their parents, for I'm certain that he never blamed me for the unhappiness I must have caused him over the years. Later, when I understood what had happened, I came to love and admire him very much, and his premature death was a cruel blow to me.

Today we have become so obsessed with the biological side of our nature that we find it difficult to believe that the romantic friendships of men for men and women for women were regarded by our forebears as a spiritual union of minds, as a union of souls, a marriage of hearts, a harmony of affection. To us it is unthinkable that there could have been no physical side to such close relationships. Herr Doktor Freud, like some serpent in Eden, has banished us all from that garden of innocence. But our parents commended romantic relationships between people of the same sex, and from all that I had experienced up to that time, I agreed with them. What, indeed, was the purpose of the public school system if not to imbue boys with ideas of friendship, loyalty, sensibility, shared tastes (including not infrequently shared beds), even camp flirtation and passion. But how far was it permissible to go? The Rev. E. E. Bradford, whose poems extolled the young men of England to 'turn away from the wench with her powder and paint', was praised by the *Times* for deploring in his poetry 'the habit of early marriage so common in cities and among industrial workers' and writing poems that were 'vigorous and refreshing', which the critic recommended 'all earnest schoolmasters' to read. Didn't Rupert Brooke epitomise all that was best in the romantic loves, loyalties and friendships of the slaughtered generation? Mother certainly saw nothing wrong in two women living together — even sharing a bed. There were, of course, nasty, effeminate men called pansies, and dreadful women who cut their hair short and wore collars and ties, and with such I must have nothing to do.

Thus prepared against the world, the flesh and the devil, I was dispatched at the age of eight to Rockells Park School in Surrey. It had been chosen for two reasons: first because it prepared boys for Eton, Harrow and Winchester; and second, because it would rid me of a dangerous Yorkshire accent. Of the two, the second was certainly the more important in the eyes of my mother and grandmother.

II

Being aware of the teasing I was likely to suffer as a new boy, my mother was anxious that I should be kitted out correctly. The school clothing list had not been revised since it was first drawn up when the school was founded in the 1880s, and was as long as a bride's trousseau. Most of the items of clothing could be got at Harrods or Daniel Neal, but for some reason the purple and gold school cap could only be obtained at the school itself. For weeks before my departure, my mother was busy assembling this regalia, which she laid out on two beds in one of the spare rooms. Everything from my trunk to my toothbrush had to be marked with my name in full — ARTHUR ANTHONY KILDWICK — either stamped or on name tags.

At last everything was bought, marked and laid out ready for packing and dispatch, luggage-in-advance, two weeks before the beginning of term. There was, however, one thing missing — my headgear. Anxious that I should be correctly dressed, mother wrote to the headmaster to ask what kind of hat I should wear, for in those days to go bareheaded was as unthinkable as to go without trousers. She was told to buy me a bowler, which proved no easy matter considering the difference in size between the head of a businessman and that of a child of eight. However, I was eventually fitted out with one that rested precariously on my ears, which luckily stuck out enough to prevent it resting on the bridge of my nose.

At last the day of my departure came, when I took a tearful farewell of Nanny and the other servants and set out to catch the train for London. By the time we had changed stations and found the right platform at Waterloo, I had had my first lesson in stiff-upper-lippery. My grandparents had accompanied my mother and me for the final parting, and the four of us followed the porter down the platform, on which were gathered little knots of parents and boys making stilted conversation and keeping their upper lips stiff. My grandfather spotted a parent he knew and asked him if his son would keep an eye on me.

'Of course you will, Tom,' said the father to his son, who looked disdainfully in my direction. When he saw the way I was dressed his face began to crease, and I could tell he was wanting to burst out laughing. However, he controlled himself as best he could.

After what seemed an age, the guard blew his whistle: the moment of separation had come. I kissed my grandmother, shook my grandfather's hand, and fighting back tears of panic, embraced my mother, who hugged me so tightly she knocked the wretched bowler off and it began to roll towards the edge the platform. Would that it had fallen under the train and been crushed beyond repair! But, alas, no; my grandfather made a dive for it, and as I stepped on to the running board of the carriage, he rammed it on my head with such force that my vision was completely obscured. Thus, blindly groping, I half fell, half jumped into the compartment, and sat down rigid with fright on the nearest seat.

There were eight of us in the compartment, of whom five were new boys. Tom looked at me with undisguised disgust. 'Why are you wearing that silly hat?' he asked. 'Haven't you got a cap?' I looked at my companions; three were wearing the purple and gold school cap, and the new boys ordinary country cloth caps. Apart from those crowning the lofty heads of fathers, there wasn't another bowler in sight.

'I don't know,' I mumbled, fighting back my tears.

'What's your name?'

'Nibs,' I replied.

This provoked a gale of laughter; even the other new boys thought it was frightfully funny. It cheered them all up immensely, for they were automatically ranged on the side of the majority, no longer outcasts. They immediately began to talk among themselves, and mercifully left me in silent contemplation of my unhappiness.

The porter had put my suitcase on the rack, so when we arrived at our destination I found out for the first time how heavy it was. I had to stand on the seat to lift it down, and as I struggled to pull it over the bar I lost my balance, and fell backwards with it on top of me. Being amply furnished with stout locks and hinges, it bruised me badly and cut my hand. By this time all the others had got out of the train, and I found myself alone and bleeding. Luckily the guard, as he walked down the train closing the doors, took pity on me and kindly carried my bag to the station entrance. He told me to follow the other boys, who were now fast vanishing into the distance.

The school was about a mile away, across a heath and through dark pinewoods. It was already beginning to get dark, and I had no idea how far I had to go, or, indeed, where the school might be, so I did the only sensible thing in the circumstances: I sat down on my horrible suitcase and burst into tears. Happily a passer-by saw me, and guessing where I ought to be, picked up my case and, taking me by the hand, led me sobbing to the school, where he handed me over to the matron.

'Are you Arthur Kildwick?' she demanded sternly. 'Why are you so late?'

No one had ever called me Arthur Kildwick before, so I looked at her vacantly.

'Dawdling, I suppose. We don't allow dawdling here.'

And with that she took me off to have a glass of milk and a digestive biscuit, showed me the bed I was to occupy in the dormitory, and left me to unpack.

* * *

The exaggerated esteem in which games were held at Rockells Park was in stark contrast to the thinly disguised contempt for all things artistic and musical. As I was hopeless at all games, but quite good at music, I found myself from the start outside the pale of convention; so far outside, in fact, that my parents were urged to seek medical advice because I spent so much time playing the piano and organ and so little playing ball. Latin, French, History and Geography I enjoyed because I was good at them, but no matter how many prizes I might collect for these subjects, they counted as nothing against my abject failure at soccer and cricket.

Religion counted for much at Rockells Park. So much time was spent in prayer that the knees of my knickerbocker trousers wore out. Private prayer (bare knees on bare boards) was obligatory morning and evening. This led to chilblains and catarrh. Public prayer in chapel was compulsory twice daily, even for the Jews. On Sundays, besides Matins and Evensong, there were scripture lessons and catechism for those about to be confirmed. As my parents were agnostic, I was not among them, so I was put with the Jews and told to learn psalms, and since I was clearly not Jewish by birth, I was made to learn longer ones to demonstrate, I suppose, how much better it was to be C of E rather than Hebrew or agnostic.

All this placed me firmly among the outcasts, and ensured a due share of bullying. I was marginally luckier than the Jews because I had fair hair and an undoubted English name, whereas most of them were dark and had foreign-sounding ones. Thus the first, and most important, thing I learnt at Rockells Park was that I was different. I count this as one of the most valuable lessons I ever learnt there, for it made me not only think things out for myself, but never to accept ready-made opinions.

Long before I left Rockells Park I had begun to experience that sensation which romantic novelists of the time described as a 'hardening of the thighs' or a 'tautening maleness'. In order to achieve this pleasant sensation I used to feast my eyes on pictures of soldiers and horsemen in books, which by no stretch of the imagination could be called pornographic, but which in some strange way reminded me of the boy I'd seen at the entrance to Olderton Park all those years ago, and of whom I'd dreamt ever since. I know it is now fashionable to blame single-sex boarding schools for all manner of perversions, so called, but whatever predilections I may have developed later in life cannot be blamed on anything that happened at Rockells Park. The only experience of this kind that I had left a lasting impression upon me for a totally different reason.

Due to my musical ability, I was the special favourite of the music master. Because of the prevailing philistinism, he was looked upon by the boys and the rest of the staff as not quite in the same category of teacher as the other masters. Unlike them he took no part in games, but this was almost certainly because he walked with a limp occasioned by a war wound.

Because I won the music prize three years in succession, he had nicknamed me Schubert, to whom with my round face and owlish glasses I bore a passing resemblance. In my third year he made me leader of the choir, and as such I had to sing solos, which required individual tuition. He went to considerable lengths to encourage me both as a singer, pianist and organist, and I grew to like him more than any other member of staff. This fondness, however, was tinged with fear, for he was a martinet and had a short temper. I think, on reflection, that he was probably in pain from his old wound, but of that, of course, we knew nothing.

Misbehaviour in chapel — not uncommon given the boredom of so many of the services — was punished instantly, and it was my duty as choirleader to keep order among the choristers. On one occasion as we were rehearsing a favourite anthem of mine and I was about to sing a high A, I caught sight of a boy opposite pulling a funny face to put me off. Instead of producing my usual nightingale tone I let out a strigine hoot, whereupon the choir erupted in mirth. Unable to see what was going on, the choirmaster concluded that I was deliberately making a hash of the solo. He stopped playing in mid-bar, came down into the choir, seized me by the scruff of the neck and frog-marched me out of the chapel, regardless of my protestations of innocence. Once outside, he boxed my ears and told me to stand at the back of the chapel during the service, just about to begin, so that the whole school could witness my disgrace.

My resentment at this injustice knew no bounds. It was, of course, taboo for me to name the culprit who had corpsed me. In any case, under the school code, I thought he was bound to own up. But he didn't. Thus, with a deep sense of grievance, I wrote to my mother telling her what had happened. I must have laid it on thick, for ten days later I was summoned to the headmaster's study. Looking grave, he told me he had had a letter from her complaining that the music master had hit me in chapel. Was this true? Although the music master seemed to have forgotten and forgiven, I was still smarting from a sense of injustice, and wanted to get my own back, so I answered, quite untruthfully, that what my mother had complained of was indeed true. Did this sort of thing happen often, the headmaster wanted to know, and again I lied and said it did.

The next day a message was posted on the notice-board requiring me to report to the music master's room that afternoon. I went, trembling, to find him in his shirt-sleeves surrounded by his belongings, which he was packing into a trunk. Pointing to the big leather armchair beside the fire, he told me to sit down. Then, to my intense surprise, instead of taxing me with my treachery, he knelt down in front of me, took my head in his hands, and gently drawing me towards him, kissed me on the forehead. There were tears in his eyes, and I thought he was going to cry. Pointing to the half-filled trunk he said, 'I'm leaving today. Someone — I don't know who — has complained about me to the headmaster. He won't tell me who it is.'

I blushed but said nothing. 'I've been accused of hitting boys in chapel,' he went on, and after a pause: 'At least I know it couldn't have been my little Schubert.' I still remained silent. He got up and walked across to his bookcase, and taking a volume of Beethoven sonatas off the shelf came back and said: 'You're the best pupil I've ever had. Take this as a present. Whatever you do, don't give up your music. If ever I can help you with extra lessons in the hols, you've only to let me know. I've no idea where I'll fetch up, but as soon as I get another job I'll send you my address.'

He kissed me again, patted me fondly on the shoulder, and said: 'Run along now or you'll be late for class. I'll miss you. Think of me sometimes. God bless you, my little Schubert.'

Clutching the volume of sonatas I got up without looking at him, without having said a word, and made for the door. I was about to open it when he came up behind, put his arms round me and almost lifting me off my feet turned me towards him, at the same time smothering me with kisses. Burying my head on his shoulders, I burst into tears. He put me down, and opening the door, without another word, pushed me gently into the passage. I ran out of the building and across to the school, my mind in a turmoil.

* * *

In 1930 my parents' marriage finally broke down and they were divorced. Nanny was left behind in Yorkshire, for my mother was offered and accepted a flat in her mother's London house, and my grandmother had absolutely refused to countenance them living together under her roof. But in spite of this domestic upheaval, my last year at Rockells Park was less lonely than the first three had been, mainly because I received a public beating for transgressing school rules. These decreed that no boy should leave the school grounds unaccompanied by a member of staff, and one dull Saturday during a cricket match, the temptation to break bounds in search of Mars bars became overwhelming, and I sneaked out to a shop on the edge of the village to buy some.

On my way out of the shop I was caught by one of the staff who reported me to the headmaster. I'd done it as a bet with a boy in my form, who, when I returned and told him I'd been caught, bet me a second time that I'd get a good hiding. I, on the other hand, thought that the member of staff who had caught me, a spinsterish teacher of extreme religiosity, would be too filled with the milk of human kindness to give me away. I was wrong. After chapel the following Monday, the headmaster in a voice charged with doom summoned everyone to appear in the school hall immediately after the service. I began to feel a strange, sinking feeling in the pit of my stomach, and this was not made any less acute by Rupert, the boy who had bet me I'd be beaten, staring in front of him from the pew opposite as if Mars bars wouldn't melt in his mouth. From the boys at large, speculative murmurs began to arise as we trooped into the hall.

It was the rule that the most junior boys sat at the front and the rest in order of seniority further back. As a member of the top form I was in the back row of all, where I took my place next the gangway, knowing what was about to befall me.

There was a long pause before the headmaster entered, grim-faced and magisterial in full academicals. The scene would have been more awesome if the headmaster had been tall, elderly, gaunt and bearded, but he was not more than forty, small, running to fat with a sallow complexion and thinning hair. What he lacked in presence however he made up for in histrionics, and like all good actors he made the most of his dramatic moment. Walking to the centre of the rostrum, he stood a couple of paces in front of his assembled staff, all similarly attired in gowns and hoods. Even matron was there in her blue dress, white apron and starched, wide-spreading veil, ready to perform, no doubt, the office of statutory medic at an execution.

He had called us together, the headmaster began, because a most serious breach of school rules had just taken place. If he had been about to tell us that one of our number had been caught in the act of rape or murder he couldn't have sounded more outraged. This crime, he went on, had been committed not by a boy in the middle school, but by one in the top form; one who should be setting a good example. There could be no excuse, no mitigating circumstance, for the boy in question had been caught *in flagrante delicto*. He paused, recalling perhaps, that those in the lower forms who had not yet got beyond *mensa* and *amo* might not understand the term. Yes, red-handed, in the very act, he thundered, the very act of — of — he paused again to make the maximum impact on his audience — *of coming out of a sweet shop!*

You could have heard a bee sneeze. Staff and boys appeared struck dumb by the enormity of the crime. Pausing again to let its true horror sink in, he then continued: 'In order to make an example of this boy, and to ensure that nothing like this shall ever happen again, I am going to punish him in front of you all.'

He glared furiously in my direction, and commanded me to come up to the rostrum. Shaking, weak-kneed, yellow as a banana, I rose to my feet, walked down the gangway, the focus of a hundred pairs of eyes. Would I make it without disgracing myself?

I made it.

On reaching the rostrum, the headmaster told me to fetch a tall stool, which was standing against the wall, and to bend over it. Selecting a cane from a collection of pointers, walking sticks, umbrellas and golf clubs in a porcelain drainpipe kept in the corner of the hall for the purpose, he advanced towards me testing it for flexibility. Apparently satisfied by its whippiness, he took a couple of paces back, and came at me with such force that I lost my balance and fell flat on the floor, pushing over the stool and bruising my shins. He stood back and told me to pick the stool and myself up and to bend over again. This time he took more careful aim, and proceeded to give me ten of the best. After this he turned to the matron, and told her to apply iodine to the afflicted part of my anatomy and change my underpants, which had become stained with my blood.

From that day to the end of the term I became the hero of the school. Coincidentally, I was playing the part of Katisha in the end-of-term production of *The Mikado*. Taking my cue from her, I placed my bottom, as she did her elbow, on view at a penny a time, and very profitable this turned out to be. Even when I had to reduce the price to a halfpenny as the bruises began to fade, I cleared a considerably larger sum than I would have won from Rupert.

Although I derived great satisfaction from being the hero of the hour, I had a lurking fear that my criminal conduct might deprive me of the privilege of a Leaver's Lecture. A profound mystery hung over this event in our lives. No Masonic secret was ever more closely guarded. As the end of one's last term approached, those who were about to set forth on what the prayer called 'the larger paths of life' were summoned to the headmaster's study one by one, there to have imparted to them some arcane message, which was to arm us against the snares of the world. Precisely what these snares might be none of us could tell, for dire punishment was decreed for those who might be tempted to reveal their nature. Those to whom the light had been vouchsafed would be seen emerging from the study with serious, puzzled faces, but no matter what inducements were offered, one and all refused to divulge a word of what the headmaster had told them.

Everything was done in alphabetical order at Rockells Park. Leavers were called for their lecture over a period of two or three weeks, depending on how many of them there were. This term Agnew went first, followed by Angus, Carlington and Dean, and so on through French and Johnson. By rights it was my turn next, but no, Macfarlane and Mayer were called, then Onslow and so on till it came to Willoughby. By now the end of term was less than a week away, and I was sure I was to be deprived of my Lecture. Having been punished once for my transgression, I was seething with indignation at the unfairness of being punished a second time by denying me this last privilege. At lunchtime on the day before we broke up, my name was at last called. Fearing further punishment, I took the precaution of stuffing the seat of my plus-fours with blotting-paper, and at the appointed hour knocked on the study door. I was bidden to enter. Mr Cattermole was standing on the hearth-rug with his back to the fireplace; he told me to sit down on the sofa facing him, This I found a trifle difficult owing to the stiffness of the blotting-paper, five or six sheets of which when stuffed into the seat of one's pants tend to restrict one's ability to bend enough to sit down in comfort. No matter, I sat.

'D'you know why I have sent for you?' asked the headmaster in a severe tone of voice.

'No sir,' I replied.

'Have any of the other leavers said anything to you about what I am going to tell you now?'

Not having the remotest idea what he was going to tell me, I could only reply that, so far as I knew, they hadn't.

'Good. I have left you to the last because you have shown by your conduct this term that you are a boy who cannot be trusted, and what I am about to tell you must on no account be repeated outside this room.'

I thought this was a bit much, but said nothing.

'You have observed, no doubt,' he continued sternly, 'certain changes taking place in yourself, have you not?'

I cudgelled my brains to try to understand what he was driving at, but could think of nothing. Was he expecting me to have detected the growth of a tail or, maybe, a cloven hoof? I had no idea, and in view of this uncertainty, I felt the safest course was to be non-committal.

'I'm not sure, sir,' I said.

'I mean, are you aware of changes to your — er — person?'

What *could* he mean? What changes to my person? Had he noticed that I had suddenly become rather popular, and was he now accusing me of the sin of pride? I knitted my brows, and suddenly it dawned on me that he wasn't referring to my personality but to my prick. How on earth did he know? My erections had always taken place when I was by myself in bed or when looking at pictures in the *Wonder Book of Soldiers*, which Dad had given me last Christmas. By what supernatural power could Mr Cattermole know about them? Had he stolen quietly into the dorm while I was asleep, whipped off the bedclothes and found me stiff? Hardly; I'd have woken up and noticed him. Since he obviously knew more about it than I had reckoned, all I could mutter was, 'Yes, I am.'

'Good,' he went on, obviously relieved to find I was not an imbecile even though I might be a criminal. 'Have your father or mother told you how babies are born?'

Unable to see any connection between this and his last question, I was now convinced that in addition to possessing the power of second sight, he was clearly crazy as well.

'My mother told me they come out of their mother's stomachs,' I said to humour him, passing on a piece of information I had imparted to the dorm many years ago, and which had thereupon earned me the nickname of District Nurse.

'Did she tell you how they got there in the first place?' he asked.

'No.'

'Well, I shall now tell you. Have you a sister?'

By now, quite convinced of his insanity, I could only tell him that I had not.

'Humph; a pity. Never mind; when you are a little older you'll find that girls are made differently from boys. Where you have a — er — person they have a....' he paused seeking the *mot juste*, '...an opening,' he concluded triumphantly,

'Oh,' I said brightly, 'I know my cousin Peggy has to spend a penny sitting down because she hasn't got a...' I hesitated, not knowing quite what word to use. Cock, dick and prick were all familiar terms, but knowing that they were rude ones, I didn't feel inclined to risk further punishment by using them. On the other hand 'little nimmy', the term Nanny used to use, sounded a bit sissy.

'Well, er, she's not like a boy,' I began to flounder. His face brightened, the awkward moment had passed. 'Quite, quite, you seem to understand perfectly. Now in a girl's... er... opening there are two... er... holes,' he continued, 'one for spending pennies and the other for having babies.'

Biology was not on the Rockells Park syllabus, so my knowledge of anatomy was vague in the extreme. By now I had lost the train of his argument, too. What on earth did he mean by one opening and two holes? Gradually it began to dawn on me that one of these holes must be the belly button. For all I knew, this was where babies did make their entrance into this vale of tears. It seemed logical; light was beginning to dawn. I nodded sagely, while he pressed on. 'When you get older and marry, you will place your... er... person into the hole for babies, and nine months later a child will be born. In order to do this your... er... person will become stiff.'

At last it was all clear. In order to beget a child I should be required, at a certain point after marriage, to pee into my wife's belly button, and lo! and behold in God's good time a child would emerge from it. Well, I thought in disgust, if that's all the Leaver's Lecture's about, I haven't had my money's worth.

'Is that quite clear?' he concluded. I nodded and made as if to get up from the sofa. 'Sit down, I haven't finished yet.'

I subsided, fearing that at last further chastisement was to befall me. But no.

'You are about to go to a public school. You will find there boys much older than yourself.' (Silly idiot, I thought, of course I will.) 'It is possible that one of these older boys may make filthy proposals to you that will involve your... er... person and his... er... person. Now I want to warn you that if anything of this sort should occur, you must go at once to your housemaster and report it. Unfortunately there is rather a lot of this sort of filth at some schools. I only hope that Templars is not one of them. D'you understand?'

Blinded by total incomprehension, I could only nod my head again and mumble something incoherent. Mr Cattermole appeared to be satisfied.

'Very well, you may go now.' He pointed to the door. The Lecture had lasted all of five minutes, and thus instructed in the subjects of copulation and sodomy, I left Rockells Park next day never to return.

III

I hated my first year at public school. My father had been to Templars thirty years before, and very little had changed since his day, apart from the slaughter of a few dozen masters and several hundred boys. Prefects, armed with the power of gauleiters, inflicted corporal punishment for fagging offences, such as burning toast and stewing tea. They ruled the house with little or no interference from the staff. Over all hovered the ghost of General Baden-Powell, whose maxims on character-building were for ever on the lips of masters, the chaplain and all those set in authority over us. Mr Cattermole had warned me about the dirt and filth I might encounter, though had not gone too precisely into details, but soon after my arrival, my housemaster told me that the training of boys wouldn't be complete if it didn't contain clear and plain-spoken instructions on the subject of continence, a word of whose meaning I was as yet almost totally ignorant.

'I have never known a boy who was not the better for having the question put to him frankly and openly,' he began, in what promised to be an enlightening half-hour. 'Indulgence and self-abuse' (another new word to me) 'are temptations more likely to assail you than other vices such as drinking, gambling or smoking. And what's more,' he continued, 'they are more harmful than any of them because they bring with them weakness of heart and head, and if you persist in them, lead to idiocy and lunacy.'

Self-abuse, he went on to tell us, wasn't even a manly vice like drinking, gambling and smoking, and was everywhere looked down upon with contempt. We could overcome these temptations, he assured us, by 'grit and determination'. They would arise, he went on, from physical causes such as eating rich food, sleeping on our backs on a soft bed with too many blankets, and from constipation. We must fight against them by washing in cold water and by exercising the upper part of our bodies with boxing and arm exercises 'to draw away the blood'. 'The first occasion will be difficult,' he warned us, 'but once you overcome the temptation, subsequent attacks will be easier to cope with.'

Since I never overcame the first occasion, and subsequent attacks were in no way easier to deal with, I soon formed the opinion that he was either a liar or a fool. None of this seemed to tie in with the filth and dirt Mr Cattermole had gone on about, so I still remained in much the same state of ignorance as before. I wasn't seduced or otherwise molested simply because I wasn't pretty enough, being fattish, owl-eyed and scruffy. But none of this prevented me going about in constant terror of molestation.

My only consolation was my recruitment into the chapel choir. My voice hadn't yet broken, and I was still able to sing alto. The War Memorial Chapel was magnificent and not long finished. I was utterly overwhelmed by its grandeur, and in my perplexity I underwent a painful phase of religiosity. In next to no time I was genuflecting and crossing myself as if my life depended on it. This pious terpsichore did not go unnoticed: I don't suppose I intended that it should. My housemaster, aware of my agnostic upbringing, wanted to know what was going on. I told him I wanted to become a Roman Catholic, at which he told me not to be a sanctimonious little prig (or words to that effect) and threatened to tell my mother, who, he knew, would strongly disapprove of my flirtation with the Whore of Babylon.

Finding this source of solace closed to me, I obediently gave up genuflection and took up masturbation instead: at least I could do this unobserved, and, on the whole, it gave me a great deal more satisfaction. When I first succeeded in unburdening myself of a fluid that was clearly not pee, though it might be cranial grey matter, thus leading to that idiocy of which General Baden-Powell had warned us, I began dimly to understand what Mr Cattermole had been trying to tell me about procreation. To quell temptation I even gave up the *Wonder Book of Soldiers* for a while, but there were so many real soldiers in the neighbouring barracks, who seemed to whet my sexual appetite, that the pictures hardly seemed necessary any more.

But great changes were about to take place. At the beginning of the academic year 1933, Dr Perkin Santon became headmaster, and many of the elderly staff retired.

Sitting in the train that night, I could not think of my present situation without reflecting on Dr Santon's educational philosophy and all that that had meant to me. Education, he once said, should aim, among other things, to enable boys and girls to achieve harmony, serenity and inner peace. A mature man was one who performed his duty to his family, his community and his country. Our education was frankly designed to make us leaders: the Good Citizen would live where there were rich and poor, manual and brain workers, old and young. With the approaching war in mind, he used to say that the officer should regard his professional honour as completely different from that of the ranker. One purpose of education was to teach us, potential officers, that all men are potential officers: in other words, education should lead to the destruction of those conventional distinctions between rulers and ruled.

The Good Citizen was above all the Good Patriot. Englishmen took their nationality for granted, and talked about it so little that they were not quite sure what they ought to call themselves — English, Scots, Welsh, Irish or British. In contrast, Germans and Italians needed an immense propaganda machine to assure them of their nationality. The Good Patriot must try in international affairs to see his opponents' point of view: this was the essence of the true democrat. Herein lay the basic conflict between Communism and Fascism on the one hand and Western democracy on the other. The Good Patriot must be ready to suffer death (and to inflict death) as a lesser evil than that the cause of justice should suffer, and the weak be overcome by the violence of the strong. He would consequently take it for granted that his country, to whose care he owed his existence, had the right to ask for his ungrudging service up to the point of sacrificing his own life.

It was here I had found it hardest to accept all that Dr Santon preached, for I believed that to be a true democrat you had to be a pacifist. I had always accepted the obligation to serve my country, but only in a non-violent manner. From what Jack had told me earlier that day, I might have to exercise much violence if I were accepted for the job he had proposed I should apply for.

Dr Santon disapproved of any system that denied its members scope for the full exercise of their human faculties. His critics said that the new regime lacked discipline, and that the boys could do as they liked. He abolished corporal punishment, drastically reformed the prefect system, and did away with fagging. His attitude towards discipline was straightforward — it was neither good nor bad; it was necessary for the orderly conduct of the school. Strict discipline inhibited initiative, he believed, for it derived from a fear of losing control over those upon whom it was imposed, and from the satisfaction it gave to those who had the power to impose it. It was useless to try to force discipline on the unruly boy. He did not trust the persistently ill-behaved boy never to commit another offence, but he did trust him to wish to be law-abiding, for it is a paradox, but nonetheless true, that people who are free to do exactly what they like, do not necessarily confine themselves to doing what they like. One of Dr Santon's aims was to get the boys to do what they liked, but there were a good many pressures on them to do things they didn't like. His cure for unruliness became the instilling of a sense of responsibility in the boys concerned. Another aim was to teach them that they could not leave the responsibility for their behaviour to someone else.

Thanks to Dr Santon and to the advent of Fascism and Communism in Europe, my faith in democracy was nourished. The main strength of totalitarian systems came from the faith they inspired in their citizens, and democracy's main weakness lay in the lack of such a faith. The Fascists declared that 'Faith without work is dead', and Hitler translated this into practice by providing countless opportunities for public service in work camps and the many activities of the Hitler Jugend. Manfred's evident enthusiasm for the movement was proof to me, at any rate, of its strength. The trouble was that democracy had ceased to inspire many young people in Britain. Nationalism was patently inadequate because it was suicidal; Communism was inadequate because it left out of account man's spiritual appetite. No system of government could solve the world's problems except one whose leaders recognised that man was dependent on God and must live by God's laws.

Recognising that adolescence is a difficult period in a boy's life, Dr Santon tended to accept as gospel some of the more revolutionary nostrums of Austrian and German psychologists. Masturbation, for example, which the old regime had considered dangerous to both health and sanity, he regarded with a more tolerant eye. One's awakening sexual instinct would manifest itself in tension and discomfort, which sooner or later would find relief in wet dreams. If this relief wasn't enough, then another safety-valve had to be opened and one masturbated. As for what he called 'Platonic affairs' between boys, the best way to deal with them was with tact. If, however, a boy was thought to be indulging in too much masturbation (and who could say how much was enough?) then a session with the school psychologist was the remedy. If things got completely out of control, and masturbation, whether solo or mutual, led to buggery, then expulsion was the ultimate sanction. Happily, sex was taken out of the realm of religion by the chaplain, who preached a gentle realism untinged by any kind of fundamentalism. He preached a gospel of reconciliation, and while not a pacifist in the strictest sense, his message was unequivocally against war and its futility, and it was largely due to him that compulsory membership of the OTC came to an end.

I left Templars as an unorthodox Christian, much influenced by Buddhism. I could see no point in trying to change people's minds by bullying them; only through the development of mutual respect, and in the spirit of truth, could friendship flourish. One of the first things Dr Santon did on becoming headmaster was to establish links with one or two German schools so that pupils might be exchanged, thus enabling us to get to know each other better. With the expulsion of so many talented German Jews, he seized the opportunity to recruit them on to the staff as teachers of art, music and languages. Consequently, I had quickly become aware of the horrors of Nazism, but on the other hand, we were left in no doubt about the injustices of the Treaty of Versailles, and of the danger of war stemming from them. Whereas at Cambridge our slightly older contemporaries were espousing Soviet Communism as the solution to our social and economic problems, we were indoctrinated with a gentler creed. It was due to this exchange system that I had met Manfred von Schrade, had become at first a conscientious objector, and now found myself about to play an active part in the liberation of Nazi-occupied Europe.

Manfred was superficially the perfect type of Hitler's German manhood. He was tall, blond, handsome, tough, athletic and ambitious. But he was far more than that. He came from an old landed family, and was related to most of the north German aristocracy.

His father had been a colonial administrator in South-West Africa, now Namibia, and had been taken prisoner when the British occupied that territory during the first war. With the loss of the colony, Herr von Schrade had returned to a starving, inflation-ridden Germany with no prospects and a feeling of deep bitterness against those, many of them supposedly Jews, who had made huge profits from the war. With great difficulty the family had survived penury, but when he was at Templars it was Manfred's ambition to follow his father's calling, and return to Africa as soon as Hitler had been able to get the colonies back. When he first came to Templars, his faith in Hitler was as firm as his belief that the sun would rise on the morrow, but the longer he remained at the school, the more it began to wane; Dr Santon's influence as well as his family's saw to that. While his parents believed Hitler had done much for Germany in the early 1930s, the time was quickly coming when he would have to be pushed on one side, and either the monarchy restored or, at least, a government animated by Christian values brought to power. Hitler had had his uses, but Manfred's family saw the Führer as an ill-educated braggart, and the sooner he was got rid of the better.

While Manfred was at Templars, two of his cousins, Peter and Berthold, were at Oxford on Rhodes scholarships. This was the Oxford of the famous (or infamous, depending on your point of view) King-and-Country debate. As patriotic Germans, they had voted against the motion, for patriotism was not ignoble to the citizens of a conquered nation. Like many other Germans, they failed fully to realise that a good many of those who voted for the motion had done so with their tongue in cheek, though there were, of course, several who had voted for it in deadly earnest. What worried Peter and Berthold was the way the vote was perceived in Germany, where it only served to confirm Hitler's prejudiced view that the British were decadent and spineless.

Manfred and his cousins greatly admired those British qualities Germans seemed to lack, whereas I, and many other English people, admired those German qualities which we seemed to lack — efficiency, a sense of duty, tidiness, seriousness and love of music. We did not, any more than they, admire the caricature of those German virtues which, under Hitler, had turned into ruthlessness, subservience, uniformity, obtuseness and sentimentality.

IV

I was extremely fond of Manfred, and though I was not then in love with him, I hero-worshipped him. My closest schoolfriend was a French boy, a distant cousin called Michel Loreau. Like Manfred, Michel had received most of his education in his own country, but had come to spend a year at a British public school to improve his English. His mother Hélène had long been adored by another of my distant relations, Charney Bassett. They had met during the first war, at which time both were married. Hélène's husband, Yves, had been gravely wounded, and had died in 1919; Rachel, Charney's wife, after repeated miscarriages, finally died in labour in 1928. Because Hélène and Charney were so deeply in love, they should have got married, but they didn't because she wanted to bring up her three sons, Robert, Michel and Philippe, as Frenchmen in France. When she refused Charney's offer they compromised; he decided to go back into the army, which sent him first to India and then to the Middle East, but he spent most of his leaves in France with Hélène and her boys, and they spent long holidays on his farm in the Cotswolds. It was on my mother's advice that Charney suggested to Hélène that she send Michel to Templars, since he and I were about the same age, and it was thought I could keep an eye on him.

Michel excelled in all those things I wished to excel in myself but didn't. His poetry and prose, in both French and English, invariably found a place in the school magazine: he was a good actor, and could draw and paint very well. He was an excellent talker with a dry wit and sophistication beyond his years.

During the summer of 1936, Michel and I spent a month at the Hawkspur Camp for maladjusted adolescents and young men, not because we were considered maladjusted ourselves, but because the Hawkspur Experiment was one of those enterprises that Dr Santon and the chaplain supported, and which they encouraged boys from Templars to visit in order to widen their social horizons.

The camp consisted of about thirty acres of East Anglian farmland, and had been bought the previous year without any buildings or shelters on it. It had begun with a few tents, a handful of adults and half a dozen young men between sixteen and twenty-five. Timber and a skilled carpenter were available in the local village to build more permanent quarters; there was enough ground on which to grow food; they had a cow and some chickens to provide them with milk and eggs, and they set out from there.

Paradoxically, the Hawkspur pioneers, who were nearly all Quakers, shared something with Hitler: they were all firm believers that *'Arbeit macht frei'* — work leads to freedom. The Hawkspur people, of course, didn't have any chips on their shoulders, were not racist bigots, and were charitably broad-minded. They considered hard, outdoor work valuable as discipline, education and inspiration. The head of camp staff, David, worked on the theory that a criminal can be defined as one upon whom it is not possible to *impose* discipline. He believed that condemnation and punishment of the kind usually meted out in prison and Borstal was quite useless, and had brought to the camp the Quaker belief in the efficacy of non-violent punishment. Since most of the young men who were sent there were in one way or another socially and emotionally disturbed, it was his aim to cure them.

When Michel and I arrived, we were put to work with three boys, Alec, Bob and Charlie. All three had got into trouble for stealing: in David's view they all suffered from the same symptoms. But you didn't have to know them for very long to become aware that Alec had a dreadful inferiority complex; Bob's father was a bully, and being a bully himself, Bob passed on to others what he had received at the hands of his parent; no one had ever shown him any affection. David saw his stealing as in some way symbolic of the theft of the affection he'd been subjected to. Charlie, on the other hand, had been brought up by very strict parents, with the result that he was overwhelmed with guilt feelings, and had a masochistic desire to be punished. Every time he stole anything he was found out — he made sure of that — but his wish to be punished was never gratified. On the contrary, David encouraged him to hit back at bullies. I remember hearing David telling him he should tell one of the older lads, a great hulk of a fellow covered in tattoos, who never stopped taking the mickey out of Charlie, to fuck off. When Charlie said he couldn't say that because it was wicked, David said there was nothing to feel guilty about sticking up for himself, and nothing about the word 'fuck' to merit eternal damnation. These three manifested the same anti-social symptoms — stealing — but suffered from different 'social disorders'. David hoped by studying their background to diagnose their disorders and hence effect a cure. On the whole he was successful. He believed that someone who has to undergo punishment tends to surround himself with a tough crust, so that society's violence will hurt him as little as possible. As he saw it, his job wasn't concerned with the tough crust but with the soft centre. He thought it would be quite impossible to get to the core if the crust was hardened by punishment.

Punishment at Hawkspur was only inflicted for breaches of camp regulations, which had been made democratically by the camp council, which, in turn, was made up of staff and boys. Bullying and fighting were fined — the boys were paid a shilling an hour — as were other offences. In this way, penalties and the need to earn were linked, the former being more in the nature of exacting restitution and of tokens of disapproval than of punishment as such. There was never any attempt to inflict pain or humiliation.

So far as it went, the experiment was a success, mainly, I think, because the majority of the boys and young men who were sent to Hawkspur had fairly high IQs. But a high IQ has very little to do with morality.

Looking back at Hawkspur after a lapse of five years, I blushed to think of my lack of sophistication, and hoped the Assessment Board I would shortly be appearing before would not pry too closely into this period of my development. Those weeks at the camp were dominated by my infatuation for Michel and by Alec's crush on me.

Alec was a slight, pretty boy about my own age, with a mop of untidy fair hair and bright blue eyes, We had not been in the camp more than a few days before he went out of his way to pair up with me whenever we had chores to do, and I quickly became aware that he was 'working' on me. I made rather half-hearted efforts to fend him off, but it was hopeless. It was soon very obvious that my lack of reaction was getting him thoroughly worked up, so I consulted Michel.

'He's getting on my nerves,' I said.

'Need you let him?' was Michel's matter-of-fact reply.

'I can't help it. He's in a hell of a state.'

'Are you worried for him?'

'I try not to think of it much from his point of view,' I said. 'I'm just aware that he's a load on my back that it seems I've got to carry. What's wrong with him?'

'What d'you think?' asked Michel in reply.

'Well, I suppose because, unlike us, he's a prisoner, and he's very lonely. It's obvious if you watch him with the other fellows that he's scared stiff of committing himself to relations with any of them. It seems to me,' I went on sagely, 'that he's got a pretty strong inferiority complex, and because I reacted kindly to him, he clings to me like a limpet.'

'You could be right,' said Michel.

'Anyway, I'm sure it's bad for him, and it's a hell of a strain on me. I've got to stop him.'

'Have you said anything to him?'

'Yes.'

'How did he react?'

'Horribly. He looked desperate.'

'How d'you feel about that?'

'I'm not sure. That's really why I'm telling you now. You see well — if it's going to hurt him so much, I don't really know what I want or ought to do.'

'Are you telling me you feel partly responsible for him?'

'Yes, I suppose I am. Though I don't see why I should.'

'Nobody can make you responsible for him. It's up to you how far you go.'

'But d'you think I ought to consider him at all?'

'I can't say. Surely it's up to David. He's the boss here. Have you said anything about all this to him?'

'No. I wanted to hear what you thought before I did.'

'Alec's clearly in a serious jam. You might be able to get him out of it. Whether you do or not depends on how fond you are of him. D'you like him?'

'Hard to say. He's always putting on an act. It's hard to know what he's really like. Sometimes I seem to get a glimpse of his real self, and then I like him a hell of a lot. I have a warm, kindly feeling for him then, but most of the time I rather resent him.'

'Does he know when you're liking and when you're resenting him?' Michel asked with a smile.

'Oh yes. He knows all right. But he's good at hiding his feelings.'

'Perhaps he doesn't completely trust you.'

'True. But I think he'd like to.'

'What I think he wants is for you to take him in your arms and comfort him. He wants to be loved, and, rightly or wrongly, he thinks you can give him the comfort he needs. I don't think it's clear to him, mind you. He's much more frightened that if he threw himself on you, you'd let him down. When you're rude to him and try to cool him off, you make it even harder for him to be honest with you. You just make him evasive, but he can't leave you because he thinks you're his one chance of salvation.'

'I say; that's going a bit far isn't it? Why me, for God's sake?' I cried.

'Can't say. He feels you can give him some of the things he lacks. You're happy and strong: he's unhappy and weak. I think that he can only be brought back to life by someone like you.'

'Wouldn't it be better if he learnt to stand on his own feet and break this unnatural dependence on me?'

'Better for you: not for him. It's up to you. If you break from him, you break one possibility of his getting on top of his problems. You won't make him stand on his own feet by repelling him: you can only do that by helping him to stand.'

'But why should I? That's David's responsibility.'

'Of course, but while we're here you can help him. He knows we're not going to be here for more than a few weeks more, so you've got your get-out anyway. But while we *are* here, you might as well try to help him as not.'

'I don't think I care about him enough.'

'I think you do.'

'I don't feel anything like what he feels for me. He told me he loved me.'

'I daresay he does,' said Michel knowingly. 'We can all see that!'

'But it's so embarrassing,' I exclaimed primly.

'Why? Don't take it so seriously. After all, we're all in a crowd of rather unhappy, misguided people. The sky won't fall because Alec loves you.'

And with that he went off to weed the onion bed.

During the next few days, David set Michel and me to work with some of the other boys, who were building a hut that was later to become the camp recreation room. Whether this was a deliberate ploy on David's part or not, I didn't know, but it clearly upset Alec. Going to bed one night I found a note from him tucked under my pillow. It read: 'Why have you been avoiding me? I don't want to force myself on you if you don't want me to. When I tried to join you on the playing field yesterday you looked at me in such an odd way. What had I come for? you seemed to be asking. I knew the others noticed this, but I didn't care much about that, except for your sake. But I do so want to work with you and to be with you. It's awful in the evening when you join the others or go out to the pub where we're not allowed to go.' And a lot more in the same vein.

* * *

Anyway, my fondness for Michel was steadily growing. He was more my type; he understood my kind of flippant humour. We appreciated the same things in life, and he was always ready for good-natured horseplay or, as I then believed, for the kind of flirting which was common currency at boarding schools and in most all-male societies such as Hawkspur. He was a great deal more street-wise than I. That was partly due to his being French. It was while we were at Hawkspur that he had lent me a novel attributed to Oscar Wilde, which had recently been published in a French translation. Needless to say, it had been banned in England on grounds of obscenity.

'It tells you everything you need to know about sex,' he told me.

'Everything?' I asked in disbelief.

'Yes; sex between men and women, between men and men and between women and women. I'll lend you my copy; I thought you'd like to read it.'

I wasn't sure whether this offer had been made because he thought my sexual education was incomplete (which it certainly was), or because he wanted to see how I'd react.

'Look after it,' he said as he handed it to me, 'and don't let the others see it.'

'It doesn't matter if they do; they don't understand French.'

'No, but David and the other members of the staff probably do. They might be shocked.'

I didn't think that a man as sophisticated as David would, but I let that pass. Although my French was above the average schoolboy standard, I'm not sure that it was up to this — as I found out many years later when an English version was published by Gay Men's Press. The book had first appeared in about 1890, and included a vast range of erotica ranging from sadism and lesbianism to sodomy and (for want of a better word) 'bottlery', a sexual exploit in which one of the protagonists at an all-male orgy is fucked with a hock bottle. When I read it at Hawkspur both the gay and so-called straight scenes had scared the pants off me.

Admittedly some of it made me laugh a lot, for it was written in an arch style of which this is one example; 'He slipped his hand stealthily up along her leg till it reached the upper storey. "No, no!" she cried, "please don't: you're tickling me." But he took courage, and plunged his finger boldly in the fine curly locks of the fleece that covered her middle parts.'

Knowing next to nothing about female pubic hair, this passage seemed incomprehensible. Furthermore, it didn't sound much fun for the girl. But when, after unbuttoning his trousers, he took hold of her 'dainty little hand', tried to introduce it within the gap and caught hold of his prick 'now stiff and hard,' I couldn't imagine a nicely brought-up girl from Cheltenham Ladies' College doing anything like that with pleasure. Girls of this kind were clearly not nice to know. And when later I read that 'the tightness of the orifice in which his cock was sheathed gave him such an overpowering sensation that he redoubled his efforts and shoved his muscular instrument with such mighty strokes that the frail woman shook under the repeated thumps', I didn't know whether to look forward to sex with a girl, or to avoid it at all costs for fear of doing her lasting damage. There was a lot more of this sort of thing, much of it apparently painful and leading eventually to 'screams, tears and sighs' followed by 'floods of tears'. To assuage these tears, the man laid on a meal of quite astonishing indigestibility, including champagne, oysters, foie gras, truffle salad and sherry trifle. This, it was alleged, 'dispelled their gloominess'. In me it would have induced appalling indigestion and an almighty hangover.

By the time I'd finished reading the book, the prospect of sex with a girl seemed both dangerous and highly over-rated. What with all the thumps, screams and tears, it didn't sound much fun for the girl, and having been brought up to be kind and courteous to women, it seemed all wrong to subject them to this kind of carry-on, unless, of course, they were tarts, in which case they were paid to put up with it. Apart from the horrendous expense, I supposed, come to the pinch, I could manage it, but only as a marital duty in order to perpetuate the Lord Mayoral line.

I felt better when I reached the point where the narrator, having one unsatisfactory encounter after another with women, at last makes love to his boy friend. I felt for the first time that, in some indefinable way, this meant more to me than all the rest. I was still a virgin, and thought of myself as straight, having accepted without question Dr Santon's sensible remarks about masturbation and schoolboy affairs, out of which, one day, I would grow. Purple though it was, I could relate to the passage where the two men come together — 'At every drop that escaped out of the body, an almost unbearable feeling started from the tips of the fingers and spread through the whole body, to end in a convulsion which annihilated mind and matter, a quivering delight too intense to be pleasurable.' This was more my cup of tea.

As I read the book, I began to look at Michel through different eyes. Much of the book frightened me, and my attitude towards him changed. I was a little scared of him and of his sophistication. The recollection of this period of my adolescence was embarrassing, too. There was the occasion when David sent us to the nearby town to collect some mail for the inmates at the post office. It was a glorious summer's day not long after I had consulted Michel about Alec. I had, to some extent, shaken myself loose from him but at the expense of attaching myself more to Michel. As we walked the five miles into the town, he had come bluntly to the point. 'Let's get this straight now,' he began. 'What's your trouble apart from Alec? What d'you want from me, how can I help you?'

I wasn't really troubled by Alec's attachment to me; it was deeper than that, and concerned my relationship with Michel far more than with him. I just had a feeling that with his greater sophistication, Michel would know what was wrong.

'You don't have to listen to me if you don't want to,' I said. 'I just feel...' I hesitated; 'I feel a bit as if I were drowning and you could save me. D'you understand?'

Michel was silent a moment before answering. 'In one way I think I do, but I don't believe it. I think you're imagining things. If I can help you I will, but I'm not sure what I can do. What's wrong? What are you afraid of?'

I told him I thought I'd missed life; we were both seventeen and he seemed so much more alive, so much more mature than I was. I blurted out that deep down I'd been frightened of something all my life; that life for me was frozen. I told him I'd always avoided scraps and fights at school, and that if anyone had threatened me I'd run away. I'd longed to grow up so as not to have to fight, but I knew that maturity would be more than an escape from childish torments. But, I went on, so far that's all it had been. I'd gained nothing and achieved nothing. I was just the same shivering kid as I always was, even though I was now fully grown. And yet, compared to him, I didn't feel a man. I daren't shake myself free. 'I think I'm scared of life,' I ended.

'Why? If you're afraid, you must be afraid of something positive, something threatening.'

'That's the trouble: there's nothing I can pin down. Oh God, if only I could get out of myself — if only someone could understand and show me. I just feel as if I've missed life: kind of cheated myself. I don't trust myself to do things for fear they'll go wrong. I can't explain it.'

'Aren't you being a bit dramatic?' he said; and then less severely, 'I believe you mean what you say, and I'm sorry, but I still don't understand you.'

I remember blurting out about a girl I'd met during the previous holidays. I couldn't even remember her name, but we'd got on well enough and liked each other, and we liked the same kind of music and so on. One day she kissed me; just a friendly, matey sort of kiss, I told him, but instead of responding to it naturally, and as she had expected me to, I'd frozen and felt embarrassed. She'd sensed this at once, and had never tried to kiss me again, with the result that I'd shrunk back into my shell.

'I didn't seem able to give myself,' I said. 'I was scared. I still am. I've always hidden behind a mask of sophistication as best I could, but I think I must be neurotic or something,' I concluded lamely.

'D'you really still feel like that?' he asked in disbelief.

'Not quite so much since we came to Hawkspur,' I said. 'It's different now: worse if anything, because I've started to want to live, and there's a kind of inner struggle going on inside me.'

'Why?'

'Because of you,' I said before I could stop myself. 'There's something about you that's got through the shell I live in. I began to feel it last term, and ever since I've felt more and more drawn towards you, and driven to break down my own shyness. I don't know why.' The words came tumbling out faster and faster. 'I've thought about it for weeks and weeks, but I still don't know. I feel as if somehow my life was bound up in you. When you look at me with approval your eyes melt the ice that's been freezing me all my life.' I could feel myself blushing, and turned away to hide my embarrassment. 'What can I say?' I stammered. 'I want to be real and give you my real self.'

Michel looked at me with an expression half patronising, half embarrassed.

'You're obviously trying to be truthful, Tony,' he said, 'I can see that. I hope it makes you feel better to get it off your chest.'

I said that it did, but in fact it had done nothing of the sort. Everything depended on Michel's willingness to meet me half way.

I really did feel he had the power to bring me back to life; to drag me out of the prison I'd got myself into. But it seemed to me then that he'd have far rather given me a boot up the arse.

We'd walked on in silence for a few minutes before he said, 'I'll try to understand and be helpful, but the trouble is that you've got a feeling for me which I don't return. It's like Alec's feeling for you. I wish for your sake that I did feel the same about you as you do about me, but I don't, and that's all there is to it. You're continually behaving as if I did. You've made me the most important person in your life, and you expect me to return the compliment. You're just not living in the real world, and every time my reactions don't agree with the imaginary ones you give me, you work yourself up into a state. For both our sakes, the sooner you come to terms with reality the better for us both.'

'Oh God, is there no way out of this?' I cried.

He told me not to be melodramatic, and I begged him not to be so defensive and hostile. 'All I ask is for you to love me,' I blurted out. 'For God's sake, just feel kind to me; let me relax; let me come to you; don't keep me at arm's length,' I pleaded.

'The best solution would be for us to leave here and go home. That'd settle the whole business. You'd forget it all in a couple of weeks. What a relief that'd be to me,' he almost shouted.

'If you go home, I'll drown myself,' I shouted back. 'Perhaps I wouldn't, but I think I would. I'd certainly feel like ending my life.'

This was too much for him. He told me, with complete justification, not to be so self-centred, and not to try blackmailing him. 'Anyone would think that my first duty to mankind was to make you happy,' he snapped. 'This doglike devotion is boring, and what's more, it's getting us talked about in the camp. It's got to stop, d'you understand?'

'Why did you work with Charlie and Bob all yesterday?' I asked before I could stop myself.

'Because David asked me to and because I wanted to. Look here, you're just being damned silly. I'm a reasonable enough chap, are you trying to drive me mad? I worked with them because I prefer working with them to working with you and Alec and the others. Is that clear?'

We walked on in silence, I struggling to hold back tears. 'Yes,' I said at length, 'I suppose I've just got to accept it.'

'Yes you have, Tony. It's neither my fault nor yours. It just happens like that,' he went on more kindly, 'You've just got to stop being so jealous.'

'I can't stop liking you,' I said. 'I just can't. I can't make myself different from what I am. It's not possible.'

'Then you'll just have to take what comes and stop whingeing. The whole of this situation between us is due to you. I didn't seek you out, and I don't need you. I know you were told by your mother to "look after" me when I came to Templars, and I'm grateful for that. But that was months and months ago, and I don't need to be looked after for ever. You can't hold me responsible for your unhappiness, and I'm not going to be made to feel responsible. I'm going to live my own life in my own way, and I'm not going to change it in the least degree for you.'

'I don't want you to change it for me,' I told him.

'If only you'd let me be free of you,' he went on remorselessly, 'there might be some chance of a genuine friendship springing up between us, but there's absolutely no chance of that so long as you go on like this.'

'Tell me how to behave and I'll do my best,' I retorted.

'You know perfectly well how I want you to behave. I want you to let me be myself and to stop pestering me.'

'I'll try. Really I will.'

'If you don't, I'll end by disliking you. Anyway, I'm getting tired of this conversation; it's getting us nowhere.'

The rest of our walk was completed in almost total silence. I felt that we had not been speaking the same language. Not because he was French and I was English, but because our attitudes towards friendship and love were completely different. I felt as if there must be nothing he didn't know; no experience of life he hadn't had. What hope was there for someone as green as me? I felt sure that most of the boys and young men at Hawkspur would have had similar experiences to Michel's, and that in some way I'd missed the boat, or been deprived. For the rest of the time we were at the camp I took care never to be with Michel or any of the other boys alone.

The day before we left, I handed him back the book he had lent me, carefully wrapped in a towel lest, by chance, one of the others might see it and ask what it was about. I would have had a hard time pretending that it was a French textbook set for holiday study, though there is no doubt that it taught me more than the *Malade Imaginaire* which was next term's set book.

The next time I saw Michel was in 1939 after he'd joined the

French navy and before my visit to Manfred at Jeven. He looked more handsome than he had done at school. Perhaps it was the uniform and the cap with its red pompom, but I had long since ceased to feel anything particular for him. Dr Santon had been right — these Platonic schoolboy affairs never lasted. There was nothing to worry about.

V

When I left Templars I was sent to France to improve my French at the establishment of General Gauthier de Fouleix. He was the long-time lover of Michel's great-aunt, Madeleine de Lusignac. They lived next door to each other at Le Chesnay in two of those huge, decaying Victorian horrors much beloved of retired military gentlemen at that time. Although in 'reduced circumstances' they took care to keep up appearances. General de Fouleix lived with four servants, three of whom were old soldiers, and his house was run like an officers' mess. Mme de Lusignac managed with five: a chauffeur, a chef, a lady's maid, a *bonne-à-tout-faire* and a housekeeper. Since neither of these large houses was ever fully occupied, and because of the dreadful economic situation, someone had suggested they could do no better than take in young foreigners and teach them to speak good French. These young people were always very carefully chosen. If they were European, they had to be recommended by people whose names appeared in *Debrett* or the *Almanach de Gotha;* if they were from the French overseas empire, they had to be royal. When I arrived, my fellow students were two Indo-Chinese princes with unpronounceable names, destined to become cadets at St Cyr, and next door, *chez* Mme de Lusignac, there were three English debs, of considerable beauty and limited intelligence, but of impeccable lineage.

Madeleine, Comtesse de Lusignac-Viveyrols, passed for a personage of some historic interest, if not importance, and was the possessor of a temperament both imperious and caustic. Having been the topic of gossip in *le beau monde* and the subject of debate in the Law Reports, Madeleine, the most beautiful and dashing of the du Buisson sisters, wasn't just any old lady yearning for the past glories of the Second Empire. Far from it: with her haughty gaze, her aquiline profile, her large bosom and her sharp tongue, she terrified the younger members of *le gratin* by the pungency of her comments.

At the age of seventeen she had been married to General Comte Georges de Lusignac-Viveyrols, an event she later compared with giving a Stradivarius to a gorilla. Such vehement sentiment was explicable only when one knew that her bridal night had been little more than rape. Her husband, at least thirty years her senior, on returning from their honeymoon confined her to the barrack life that formed the limits of his horizon. This life was made all the more uncongenial by the fact that the general was soon revealed to be a brutal and greedy fortune-hunter, obsessed by his conjugal rights, and lacking all consideration in their exercise. It was not long before Madeleine had fallen in love with one of the general's still more handsome and dashing subalterns, Gauthier de Fouleix.

It was rumoured (and no one seriously doubted it) that she had caught the eye of the Prince of Wales during one of his many visits to Biarritz, and that her daughter Albertine... Well, you never know; you can't be sure, can you? And with that dreadful husband of hers... Certainly the locket with the royal miniature inscribed 'A Madeleine, pour toujours. Bertie' and the date, 1898 — the year before Albertine's birth — was no ordinary memento.

Eventually, after enormous difficulties, Madeleine was able to secure a legal separation from her odious husband, but not before he had possessed himself of all her property, which under French law at that time he was entitled to do, though she refused point-blank to quit her home. Lusignac then sued her for the restitution of his conjugal rights, but since she refused to budge or to cooperate in any way, she found herself subject to a huge fine. This she likewise refused to pay, and as a result, she was summarily arrested and sent to prison, where she languished for several days before friends of the family persuaded the Minister of the Interior to annul the sentence. She was set free amid scenes of delirious enthusiasm on the part of the champions of women's rights and became the heroine of the hour.

General Gauthier de Fouleix was a short, dapper man with a clipped military moustache, who wore spats and a curly-brimmed Homburg hat in both Paris and the country. He had had a distinguished career, and since his retirement from active service had been military attaché in several European capitals. He had served as governor of a French colony, and was a subscriber to Action Française and a member of the Ligue des Camelots du Roi, whose aim was the restoration of the French monarchy and the establishment of a fascist regime. Although they had been lovers for more than thirty years, and had spent the greater part of their lives together, Gauthier and Madeleine preserved appearances by not sharing the same house. Because of the 'paying guests', as the language students were called, the twin establishment was known as the Ecurie Fouleix-Lusignac.

The formality of the two households was stupendous. The general always addressed Madeleine as *vous*, only employing *tu* for the three old soldiers and the dogs. The mealtime conversation, in which we were supposed to join to improve our French, usually declined into a monologue by the general, whose favourite topics were the iniquities of successive French governments, of the Jews, of the Communists, and above all, of *les sales boches* and *les macaronis*. This last was a difficult attitude to sustain, for he had to admit that what France needed was someone like Mussolini to get the country to 'come to its senses'.

Early in June, both households uprooted themselves and made for the Château de Jovelles, Mme de Lusignac's place at Montabourlet in Périgord. The journey thither was planned and executed, as was to be expected of a general, like a military operation. The butler, a former sergeant-major, was in charge of the commissariat. He was despatched each morning, an hour or more before the rest of us, to a pre-arranged stopping place along the route. Since the weather was hot and sunny, the 400-mile journey was to take five days, for Mme de Lusignac was determined to show us as many châteaux, abbeys and cathedrals as she could manage, and to visit as many of her friends and relations as she could bludgeon into entertaining a party of eleven. As most of these lived in large châteaux, this presented fewer problems than might otherwise be imagined. Lunch would be a *pique-nique* in some forest, where we would arrive to find that a fine meal had been prepared by the advance party.

We travelled in three vast Hispano-Suizas. In the first, a proto-estate-car, went the butler, the chef, and the lady's maid, along with the dogs and the baggage. They had a cramped journey. The second car, commanded by the general, carried the two princely cadets and myself. The third was Mme de Lusignac's, driven by Benoit, formerly a footman, then her coachman, and now in his old age her chauffeur, and in it travelled the three debs and Madeleine. All three cars were old, and had been bought when times were better. The estate-car was the oldest. It was fitted with a somewhat austere wooden body, and being designed for the exclusive transport of servants, dogs and luggage, was not very comfortable. The general's car, as befitted a military man, was upholstered in black leather with silver fittings, which included such essentials as a top-hat rack, a cupboard containing a brandy flask and silver goblets, a vase for carnations and coconut matting. Mme de Lusignac's, on the other hand, was tricked out in petit-point tapestry with a pattern of pink roses and mauve wisteria entwined round trellises. The fittings were gilt, if not gold, and comprised a built-in dressing-case for scents, sal volatile, eau de Cologne and face powder. The two chauffeurs wore maroon liveries to match the bodywork of the cars, with breeches, leather leggings and peaked caps with cockades. The arms of Fouleix and Lusignac-Viveyrols quartering Buisson were emblazoned on the doors of the cars of their respective owners.

There's no doubt that had they been contemporaries, Madeleine de Lusignac and Marie-Antoinette would have got on like a house on fire. They would have discussed at great length the best kind of cake to give to the starving poor, but, unhappily, in 1937, it wasn't easy to ignore the presence of the Third Republic completely, though Madeleine did her best. At Chartres and Chinon, at Chambord and Chenonceaux, at Richelieu and La Rochefoucauld she took a delight in pointing out to us the architectural beauties that had survived the wanton damage done by the republican philistines. Every empty niche, every headless statue, every unfurnished salon, every once-stained-glass window was the cue for a diatribe against the *canaille*, the rabble. Voluble official guides were swept aside with an imperious gesture, their gramophone patter rendered mute, while Mme de Lusignac held forth on the infamy of equality, fraternity, licence, democracy, atheism and mass education. It was as if we were back at the court of Louis XVI. For her, nothing of any worth had been created since 1789. I simply adored her!

After four months, during which my French improved and my politics veered towards the left, it was time for a change, and I was sent to spend the rest of the year with an Austrian family to improve my German.

VI

If life was uneventful at the Ecurie Fouleix-Lusignac, it was anything but at Schloss Drachenfels. To begin with, the castle was romantic in the extreme, set on a rock commanding a gorge through which the Salzach forced a passage from the mountains to the plain. It had belonged to the Tessenberg family since the fourteenth century. Towering above it to the north was the great mass of the Hagenberg beyond which lay Berchtesgaden and the menacing presence of Adolf Hitler. Not that we were very aware of him when I first arrived during the late summer of 1937, for the milieu in which I found myself held him in utter contempt. If they feared him at all, it was less than they feared socialists and communists.

If Hitler had died in 1937, he would, without doubt, have gone down as one of the greatest figures in German history. Throughout Europe he had millions of admirers: people as different in political outlook as Bernard Shaw, Gertrude Stein and King Edward VIII. His appeal was not just to the disgruntled and the disenfranchised, of which, God knows, there were then more than enough in Britain, but to many responsible men and women of good will. Much of his support came from the German establishment — the army, the church and the law — all of whom were united in their fear of communism. It was Hitler's genius to draw together the youthful elements in society as well as intellectuals, who found his ambition to restore Germany's wounded pride and shattered economy a refreshing alternative to the weak liberalism of the Weimar republic. Furthermore, unlike many of Europe's leaders at that time, he was a man still under forty, who had been decorated for bravery in the trenches, even though he had not reached any rank higher than corporal. As such, he spoke for the younger generation and for the future. Therein lay his power and his menace.

Graf Wolf von Tessenberg and his wife admired all things British. He had commanded a Jäger regiment against the Italians, and taken part in the overwhelming Austrian victory of Caporetto during the first world war. Like many of their class, the Tessenbergs had lost most of their money after the Austrian defeat, and had been obliged to recoup their finances by opening their houses to language students and paying-guests. The family consisted of two sons — Arnulf, the elder, then an art student in England, and Christoph, about my age, then doing his military service — as well as a married daughter, Hermine, four or five years older than me. Not long before I came to Drachenfels, she had married a widower much older than herself, the father of two girls only a few years her juniors. Hermine had been employed by her husband's late wife in a successful dress shop in Vienna, and had become her companion and helper during a long illness from which she died. For his children's sake, and the sake of the dress shop as well as for his own, he had asked her to marry him. But it was not a happy marriage, partly because of their great disparity in age, also because he was an almost penniless bore, who lived off a meagre army pension having lost all his family estates in Slovakia when that country became independent of Austria at the end of the war. His marriage to Hermine did little to better him financially, and much to cause her discontent. While not entirely penurious because of the successful dress shop, money was tight and her tastes extravagant.

I had not been at Drachenfels very long when Christoph came home for a week's leave. One morning we went into Salzburg to do some shopping, and agreed to meet at a café in the square not far from the cathedral. I turned up a little after him and had just sat down to order a hot chocolate, when I chanced to look up and saw coming across the square towards us a tall, fair-haired young man dressed in lederhosen, white stockings and a green loden jacket. As he approached I exclaimed to Christoph: 'There's someone I know. He was at school with me in England.'

Christoph looked in the direction I was pointing; 'I know him too,' he exclaimed, and getting to his feet he shouted: 'Hi, Manfred! Wie geht's dir? Hier ist einer deinen englischen Freunden!'

As he turned, Manfred broke into a broad smile, and running towards us, he took me in his arms and embraced me warmly. 'Tony, this is marvellous! What are you doing here?' His English was perfect, and his accent much improved since we had last seen each other two years before.

'I'm staying with Christoph's people to learn German.'

'No! That's fantastic,' and turning to Christoph he went on in German: 'And what are *you* doing? They told me you were doing your military service.'

'I am, but I've got a few days' leave, and we came into town because Tony and I had some shopping to do. I go back to Linz early tomorrow.'

'What a shame! I've not been called up yet, but I expect to be very soon. I'm here at least until Easter, unless my call-up papers come through before then.'

'Are you studying here?' I asked.

'Yes. I'm taking violin lessons and reading musicology at the university. I'm going to write a dissertation on Mozart's violin concertos.'

'That's marvellous. I'm taking music lessons, too. You remember how badly I played the clarinet at school! I thought I'd take the opportunity to try to improve my technique. I'm also taking piano lessons as well, in between my German ones. Christoph's mother is teaching me German.' Turning to Christoph, I went on, 'Did anyone ever tell you what a good teacher your mother is?'

Christoph smiled: 'I'll believe that when you speak German more grammatically than you do now.' We all laughed. 'Where are you staying, Manfred?' he asked.

'Oh, with Sonja Helmuth, who else?'

'Of course,' said Christoph, 'who else?' and turning to me he explained that Manfred was a cousin of one of Hermine's oldest friends. Sonja had a secretarial job at the Mozarteum and was on the festival staff.

'You must come out to Drachenfels, Manfred,' he went on. 'Mother and father would love to see you. Arnulf's in London and Hermine's in Vienna, but,' turning to me, 'you'll have Tony, and I'm sure he won't mind a bit of company of his own age. It must be dull for you on your own, isn't it?'

I had to admit that it was, and I said I'd look forward to seeing Manfred whenever he could get away. 'Oh, that's easy. I'm free every weekend. I'm sure I won't be missed if I pop over to Drachenfels now and again. We could have some music, couldn't we? I believe your mother' (to Christoph) 'still plays the cello, doesn't she? There's not much room at Sonja's,' he went on, 'and I'm sure she'd be only too glad to have the place to herself now and again.'

'How will you get there?' asked Christoph. 'D'you have a car?'

'No; but I've got a motorbike. That'll get me anywhere.'

In the short time since we had been at school together, Manfred had filled out and become even better-looking than I remembered. He was obviously glad to see me, and that pleased me enormously. We'd exchanged one or two letters after he left Templars, but neither of us were good correspondents, and we gradually slipped into the habit of sending postcards to each other at longer and longer intervals.

'You know I've been in France,' I said. 'I was staying with an aunt of Michel Loreau's. You remember him at school, don't you?'

'Of course. What's he doing now?'

'He's joined the French navy. He's going to be a professional sailor.'

'Did you see much of him while you were in France?'

'No, only once when he came home for a day or two's leave before joining his ship at La Rochelle.'

'He's some kind of relation of yours, isn't he?'

'Yes, but a very distant one. By marriage, you know.'

'I remember what great friends you were at Templars,' Manfred went on, giving me what I thought was a slightly sly look.

'Yes, we were. We spent part of last summer holidays together at a camp for juvenile delinquents.'

'That sounds most appropriate,' he said, laughing.

I smiled. 'We were sent by our parents to enlarge our horizons,' I said. 'It was okay.' I hesitated: 'We got on all right, but our paths went in different directions, that's all.'

'Like yours and mine?' said Manfred, smiling.

'Yes, but we've met up again, haven't we?'

'By good fortune — yes.'

Christoph summoned the waiter to pay the bill. 'I'm afraid we must be off now. We came in by train, and the one that gets back in time for lunch leaves in about ten minutes.'

'Give me your phone number, Manfred,' I said, getting up to go. 'You've got mine, I expect. If not, Sonja will have it. I mean your college number; Sonja's always out. I'll give you a ring when I've spoken to Gräfin Tessenberg and asked when it would be convenient for you to come over.'

Manfred and Christoph shook hands and sent greetings to their respective parents. Turning to me, Manfred took my outstretched hand in both of his, and looking me straight in the eye, said in English: 'I'm thrilled you're here. There's so much I want to talk to you about. So much has happened since I left Templars. I couldn't have wished to meet anyone more than you.' And squeezing my hand tightly, he went on: 'Let's meet as soon as we can. Have you got your riding gear here? Perhaps we could get a couple of horses and go on an expedition while this lovely weather lasts.'

'That'd be great,' I said. 'I'll ask the Graf if he knows where we can get another horse. At the moment I ride by myself. It'll be fun if we could go off somewhere together.'

On the way back in the train, Christoph asked me how Manfred had got on in England. I told him I thought very well.

'The von Schrades are very distant cousins of ours, you know' — and after a pause — 'He's a member of the Hitler Jugend, isn't he?'

'I expect so. They've all got to be, haven't they?'

'Yes, but is he very pro-Hitler?'

I said that I knew he admired Hitler for what he'd done for Germany, but that I didn't think Manfred was a fanatical Nazi.

'We don't trust the Germans. Not even our relations. It won't be long before they invade us. Father says they think there'll be an Anschluss before Easter.'

'If there is, it'll mean war,' I said.

'We think so, too. But they're working on the Viennese riff-raff all the time. We're all pretty worried because we're so close to the frontier. If Hitler invades, we'll be in the front line. That's why I asked about Manfred.'

'You're not suggesting he may be a spy, are you?'

'How can you tell? I hope not, but you can't be sure.'

'Well, from what I remember of him at school, I think it is most unlikely.'

Christoph looked out of the carriage window and sighed. 'It's all a bloody mess anyhow,' he said, and lapsed into silence.

VII

Manfred and I saw a great deal of each other that autumn and winter. He would come nearly every weekend to Drachenfels, and if it was fine, we would ride out together into the surrounding countryside. If it was wet, we played violin sonatas or chamber music together, depending on who was staying in the house, for nearly every-one who came seemed able to play an instrument. Whenever I went to Salzburg for my music lessons, we would meet for lunch, or for a drink before I caught the train back to Drachenfels. We became inseparable, and the attraction I had felt for him at school grew steadily stronger.

We both knew in our heart of hearts that time was short, and that the political situation might change at any time to our disadvantage. We had met again by pure chance, and made the most of the circumstances in which we found ourselves. As the weeks went by, we fell more and more in love with each other. The rather shy admiration I had had for him at school ripened into deep affection. He had matured, and now was everything I admired in a young man. What seemed wonderful to me beyond words was that he seemed to see in me something that he also loved and admired. If, from time to time, I asked myself what it could possibly be, I quickly banished the thought, and thanked God that I had found a friend who returned my love.

In those days, boys of our age and upbringing seldom, if ever, declared their physical feelings for one another, even when they were as deeply in love as we were. Neither of us ever alluded to sex, except flippantly, when, in the course of a walk through the town we might meet one of Manfred's fellow students on the arm of a pretty girl, when he would say something disparaging, such as: 'Oh there goes old so-and-so; thinks he's a deb's delight, as you English say. Can't think what he sees in a silly girl like that,' or something equally dismissive.

Not long after we had met by chance in Salzburg, just as the September leaves were beginning to turn, Manfred came to Drachenfels. The weather was beautiful, and Graf von Tessenberg suggested that we take a couple of horses and ride up the Salzach valley to a property he owned to deliver a letter from him to his tenant. It was a gorgeous day, and after a couple of hours we came to a meadow by the side of the river, where I suggested we tether the horses and let them graze while we went for a walk along the river bank.

From what Manfred had told me at Templars, I knew that he admired Hitler, and had joined the Hitler Jugend of his own free will. At the same time, I wanted to find out what effect, if any, his two terms at Templars under Dr Santon had had on his attitude to the Nazis.

'I appreciated that what Dr Santon had to say was valid for you,' he said in answer to my question, 'but what applies to you doesn't always apply to me. If I were an Englishman, I would certainly agree with most of what he said, but I'm not. My country was defeated in the war, and we have suffered more than you have as a result. What does that prove? That Germans are inferior or wickeder than Englishmen? That you are morally superior to us?'

'Of course not. It merely means that we had more guns than you. That's all it can mean. Our soldiers weren't braver than yours; our generals were certainly stupider.'

'Maybe; but you weren't stabbed in the back by the Jewish profiteers as we were.'

'We might have been if we'd lost. There are a lot of people in England who dislike the Jews as much as Hitler does. I should know because I had a Jewish grandmother. But a lot of true-blue Britons made just as fat profits, one of my uncles among them. If we'd lost we would have made them the scapegoats just as Hitler is doing now. It's very easy to point the finger at Jews because they're different and unpopular.'

Manfred sighed, and taking a pebble, threw it into the river. Turning to me, he said: 'Tony, what are you going to do if it comes to war?'

'I don't know. I've no intention of killing Germans, that's for sure,' I said making light of his question and laughing.

He looked at me, his expression serious, unsmiling. 'It's nothing to laugh at, Tony,' he said, stretching out his hand and touching my shoulder. 'You and I might find ourselves face to face in battle, and it would be our duty to kill each other.'

'I know. That's why I'm going to be a conscientious objector.'

'But that's a cowardly thing to do,' he expostulated.

'Is it? I'd probably be sent to prison if I do object. That wouldn't be much fun.'

'Nonsense. Not in England. In Germany, yes. In Germany they'd probably shoot you.'

'In the last war we did almost the same, though we were more hypocritical about it. We gave objectors exemption provided they agreed to do non-combatant service, and then we made sure that the work they were required to do was so dangerous they'd probably get shot. We got your lot to do our dirty work for us so that our consciences could be clear, and so that the army could write and tell their wretched parents that their son had died a hero's death.'

Manfred looked at me in amazement. 'Are you serious?' he said.

'Yes; I'm afraid I am. We're clever at disguising things like that, but we have a nasty side to our national character just as you Germans have.'

We were silent a while as we lay side by side, each lost in his own thoughts. What would I really do in the coming war? In a war that would probably start with mass air-raids on a devastating scale, it wouldn't be so much a question of what Manfred and I would do, as what would be done to us. There would be no sure way of getting out from under the enemy's bombs, or from either of our countries' condemnation, or from the fury of the mob, who would be persuaded to believe that those who had led them into the war were their saviours, and that those who had tried to lead them away from it were their enemies. In the final analysis, was there a pin to choose between Hitler and Chamberlain? Were they not both determined to fight it out to the finish when war eventually came, as come it must? As far as I could see, the only difference was that Hitler was undeniably a paranoid yob, whereas our rulers were bellicose old gentlemen. When it came down to it, there wasn't much to choose between yobs and gentlemen, when both were obstinate chauvinists.

Since the last war, the technique of attack had advanced far further than the technique of defence, whether the attack of nations on their enemies by bombs and poison gas, or of governments on their own people by suppression and poisonous propaganda. In the first war, the actuarial value of an objector's life was very much higher than that of a front-line soldier's. In the coming war, civilians would be in at least as much danger as the infantry, especially citizens of big cities, so pacifists would have to face the added perils of their own states as well as of mob law.

'I can only answer your question by saying that I shan't contribute to the process of fighting by any deliberate act,' I said, 'but I don't expect to escape by not taking part. I have no quarrel with you as a German, or with the German people as a whole, but I'm afraid I may find I have a quarrel with Hitler and the political system he has given you.'

'But Hitler has done more for Germany than any other politician since Bismarck,' protested Manfred. 'He has given us hope and self-respect.'

'That I'm perfectly ready to concede,' I said, but if we are to believe *Mein Kampf*, he intends to get back all the territory that was taken away at Versailles, kill all the Jews, and claim German *lebensraum* in Russia. How will he do this without a war? I simply fail to see it.'

Manfred didn't answer. He took up another pebble and threw it in the water.'You asked me what I was going to do in the coming war,' I went on before he could answer my question, 'but what I said, though definite, wasn't an altogether adequate answer. I've got to justify my pacifism, not just to myself but to others. I've got to satisfy my conscience that what I do is right, and because I have some Jewish blood in my veins, this will be very difficult. I've got to be sure of my intellectual, moral and emotional reasons. I've got to be prepared to act rationally in the face of war hysteria.'

'What d'you mean by war hysteria? Is it hysterical of us to demand the reunion of Germans who were separated from us by Versailles?'

'Of course not. That's not what I mean. I'm thinking of the mindless hysteria there was last time. People just gave up thinking intelligently and rationally. They actually believed that your soldiers went about cutting off the hands of Belgian babies; that you took corpses from the battlefield and sent them to sausage factories to make grease; in England, people kicked dachshunds because they were German dogs, and refused to listen to Wagner, Bach and Beethoven. They said your soldiers raped nuns and hanged priests from the belfries of their churches. It's already beginning; we're hearing horror stories in England about German concentration camps. I've no doubt that you've heard similar tales about us. But it doesn't end there. There was a story at the beginning of the last war, which you remember began in August, that the Czar had sent a huge army from Archangel to fight on the western front, and that Russians had been seen getting off trains in England with snow on their boots. Snow! I ask you, in August after a two-week journey by sea. And there were thousands of people who really believed that. It's mad, mad, mad.'

He turned to me and smiled. 'I agree, but they're not all lies. Our soldiers returned from the front and what did they find? All the food, all the jobs, all the houses taken by Jews. My family lost thousands of hectares in Posen to the Poles. The communists, here in Austria, nearly succeeded in taking over the country as they have in Russia. If they'd succeeded here and in Germany, d'you think I'd be here talking to you now? Wouldn't they have slaughtered us like they slaughtered the Czar and the Russian aristocracy? Would *you* like to live under Stalin?'

'Of course not. Nor would I like to live under Hitler and Goebbels and Goering.'

'You can leave Goering out of it: he was a great war hero. Next to Richthoven he was our greatest air ace.'

'Maybe. All the more reason why he should be ashamed of being associated with riff-raff like Hitler's gangsters.'

Manfred shrugged: 'I have to admit that there are a lot of nasty pieces of work in the Party. People like us wouldn't have anything to do with them if we could help it. But in the dire situation Germany found herself eight or nine years ago, we all had to work together if we were to survive, and whatever you may say about him, Hitler did save us from bolshevism. We'd have been slaughtered; so he's saved our lives. Why, even the Kaiser's grandsons have lent him their support. They should know, after what happened to their Russian cousins.'

'But all that's in the past,' I said. 'The way things are going, and Hitler has said so quite plainly in his book — sooner or later there's going to be a war between England and Germany.'

'England needn't take part. We've no quarrel with England.'

'What about South-West Africa?' I said slyly. 'I remember you telling me at Templars that your father had been out there, and it was your ambition to follow in his footsteps.'

'Yes I did. But if England is as fair as she claims to be, she'll give it back to us.'

'I wonder.' I looked away, and then, 'But we were discussing what I would do in the war. D'you remember when your cousins, Berthold and Peter, came to take us out from Templars on their bikes?'

'Yes.'

'D'you remember all the fuss there was about the Oxford Union debate on the motion that "This house will never again fight for King and Country", how shocked Berthold and Peter were, and how they said they'd voted against the motion?'

'Yes I do.'

'Well, haven't we been told that the Great War was fought to end war? Very well; the purpose of the debate was not wanton. "King and Country" stands for the blind appeal to patriotism — my country right or wrong. Those who supported the motion made not so much a confession of pacifist faith as a claim to consider and judge the true issues of war. Whatever the issue, "King and Country" will be again, as always before, no more than a cloak. What they were saying was not "never again" but "never blindly again". That's the important thing to remember. There was a huge outcry against these so-called decadent, unpatriotic, cowardly undergraduates. You know because you were there. D'you remember how Churchill compared them to people like you — to German youth — who were admirable, and how he urged us all to follow your example? Have you ever thought what that means? It means that one old man was urging me to go out and shoot you — yes, shoot you, probably the dearest friend I've ever had, the person I admired as much and more than any of my other contemporaries.'

He turned towards me once more and put his hand on my shoulder.

'D'you really, really mean that about me?'

'Yes,' I said without hesitation and looking away, I went on, 'You must have realised how much I admired you.'

'You know how much I admire you, too, Tony, don't you?'

'Oh nonsense,' I said embarrassed, and wishing I hadn't let

myself be quite so carried away. 'Quite apart from anything else,' I went on, trying to change the subject, 'the Bible tells us not to kill one another.'

'Of course, I know it does, but d'you really believe that the use of force, even to the length of killing, is always and inevitably wicked?'

The moment of embarrassment had passed, and I had regained my equanimity.

'No, I don't believe it is always wicked. But I feel bound to make it clear to myself, and not just to myself, what the basis of my pacifism is.'

I paused, thinking before I spoke. 'I think that any war I can conceive of involves such infinite evil to humanity as a whole, that it outweighs any possible chance of good that might come out of it.'

'What kind of war would that be?' he asked.

'Well there are several kinds of war I can think of. There's the patriotic war of which the last one was a prime example. It sprang from the pitting of one set of national ideals, aims and ambitions against another. It showed fanatical passions on both sides; it demanded the devoted adherence of scores of millions of apparently sane people, arrayed in bitter enmity against each other. There was an English verse that summed it up neatly. I wonder if I can remember it. It went something like this:

'God heard the embattled nations sing and shout
"Gott strafe England" and "God save the King".
God this, God that and God the other thing,
"Good God," cried God, "I've got my work cut out."

'Patriotism that can produce that kind of rubbish stands self-convicted in my opinion. If "My country right or wrong" is appropriate for me, then it's appropriate for you.' I went on to say that I believed the people of one nation should respect those of another; that Englishmen should respect Frenchmen, Germans and Italians because each nation had contributed its share to European culture. As an Englishman I wanted to make my compatriots aware of the crimes that had been committed in its name by government, and that would be committed when war came, more especially because the English government had been freely elected.

'For you to do the same,' I went on, 'will be much harder, because your government is trying to deprive you of your spiritual liberty, which is your birthright. They can take away our physical liberty easily enough, but all the armies and all the Gestapos in the world are powerless to deprive us of our spiritual liberty, unless — unless, my dear Manfred, you cooperate with them. Whether you do so or not is not for me to say, and I certainly wouldn't presume to tell you. Only time will tell whether Germans will be allowed full spiritual liberty unimpaired by propaganda and lies. You'll find out soon enough.

'If I had my way, I'd do everything I could to debunk patriotism — all that martial music, the medals, the religious blessing of regimental banners, the picture of the soldier as saviour rather than destroyer. It's by ruses and disguises like this that adults are made to look childish.'

'But martial music, medals and uniforms are fun,' Manfred protested.

'That's the trouble; they are. They're very beguiling indeed for all sorts of reasons,' I added, smiling at him. 'Have you ever asked yourself why Hitler's done so well with the young? It's because he's dressed them up in pretty uniforms and made them think they're great kids. And that goes for the adults as well as for people of our age. I love martial music and uniforms, but I have to acknowledge that using them for the purpose Hitler uses them is very dangerous, and rather childish.'

'Perhaps you're right. But how else would Hitler have got the country out of the mess it was in? None of your politicians have been very successful in uniting English youth for the common good of the country. What you say about blind patriotism is all very well, but what about wars of self-defence?' he asked. 'Germany is surrounded by enemies who may attack her at any moment.'

'Oh come now, Manfred, how can you say that? The Dutch, the Danes, the Swiss, the Austrians, the Czechs, the Poles — none of them want to attack you. The French and English lost so many men in the last war they certainly don't want to risk losing as many more again. So that leaves the Russians. They might wish to attack you, but all the evidence suggests that Stalin is quite prepared to destroy the political system under which we live in the West by subversion, even if it takes him till the end of the century. Anyway, he's just shot all his best generals, so he can't be much of a threat to you now. So what have you got to fear?'

'It's all very well for you to say that, but international Jewry is out to destroy us if it can, and it's much more powerful than bolshevist Russia. Russia and America are dominated by Jews; the Jews are the biggest revolutionaries as well as the richest capitalists.

That's what makes them so dangerous. Just think of it — Marx, Trotsky, Zinoviev, Kamenev — were all Jews. Jews dominate the American economy, just as they dominated the bolshevik revolution to destroy capitalism. They are just biding their time till they're strong enough, and then they'll attack us. Just you see! Haven't you read *The Protocols of Zion* in England yet? Get hold of it, and then you'll see what a menace the Jews are.'

'I've not read it, but I've heard my people talking about it. I can't see English Jews taking part in that sort of thing. There were quite a lot of nice Jews at Templars.'

'There are quite a lot of nice German Jews — Mendelssohn and Heine, for example. It's not that kind of Jew I'm thinking about. They've contributed to the countries they've settled in. I'm sure your Jewish great-grandfather contributed a lot to England.'

'I'm sure he did, he made umbrellas,' I said laughing.

'I was talking about the Jews who have contributed nothing and are social parasites.'

I sighed. 'I can't agree with you about the Jews, but I do agree with you about the communist threat. It is an evil system, and we must try to put a stop to it.'

'It's not just communism; it's the Russians themselves. They're almost as primitive as Africans. It would be appalling if they over-ran Europe.'

'Now that's utter nonsense, Manfred. How can you say that men like Tolstoy, Tchaikovsky, Chekhov or Dostoievsky are primitive savages. All that racial stuff Hitler has been filling your head with really *is* rubbish. Surely you don't believe it, do you?'

He looked at me sheepishly.

'Perhaps not all of it,' he admitted.

'Not any of it, Manfred. The idea that war is an integral part of the struggle for existence, and that it is possible to breed a race of supermen, all looking like you with your looks and brain and intelligence, is nonsense. To say that war is nature's way of securing the survival of the fittest is pure and utter codswallop.'

'Codswallop? What's that? I don't understand the word.'

'It means rubbish, balderdash, twaddle, bosh, rot, drivel, un-scientific nonsense. The Nazis have served it up with a lot of bad eugenics: it's no more than misapplied half-truth. It's based on a deliberate misunderstanding of Darwinian theory. Just think about it. If you were old or cunning enough to escape active service, or if, by some fluke, you were resistant to the effects of poison gas, and if, which they are not, these were heritable factors, they are not therefore variations we would want to predominate at the expense of all other and more distinctively human characteristics, are they? And furthermore, don't wars kill the youngest and fittest in society? I'm sure that your army rejects cripples, idiots, those who are blind and deaf due to inheritable diseases. I've heard that Hitler wants to kill these sorts of people because they are a burden on the state, or does he want to conscript them into the army so that the enemy can kill them?'

'You're changing the subject, Tony. We were talking about a war of self-defence.'

'All right then. But if Germany attacks eastward to stop the spread of communism in its self-defence, won't that prove to the Russians that the war they are fighting is one of their own self-defence? What we've got to ask ourselves is this: "What is it we actually want to defend by fighting?" The answer must surely be our lives and our culture — our standard of living, our way of life, our very well-being. You must know La Fontaine's fable of the tame bear that wished to defend its master against a bee that was about to sting him. He took up a rock and crushed the bee on his master's bald head and killed him. I can cure a cold in the head by decapitating myself, or I can save the contents of my house from being burgled by burning it down. Tell me this: how often has a nation attacked another one which it didn't think it could easily defeat?'

'We lost the last war,' he said.

'Yes, but that's not the point. The Kaiser thought he could repeat 1870 when he declared war on France.'

'He didn't declare war on France: France declared war on us.'

'Well, when Austria attacked Serbia after the archduke was killed. The whole thing got out of hand after that. The English didn't care a hoot about Serbia, nor did the Russians care a hoot about Belgium. Only a totally unprovocative country can really claim its war would be one of self-defence, but unprovocative countries don't declare war on each other. Can you imagine a situation where Holland would declare war on either Belgium or Germany, or on Denmark or Sweden? The only war I could justify is one to destroy a tyranny that is enslaving a people, who cry out to be liberated.'

'Precisely. You're right there. That's why we would be justified in attacking Czechoslovakia and Poland because these people are enslaving Germans.'

'But Manfred, are you really sure that they are?'

'Yes I am. That's why I shall support Hitler in everything he does to rescue our people from them.'

I turned away. There seemed no more to say.

'But that's no reason why Germany and England should fight each other,' he continued. 'It's our affair. We want to solve it in our own way.'

With that, he got up, and started to saddle his horse. I watched him for a second or two, and then followed his example. We rode home in silence.

In November the Tessenbergs took me with them to Vienna for three weeks. We stayed in a palace belonging to some cousins, visited the opera, and went sightseeing and socialising. Most of the people I met were living in a world of illusion, doing their best to shut out everything that was unpleasant or revolutionary. So far as they could, my hosts lived the kind of lives they had lived under the Empire, looking to the day when the monarchy could be restored. I doubt if I met anyone who was not a prince, a count or a baron — or more accurately a princess, countess or baroness, since most of the young men of my age were doing their military service.

We returned to Drachenfels for Christmas, and though I saw Manfred briefly before he went home to his people in Germany, I was alone with the Tessenbergs until the New Year. It was during this time that I got to know Hermine. We had met briefly when I first arrived, and she had been at Drachenfels in October, but as most of my time, when not studying German and music, had been spent with Manfred, I had not seen much of her. In Vienna she introduced me to many of her friends, but the time we spent there was one round of parties and it was not until we found ourselves thrown together at Drachenfels over Christmas that we had a chance to get to know each other more than very superficially.

Hermine von Branden, I have to admit, was quite entrancing. Vivacious and witty, she had the kind of beauty that cries out to be loved. Today she would be described (by the gutter press, at any rate) as 'fun-loving', which in their parlance means that she possessed a high-powered sex-drive, and it is certainly true to say that she had what I can only call a mega-lust for handsome young men. Unhappily, her middle-aged, corpulent husband failed totally to satisfy her, and her gaze had become focused on Manfred and me, as the only young men who were not either her brothers or discarded former studs.

As I have already indicated, Manfred and I that autumn were inseparable. The feelings I'd had for him at school had been tempered by shyness and my attraction to Michel, but since we had been so much together, I had fallen in love with him and he with me. There were so many interests we had in common. Not only were we more or less the same age, but we both loved music and riding, and that glorious autumn we had our fill of both. Hardly a day passed when we didn't see each other, and none of this had escaped Hermine's notice.

'You are very fond of him,' she said one day when we happened to find ourselves alone in the drawing-room before dinner.

'Yes I am.'

'You Englishmen share with us Austrians these romantic friendships with other young men, but you mustn't let them go on too long.'

I didn't answer, and I don't think she expected me to.

'It's better to have that kind of relationship when you are at school, and you and Manfred were at school together, I know. It's natural then, but now you are a man you should fall in love with a woman. You need an experienced woman, a little older than yourself, with whom you can have a relationship. She could teach you how to love and cherish the woman who will one day be your wife.'

I smiled enigmatically, mainly because I wasn't sure how to answer her in German — or in English for that matter. Coming closer, she put her hands on my shoulders, and looking me straight in the eyes, said very softly, 'I could be that woman, Tony, *mein lieber.*'

I was exceedingly flattered by Hermine's obvious interest in me, but was saved from having to say anything further by the Gräfin's entrance with some of the other house guests.

'Don't forget,' said Hermine, as she took her hands from my shoulders, and turning away from me, she walked over to welcome her mother's guests, and spent the rest of the evening chatting to an elderly prince with a handlebar moustache, who had come to spend the weekend shooting chamois.

* * *

Not long after Christmas, Manfred returned to Salzburg to resume his studies. Christoph had Christmas leave, and Arnulf had joined the family from England. The weather was sunny and frosty, and someone suggested an expedition to the mountains to ski.

In those days, only fashionable resorts like St Moritz and Kitzbuhel had ski lifts, so in order to reach the higher slopes above the treeline we had to walk up on skins, or go by horse-drawn sleigh to the base of the runs and climb from there. On this occasion it was decided to go by sleigh, and to start from the Count's property Manfred and I had visited on horseback in the autumn. This time we drove by car to the farm, where we changed into sleighs. There were three of them; Hermine and Arnulf led the way, Christoph and Sonja were in the second and Manfred and I brought up the rear. It was a long, twisting road up to the ski slopes, and the journey took an hour or more. We eventually reached a small chalet the farmer used in summer while tending his cattle grazing on the mountain pastures. It was quite small, consisting of a living room with a box bed fitted into one wall, and a large porcelain stove in the corner. This room was built above the stable, which was divided into a store for hay and standings for the horses.

After we had unharnessed the horses and tethered them in their stalls, we took the heavy fur rugs, which had kept us warm on the sleigh ride, together with the food and drink we had brought with us to consume after the ski run, and put them in the chalet. Arnulf lit the stove to warm the place up, and then we set off on our skis. There was some discussion, I remember, about which of two or three runs we should take, as they were not all equally easy. Arnulf and Hermine chose the hardest, while Christoph and Sonja said they would take us down the easiest, agreeing that we would all meet at the gasthaus at the village where we had left the car. If, by any chance, we couldn't make the gasthaus, then we could sleep in the chalet and go down by sleigh in the morning.

The four of us set out together, but Christoph and Sonja soon got ahead of Manfred and me, though there was no difficulty finding the way, for it was easy to follow their tracks in the new snow. In those days, the number of skiers was small, and there was no one else on the mountain that day. Eventually we reached the point where Christoph and Sonja had stopped to take off their skins to start their run down.

The weather was still fine, but as we climbed, clouds had begun to gather, and by the time we had rested and thought about our descent, they had closed in in the valley below. Neither of us was unduly worried by this, for all we had to do was follow the others' tracks. They knew the way well, and sooner or later we were bound to get back to the chalet. Easier said than done. Although Manfred was a better skier than I, neither of us were up to the standard of the others, and consequently we were far slower than they were. As we entered the cloud, we found to our dismay that it was by no means easy to follow the tracks, which in the sunshine had shown up clearly enough in the untrodden snow. We kept getting lost and having to retrace our steps, and it was getting dark, and long past the time when we had planned to meet in the gasthaus, when we at last reached the chalet, by which time the light had all but gone.

The others had taken their sleighs, and left us a note telling us on no account to attempt the descent in the dark, and that we should spend the night in the chalet and come down in the morning. By now it had come on to snow, so we set about stoking up the stove, and cooking the food we had brought with us in case of just such an eventuality.

While Manfred was making some glühwein, I went to feed the horse and collect our rucksacks from the sleigh, and we quickly made ourselves warm and comfortable. After we'd eaten our supper, Manfred took a hip-flask from his pocket and two silver goblets, and poured out some schnapps. 'Prosit,' he said, smiling, as he offered me one. 'To us.'

'Yes, to us,' I responded.

I sat down on the bed to take off my ski-boots, and while I was doing so, he came over and sat down beside me. Draining his goblet, he turned, holding out his hand. Taking it, I knew then how much I loved him, and bending towards him kissed him on the forehead and then on the lips.

For the first time since we met at Templars, I felt completely at ease, and no longer shy of him, and I was glad of the storm of kisses he showered on me in return for mine. As his hands clenched my head, he kissed my lips and my throat and ear lobes, nuzzling his whole face against mine as if he wanted to devour me. In his eagerness, he had pushed me down on to the bed, and at first I lay passively enjoying the fierceness of his kisses.

After this initial outburst, he got up and held out his hand to me. I had always feared physical love, but I now saw how natural our primitive abandonment had been. We looked at each other without speaking, and coming closer, Manfred broke the silence, telling me how much he had loved me at Templars and how much he had thought of me since.

'But why didn't you write to me more often, or tell me?' I

asked.

'I was afraid to. And I didn't think you cared. You English are so reserved. Anyway, I was sure you were fonder of Michel.'

And then it came out in a torrent of words: how he was no longer ashamed of feeling about me as he did; about his family; about the great pressure he was under to give up his English friend; how little time there was before he would be called up — on, on, on he went in an outburst of love and emotion.

Still holding his hand, I drew him down beside me, and once again our lips met. Gently he stripped me of my clothes and I of his, until we lay naked on the soft, fur rug we had put on the bed.

Down below I heard the soft whinnying of the horse, and the clink of the halter chain as it moved in the stall.

We feasted our eyes on each other hungrily. His blue eyes seemed to pierce me to the very core of my being, making my blood flow more rapidly. He bent down and caressed me with his hands everywhere, pressing his lips on every part of my body, lavishing kisses on my nipples, my ears, my arms, my legs and then my cock. He pressed it to his lips, which seemed to electrify me, and then, gently, lovingly, took the tip, and afterwards all of it, into his mouth. Every nerve tautened with a sensation so keen it almost overwhelmed me; even the soles of my feet were tingling as if pierced by a thousand tiny needles, fire seemed to course through my body, and my whole body seemed to melt as I came in urgent, convulsive spasms.

Then recovering myself, eager to take his place and return the delight I had just experienced, my overwhelming desire was to repay him for the wonderful gift he had bestowed upon me. Clasping each other we wrestled together, laughing, twisting, writhing, exciting each other into a state of near frenzy. At last we calmed down, and I feasted my eyes on his beauty, on his lips parted in a happy smile, and on his perfect body. I laid him down gently on his back, and kneeling astride him, bent down and kissed him. He began to move beneath me, gently at first, then thrusting a little faster and further until our movements synchronized. I pressed him ever more tightly till I felt him shudder, and just as I had done, he shouted for joy, and I knew that I had repaid the debt I owed him. His arms gripped me convulsively; I became rigid, and then together our nerves relaxed in harmony and we fell once more into each other's arms.

I don't know how long we slept, but it was still dark when I woke, and the oil lamp was still burning. Manfred lay beside me, his head cushioned on one arm, a faint smile on his lips, his tousled hair just glinting in the lamplight. I raised myself on my elbow and looked down on him, his face half hidden in the shadows, the clean line of his jaw and throat pale against the dark fur of the rug on which we were lying. I was lost in admiration not only of his beauty but also of his steadfastness of purpose. He was a true patriot; one who was prepared to give his life for his country; for a country that had suffered much; that had been subject to a vindictive treaty; the country of Bach, Beethoven, Goethe and Luther; the country that had been at the very core of European civilisation, and which had been vanquished, as he believed, by the greed and treachery of men who bore it no true allegiance, and who had so woefully let down the soldiers at the front. We had no quarrel, this Parsifal and I, but inevitably in a few months — at most a couple of years — we would be enemies, bound by stupid laws and stupider politicians to kill each other should our paths cross on the field of battle.

I thought how absurdly young he looked, and could not stop myself from stretching out my hand to stroke back a lock of hair that had fallen across his forehead. As I did so, he opened his eyes and smiled. Raising himself slightly, he leaned towards me and kissed my forehead.

'Ich liebe dich, Tony. Ich liebe dich,' he whispered.

'Yes,' I replied softly. 'Yes, for ever and ever until death do us part.'

'Sprich nicht von Tod. Sag nur "bis in alle Ewigkeit" — for ever and ever.'

In the stall below, the horse stamped its hoof on the stone floor, and clinked its halter as it shifted its weight in sleep.

There could be nothing shameful in love such as Manfred and I felt for each other, but that terrible line 'You were the enemy I killed, my friend' came into my mind, and I wanted to cry out in agony: 'No never — never, never, never, never.'

I *would* have a choice, I could object, stand away from the utter lunacy of war; I would go to prison, if need be; but Manfred? What choice had he? He must obey or be shot, but I would rather he obeyed, no matter how wrong I might think the cause. We both loved our country, but I loved him more, and at that moment, I believe he, too, loved me more than anything else in the world.

The conviction came upon us that this would be the last time we would make love. We knew the moment must be held and cherished...

'I could never, never hate you, Manfred,' I whispered.

'Du bist mein ewiger Freund, Tony,' he whispered back. 'Du bist mein ganzes Herz.'

Next morning, when we got back to Drachenfels, there was a telegram for Manfred from his father, summoning him home at once. His call-up notice had come, and he must report for duty early the following week.

VIII

Not long afterwards I received a letter from Manfred. It was addressed from his home in Husum and dated 20th January 1938.

My dear Tony,

You will understand, I'm sure, why I haven't written to you before. It took me two days to reach home because, for some reason, the train service was interrupted, and I was obliged to spend a night in Nuremberg because I had missed my connection.

When I got here I found that my request to join the regiment of my cousin, Claus von Stauffenberg, had been granted, and that I had to report to it at once. I am not at liberty to tell you where I have been posted, but only that I reached my unit five days ago.

I shall always look back, Tony, on the past few months as the happiest of my life. Our music, the rides we had together, our ceaseless conversations, *and* above all, our trip to the mountains, will remain treasured memories for ever. I now have to do my duty to the Fatherland, and as a soldier, I have had to swear an oath that I will render unconditional obedience to the Führer and German People. This is a duty I undertake willingly, and an oath I am prepared to fulfil to the letter, though I shall not easily forget what you said about patriotism and war. I only pray solemnly to God that our countries will never have to fight each other.

But no matter what fate has in store for us, part of me will always be yours.

D'you remember that old Greek legend we found so strange at school? I mean the one that went something like this: In the days of the Giants and Titans there were three sexes, male, female and hermaphrodite. In those days men were not like us, for they had four arms, four legs and faces on both sides of their heads, but they only had one soul. They were so clever that the gods became jealous and frightened of them, and appealed to Zeus to do something about it. He looked down from Olympus and saw what marvels they had achieved, and he, too, became afraid lest they should become gods themselves. So he decreed that they should all be cut in two and scattered to the four corners of the earth. But in doing so, he cut their souls in half, and ever since human souls have been seeking to reunite themselves with their missing halves. This explains why men couple with women, men with men and women with women.

During that night on the mountain, our bodies found each other and our souls were at last united and became one. Though we may not meet for a long time, our souls cannot be sundered again, for whatever happened that night cannot be undone, and no one can take it from us. You have an English word for it — soul-mate. You and I are soul-mates, and we shall be till the end of our lives.

I shall try to write to you as often as I can, but it won't always be easy — they keep us busy here, and our training is hard. It leaves us little time for leisure. You can always write to me at Husum; mother or father will forward your letter, but it may have to be opened and posted again in Germany — we are not supposed to receive letters from abroad here. But I shall be thinking of you always, just as I know you will be thinking of me, and never more than when you are listening to or playing the slow movement of Schubert's last quintet, which we both love so much, and which we used to play at Drachenfels.

I must stop now, Tony. Ich liebe dich

Dein

Manfred.

Even after that rapturous night with Manfred in the chalet on the mountain I did not think of myself as queer. Queers were limp-wristed pansies, and clearly neither he nor I were handbag-swishing queens. That syndrome was something quite, quite different. Our physical love had been no more than an extreme expression of our friendship — an extension of the intellectual rapport we both felt for each other. It had been as natural, as inevitable as holding hands or embracing, which people did every day. I felt no guilt or shame — far from it. On the contrary I felt that we had cemented our friendship in a very special way that we would both treasure for the rest of our lives. I simply couldn't see that there could have been anything wrong in what we had done, and certainly nothing to be ashamed of. What's more, I was certain that Manfred felt the same.

I found it hard to know what it was about me that Manfred loved, but I knew very well that he did love me, and what it was about him that I loved. To begin with, there was his physical self — his masculinity, his good looks, his skill as a horseman, his musical talent, his honest patriotism, his ambition, his sense of honour, and his determination to do what he could for his country.

What *could* he see in me, though? I was not outstandingly handsome, not particularly athletic, though I too, was a good horseman. I was not nearly so musically talented as he was, I could not speak German as well as he spoke English. I was certainly not effeminate, but my pacifism, which he seemed to accept on the intellectual level, was very different from his wish to become a soldier and fight for his country. I could not draw or paint, or write poetry or prose of any distinction — what was it then, that attracted him? After that wonderful night together, there could be no doubt, no matter how naif I might be, that our sexual encounter had been one between equals. Neither had dominated the other; to both it had been equally fulfilling. We had come together as equal partners, expressing physically the intensity of our love and affection for one another. If he had tried to fuck me, it might have been otherwise — I would have thought he was using me as a surrogate woman, and I could not have stood for that for a moment. Had he made the attempt, our relationship would have been shattered at once. I neither wanted to be dominated by him nor to dominate him. I wanted only to return the physical love he had given me in the most sensitive way I could. Our sex had therefore been pure, passionate and mutually fulfilling at every level. It would have been blasphemous to regard it as filthy or perverted. Surely what we had done could not be classed as the 'unnatural vice' the moralists went on about. Ours was the kind of love and friendship Plato and the Greeks had held in such high esteem. And now I knew why. It had absolutely nothing whatever to do with effeminate men who, if they could not help themselves, were rather to be pitied than condemned, but who, if they adopted that pose deliberately to shock, then deserved the obloquy that came their way.

About a week after Manfred had left, Hermine proposed a skiing expedition to the Gross Glockner. She phoned a number of friends and we went in two cars, Sonja and some Salzburg friends in one, I in Hermine's. We reached the Fuscher Törl about midday, and, putting on our skis and skins, climbed the lower slopes of the

Edelweiszspitze. It was one of those crisp, sunny days following a fresh fall of snow, which gives the best kind of skiing, and it was getting dark when we made our final run down to the gasthof, where we'd left the cars. After a couple of glasses of glühwein it was time to start back, and we set out as we had come.

When she'd got into the car, Hermine took off her woolly cap, and shook free her hair, which was marcel-waved in the current fashion, and carefully coiled in a long sausage roll round her neck. She was wearing a bangle of charms. I remember, which included a little golden bell, a tiny violin, and, incongruously I thought, a golden boot, and in her ears little diamond clips. There was no doubt about it, Hermine was an extremely attractive woman, and I found myself stealing sidelong glances at her as we drove along.

'I hate driving at this time of day,' she said as we negotiated the hairpin bends down the pass. 'It's not light enough to see properly, and too light for your headlamps to be much help.' She leaned across me to the glove compartment for a packet of cigarettes and offered me one.

'No thanks.'

'Light one for me, will you?'

I had never been asked to do this before, and as I took the cigarette from my lips and put it in hers, I caught the unmistakable whiff of sexuality. We drove on in silence, I fretful of my inadequate German, but shy of her. She? It was hard to tell; but without saying a word, she had made me feel uneasy. Uneasy because as we drove down that tortuous mountain road she let her elbow or her knee brush against mine in spite of the impediment of the gear shift and handbrake. Without a word spoken, she had made it crystal clear what she wanted, not just when she took the cigarette from my lips, but throughout the whole drive home.

It happened, by chance or design, I don't know which, that my bedroom was next to hers. That night she came to my room just as I had turned out the light, and remained till morning.

* * *

In February 1938, the German propaganda campaign against the Schuschnigg government of Austria became more and more strident. Everyone at Drachenfels was convinced that the Austrian Chancellor would resist any attack Hitler might launch against the country, and that he would never agree to a union of Austria and

Germany. I don't suppose that at eighteen I fully grasped the significance of all that was going on around me, but my attitude towards Germany and the Nazis had been deeply influenced by Manfred. If he could approve of what Hitler was doing for his country, who was I to think otherwise? I therefore decided to go and spend two weeks in Munich to see for myself.

I am glad I did, though my trip did not work out quite as I had planned. Munich was plastered with posters for an exhibition entitled 'Der Ewige Jude' (The Eternal Jew) which was designed to show how Jews owed no allegiance to any state, and how they had been responsible for every misfortune ever suffered by the German people from the Thirty Years' War to the present day. It was attracting huge crowds, much as an art exhibition at Burlington House would attract visitors in London. How willingly people were visiting it was hard to say, for some undoubtedly went out of a fear of being denounced by their neighbours if they had stayed away. But listening to the comments as I went round, I was under the firm impression that most people were approving. I, myself, found it sickening and bewildering.

Walking back to my hotel I had to pass the Feldherrnhalle, outside which there was a pompous memorial to the Nazis who had died in the abortive putsch of 1923. In those inter-war years it was usual for men to raise their hats when passing the cenotaph in Whitehall out of respect for those who had been killed in the Great War; in Munich it was obligatory to raise one's right arm in the Nazi salute when you passed the Feldherrnhalle. I didn't, and as I sauntered by with my hands in my pockets, I looked at it across the street as any sightseer might look at a public monument in a city he was visiting for the first time. As I drew level with the first of the two sentries, who were standing stiffly to attention on either side of the monument, I glanced at it casually and continued my stroll. I had not noticed an SS-man standing in a doorway on my side of the street. As I passed by, he jumped forward, seized me by the arm and frog-marched me up a side street to a nearby police station. Although I understood German pretty well by that time, I pretended to understand nothing, while he accused me of insulting behaviour, and threatened me with all kinds of penalties. Luckily I had my passport on me, which requested and required in the name of His Britannic Majesty in the most peremptory terms all those whom it might concern to allow the bearer to pass freely without let or hindrance.

At first the Bavarian thug to whom I pointed this out had not been impressed. Luckily his superior was a man of milder mien and profounder knowledge, for he recognised Anthony Eden as a man of whom he had heard, and that someone might have something to say if I were not allowed to pass without let or hindrance. Though unwilling to afford me the assistance Anthony Eden was demanding in the foreword of my passport, he let me go with a caution to do in Munich as the Müncheners did. I withdrew with as much dignity as I could muster, relieved that a British passport still counted for something in Nazi Germany, and returning to my hotel, packed my bags and caught the next train back to Salzburg and civilisation.

While this was happening to me in Munich, Dr Schuschnigg was being browbeaten by Hitler in Berchtesgaden. During the next two weeks the situation became increasingly tense. The Tessenbergs decided it would be wiser if I returned to England until things settled down. They feared that Hitler would attack, and that the Austrian army would resist. Given the situation of Drachenfels so close to the frontier, there was a strong possibility we would find ourselves in the firing line. Count Wolf sent his wife to stay with Hermine in Vienna, and put me on the train for Paris. I arrived in England on March 12th, to be greeted by screaming headlines: **HITLER INVADES AUSTRIA**. Everyone held their breath awaiting the outbreak of war. Nothing happened.

Part Two:
Love and Friendship in the Shadow of War

I

The eighteen months following Hitler's absorption of Austria were punctuated by one international crisis after another, which led inexorably to the conviction that war was inevitable. I was of that generation that would be most affected by it, and I had to decide what, if any part, I would play in it. I had two choices — to conform, or to register as a conscientious objector, when the time came for me to be called up for national service. I decided to object.

My premature return from Austria, and my separation from Manfred, plunged me into a deep depression. I didn't know what I wanted to do, or what career I wanted to follow. Until then, I had not thought of going to university, as I had considered that two years abroad would furnish me with fluency in at least two, if not three foreign languages, and that this would be enough to get me a job in the Foreign Service, or in some international organisation. My father, who had acquiesced in all the decisions my mother had taken regarding my education, thought I should go to university, but he did not mind which. Nor did he mind what I read, but sensibly suggested that as I was now passably fluent in French and German, I should read Modern Languages. I would have preferred to read history, but as neither of my parents could see any commercial advantage in doing so, I fell in with their wishes. In any case, in June and July 1938, the future looked so black that it didn't seem to matter very much, as I would almost certainly be called up the moment war was declared.

The Munich crisis of September postponed war for a year, and so I went up to St Sergius's College, Cambridge in October. So far as I was concerned, it was a good choice, for among the freshmen that year were one or two old Templarians, and one, in particular, who shared my pacifist views.

I was convinced that the Nazi philosophy was utterly revolting, bigoted, cruel, and, above all, stupid. Morally and intellectually, I was now persuaded that we were struggling against an odious and pernicious system. At the same time, I was certain that, as Manfred got to know the Nazi system better, he, too, would share my opinion. He had joined the army as a regular soldier, and thus his life would be governed by a strict code of honour. In the event of war, he would no doubt serve his country loyally, while hoping that in time Hitler and his thugs would be ousted from power.

Many British pacifists, among them myself, based their objection to the war on the premise — false, alas — that nobody wanted war; the dictators no more than the rest of us. But my overriding objection to war was that the wrong people would be killed in it. Not just the wrong people — innocent children, women, the elderly and infirm — but I also objected to the fact that the evil cause was just as likely to triumph as the moral one, depending upon which side had the bigger resources. The whole character of war had changed since 1918. Then the direct risk to women and children was slight compared to that of the soldier at the front. Now, the development of military hardware ensured that the civilian population would suffer just as much, if not more, than frontline soldiers. Air raids would wipe out whole cities, as we had already seen at Guernica, and their inhabitants would all be poisoned by gas or bacterial weapons.

The machinery of regimentation, too, had been perfected, especially by the totalitarian states, to the point where personal liberty, which we were supposed to be fighting for, would be severely curtailed in the interest of the production of more munitions and more cannon-fodder.

The dilemma that gave me the most trouble was the conflict between my duty to the state and my duty to God, which was not quite the same as my duty to my conscience. If the good of the state was the criterion of good and evil, and the supreme reality to which I must sacrifice myself, then the state came very close to usurping the place of God, just as it had done in Germany. The slogan 'My country right or wrong' equated the government of the day with the divinity, and gave people the excuse to commit frightful acts of cruelty and barbarism in its name. That was something I could not accept. I had to decide the limits beyond which loyalty to the state could not be taken.

There is another more idealistic, almost religious motive for going to war: a passionate devotion to the Nation or a Cause. With this goes the desire for self-sacrifice. This impulse of heroism for the welfare of the nation or cause is by far the noblest of the motives that make for war. Being in itself essentially religious, it can only be adequately combated by a wider religion, extending the boundaries of one's country or cause to all mankind. It was this, more perhaps than any other, which was the reason for my uncertainty. Unlike some of my (now notorious) contemporaries at Cambridge, who had caught Communism as most people catch flu, I had no certainties. I thought of myself as a democrat and as a European. I was related by marriage and cousinship to France, and I was deeply in love with a German.

The Fellowship of Reconciliation, which I joined soon after going up to Cambridge, was founded in 1915 by Christian pacifists. It was never very large, and never appealed to the masses like the Peace Pledge Union. It tended to recruit absolute pacifists, who wanted to use it to convert the churches to a 'Stop the War' campaign. It also included those who believed its outlook should be 'humble and constructive'. There were Quakers, who insisted that socialism was essential to Christianity, and many who believed in peace at any price.

There were many pacifists, of whom I was one, who believed that English freedoms would disappear due to the subordination of all values to the needs of war, and that the nation would become as regulated as Germany, which it was set on defeating. Our chief fear was the introduction of conscription and any form of national service that would aid the war effort, and the FOR offered help to those who wished to register as objectors when they were called up. Other pacifist groups were less extreme. They drew a distinction between compulsion for home defence and compulsion for service abroad, but all groups sought to make sure that conscription never became a permanent feature of British national life.

The underlying philosophy of the opponents of conscription was simple. All human life is sacred. Whatever else the state may or may not do, there is one interference with individual judgement that no state in the world has any sanction to enforce: that is to tamper with the right of every man and woman to decide for himself or herself the issue of life and death.

But the most difficult dilemma of all presented itself only gradually, as people became aware of the appalling barbarity of the Nazi system. It began to dawn on pacifists that war against Hitler *could* be the lesser of two evils. Much as many older pacifists hated the Nazis and the Treaty of Versailles, they had believed it was necessary to explore every possibility of reaching a negotiated peace with Germany, believing, in other words, in a policy of appeasement. Up to the end of 1940, many were sceptical about alleged German atrocities, and this included tales about the horrors of concentration camps. While it was possible to condemn these institutions on the ground that people sent to them were being deprived of their liberty for political reasons, few seriously believed the tales of horror that later proved to be all too true, thinking that they were most probably our own propaganda. Likewise, many pacifists were ardent defenders of Russian communism.

It was into this ferment of argument that I went up to Cambridge in October 1938. The question I had to ask myself: what good could I do? For this is where I stood: amid such universal distress — unemployment and poverty at home; despair and humiliation in Germany; cynicism and vengeance in France — how could I reduce that distress in any way? That was the nub of my problem, and in the face of it, I knew that I could do almost nothing. This was where I differed so much from Manfred: he sincerely believed there *was* something he could do. And yet he was no fanatic, far less a bigoted convert to fascism. Both of us were seeking our ways gropingly; neither of us knew whom to trust, though Manfred trusted Hitler more than I trusted Chamberlain or Daladier. I had told Manfred before we parted to believe those who were seeking the truth; to doubt those who said they had found it; to doubt everything, but not to doubt himself, for this was the creed by which I was trying to live. This seemed to me then to be the only rational position that either of us could adopt if our love for each other was not to be extinguished by the external pressures that were closing in around us.

It was at this time that I first began to think of myself as one of a minority. In matters of religion I was a Unitarian; I was a pacifist; I disliked and took no part in college sports; I began to think that perhaps, after all, I might be what people then called 'one of those'. I began to long for that oneness with large bodies of my fellow men and women that is experienced by enthusiastic crowds. I had seen on my brief visit to Munich how such crowds responded to Hitler's magic, for one of his bellicose speeches had been publicly broadcast while I was there, and I had witnessed the frenzied behaviour of the huge crowd that had gathered in the square near my hotel to hear it on the public address system.

I suppose my longing must be the common lot of members of all minorities, but my scepticism cut me off from such facile enthusiasms, and had transported me into a troubled solitude. This feeling had to some extent vanished once I got back to England, but there were occasions when, during my first term, the ghost of it returned to worry me.

What made things harder for me was my lack of fanaticism. Fanatics are always certain that they are right: I was only certain of one thing — that I was uncertain of where the truth lay, and of what I should do to find it. I soon discovered that most of my fellow members of the FOR were vehemently left-wing or ultra-religious. I was neither. Like Manfred and my French and Austrian friends, I was vehemently anti-communist, because in my view, an all-powerful state denied freedom to the individual. I owed as much to the teachings of Buddha and Gandhi as I did to those of Jesus Christ. I regarded myself as a patriot, and I wanted to share the hardships my friends would have to endure when war came. Failure to do so would spell dishonour, so I had to come to some kind of compromise.

By going to prison I might assert my total abhorrence of war, but by relieving suffering in a non-military role, I would at least be doing something, no matter how trivial, of a more positive nature than sewing mailbags in gaol. If I joined the army, and asked to serve in the Royal Army Medical Corps, it was most unlikely, as a linguist with no medical knowledge of any kind, that my request would be granted. If I joined any other so-called non-combatant organisation, such as the Pioneer Corps, I would only be releasing a man for the front. In any case, the Pioneer Corps was reserved for men with minor disabilities, such as colour-blindness or asthma, and I was extremely fit.

I, and most of my friends, believed that the threat to democracy came from within as much as from abroad. Our ideals were safe from everything except the attempt to defend them by the wrong means. Many of us believed that fascism was the result of the failure of democracy to provide society with a decent standard of living, that it would flourish so long as people believed that a dictator was necessary, and that violence was the only method which was understood and practised. It was a problem that ultimately only time would settle. Alas! if only it had been. But in 1939 we were still living in a fundamentally optimistic age where Progress would surely lead to a sea-change in human nature.

In one breath the churches forbade the doctor to carry out an abortion to save a mother's life, yet blessed the airmen and their planes who dropped bombs on crowded cities. This seemed to me quite outrageous. But to love one's enemies — that was another matter. Who were my enemies? Could I sincerely love them? Well, I could no doubt love such Germans and Russians as I might encounter in the course of my life, but this love would be an entirely personal one. Was it indeed possible to love an abstraction as vast as the Nazis, the Communists, the Jews, the Blacks and so on? The Gospels didn't help in the least. All the relevant texts referred to personal situations: 'Bless them that curse *you*, pray for them that persecute *you*, resist not *him* that is evil, return not evil for evil.' There is no room here for the defence of the defenceless against attack by blanket bombing. How could I reconcile my duty to my neighbour who is wounded in an air raid, or thrown into prison for his beliefs, if I fail to do all in my power to help him? Search as I might, I could find no passage in the New Testament positively justifying or recommending the legitimacy of active or violent resistance to injustice. If there is a question of resisting, it is only of resisting the Devil or God; never of resisting men. But how can one resist evil without resisting men who do evil? And what *is* evil? Was it not possible that my evil might be another man's good? The evil of taking from the rich is certainly the good of the poor who receive it. When two men love one another, and live together, was it not good for them because by their nature it was the natural thing for them to do? But in the eyes of those who are attracted to the opposite sex, it is an evil because what these men are doing is said to be against nature and against the ordinances of God whom they say is good.

It came down to this: only those governments which had been freely elected (with the accent firmly on freely), and which exercised tolerance and behaved in a moral fashion, had the right to expect implicit obedience. As I saw it, there was a great dearth of these in the world. I wasn't satisfied that the good for which the state was striving led to the establishment of liberty, fraternity and equality of opportunity, or that there was an absolute definition of public morality. Public morality then was not very different from what it is today, except in one important respect: it was then even more smug and self-satisfied than it is now, and the young then were not so well-informed or sophisticated as they are today.

In reaching my decision to become a conscientious objector I was constantly asking myself what my true motives were. I could not truthfully say that I loved my neighbours for I loathed Hitler and the Nazis and what they stood for. There were lots of people I didn't love. When someone indignantly demanded to know (as they did of most pacifists) what I would do if a Hun came and raped my sister, I had to confess that, given the chance, I would try to stop him, even if I had to use a lot of violence to do so, and that if I were armed I would probably try to shoot him. I could not pretend that any argument or sweet reasonableness would have the slightest effect in such circumstances. But that didn't seem to me to be in the same category as dropping bombs indiscriminately on German women and children. Although I greatly admired Gandhi's gospel of non-violence, after what I had seen in Munich I doubted if the SS would have cared two hoots if we all sat down in the road to bar the way to the German tanks.

Since the war seemed inevitable that summer, it was only prudent to take practical steps for action when, at last, it broke out. Together with some like-minded undergraduates from Oxford, I decided to join an ambulance service if I obtained exemption from the Conscientious Objectors' Tribunal when the time came for me to appear before one. I never contemplated opting out as some extreme pacifists did. If there was to be a war, there would be no escape from it; one would have to take some part in it whether one wanted to or not.

Early in May 1939, I got a letter from Manfred, in which he told me he would be getting three weeks' leave from the middle of June, and that he proposed to spend it at Jeven with his family. Would I be able to come, so that we could make up a musical party? He said that his sister, Helga, and her fiancé, and a Swedish friend of hers, Clara Edelstedt, who was a fine musician, would be staying, and he thought of asking Andrew Dahl, the son of a friend of his father's, who was studying medicine in England. Together with Herr and Frau von Schrade, we would make up an octet. 'Please say you can come,' his letter ended. 'This may be the last chance we'll have of being together for some time.'

Manfred had told me a little about his family. He was a few years younger than his sister, Helga, who was engaged to a former schoolfellow of his called Hans Streiter. I had gained the impression that Manfred didn't like Hans very much. He said he was a fanatical Nazi, and he didn't trust him. He was, however, a talented flautist, which was one point in his favour. Andrew Dahl's father was German, but his mother was English, and as he had been born in South-West Africa after that territory became a South African mandate at the end of the Great War, he held a British passport. His father and Manfred's had been neighbours in Africa, where their plantations were in the same district. Andrew, like Hans, was a good musician, but he was also a keen bird-watcher, and was spending his vacation studying bird life along the Danish coast, so would not be far from Manfred's home at Jeven. It sounded like a good idea, and I replied at once that I would come as soon as I could after the end of term.

II

Schloss Jeven stood on a small eminence about half a mile from the sea. A broad avenue of limes led down to low sandhills and an inlet where fishing boats were moored. It was not a very big house: more a large farmhouse than a country mansion, but handsome in a simple way, flanked by ranges of stables and barns on two sides, and crowned by a lookout platform and lantern, from which you could get a splendid view to the west and north towards the low-lying islands of Pellworm, Hooge and Amrum.

Anchored off the inlet you could see sailing barges like those that once plied the Thames, bluff-bowed, high-sterned, of about fifty tons, fitted with leeboards and with long, tip-tilted bowsprits. There was a pilot's house at the end of a short jetty close to the entrance of the inlet, and it was here, safe from open water, that the von Schrades kept their small yacht. 'Yacht', perhaps, was too grand a name for what was an open boat not much bigger than a dinghy, with an outboard motor and a single sail. The family used it mainly for duck shooting expeditions among the myriad creeks and islets that stretch in a northerly direction from Husum to the Danish border some fifty miles away. The coast here is fenced in behind a fringe of sand, with only one sizeable river, the Eider, entering the North Sea a few miles south of Husum.

The von Schrade family, like the Tessenbergs, had lost much of their wealth after the war, mainly because Manfred's father had owned a large plantation in South-West Africa, where he had also been a colonial official. The plantation had passed under South African control under the terms of the Treaty of Versailles, and Herr von Schrade's official position had been handed to a South African. The family estate at Jeven was not large, but it had the advantage of being on very fertile soil, on which Frisian cattle and Holstein horses thrived. Herr von Schrade had settled down in 1920 to farm it, and to make it as profitable as possible. It was now among the best-run estates in the district.

Manfred's mother was a small, plump woman with twinkling blue eyes, fair, greying hair done in a bun, with no pretensions to fashion. She was responsible for the poultry and the orchards on the estate. She had the same sweet smile as her son, who adored her. Helga, Manfred's sister, was buxom, blonde and bumptious — a dedicated Hitler Maiden, and leader of the local troop. Her fanatical adoration of the Führer was not shared, I was sure, by her parents any more than by her brother.

I had crossed from Harwich to Esbjerg in Denmark, where I had taken the train to Schleswig. There Manfred had met me in his new Volkswagen Beetle. We hadn't seen each other for nearly eighteen months, though we had exchanged a few letters, I was conscious, as we drove through the pleasant countryside with its small, neat farms and windmills, of an element of constraint, although he was clearly glad to see me. It was nothing I could put my finger on, and I attributed it to the fact that he had been under military discipline since we had last been together. On the way to Jeven we chatted about mutual friends in England and Austria, studiously avoiding politics and the worsening international situation. I had no wish to discuss these topics unless Manfred raised them; this was to be a musical holiday, and the less we concerned ourselves with such matters the better.

After we'd been going about fifteen miles and were close to our destination, Manfred turned to me and said: 'I'd better warn you about Helga and Hans. They're both very keen Party members; Hans is in the SS. He's just been promoted Hauptsturmführer — that's the equivalent of captain in the army. Mother and father don't like him very much. Nor do I. I didn't like him at school. In fact, I was pretty fed up when Helga told us she was going to marry him, but there was nothing *I* could do about it. Mother and father did their best to put her off him, of course. I'm only telling you this to warn you that they may try to preach Party propaganda at you.'

I said I thought I could cope with that, but promised to be as tactfully noncommittal as I could. I had been invited to spend a couple of weeks at his home in order to meet his family, to make music and to go sailing and riding with him. I'd been looking forward to the visit very much, and was determined to make the most of it, and to avoid difficult subjects of conversation. I didn't feel that it was my business to preach to any of Manfred's family, and as a guest in their house it was nothing more than good manners to keep my mouth shut.

Because Hans was stationed at Kiel, and Andrew Dahl had been bird-watching on the island of Fehmarn in the Baltic, they had been joined by Clara Edelstedt, Helga's Swedish friend, in Kiel and had all driven over together.

We were having tea on the terrace when we heard Hans's car crunching up the drive, and a moment later he strode in, dressed in his black SS uniform, followed by Andrew and Clara. He marched up to Frau von Schrade, clicked his heels, shot his right arm out in the Hitler salute, then bent to kiss her hand. He turned to Herr von Schrade, clicked his heels again and almost shouted 'Heil Hitler'. Next he turned to greet Helga, who was sitting between her father and mother. Any normal, engaged couple would, I thought, have embraced, but not these two. Helga stood up and bowed, and both their arms shot out in yet another Hitler salute, a glazed expression of bliss suffusing their faces — the ideal Teutonic couple. Hans clicked his heels yet again, bowed stiffly to his fiancée, and then turned to Manfred and me. In true British style, I held out my hand to shake his, and because he was about to 'heil' me, we failed to make contact, so I just smiled and said, 'Hello; nice to meet you!'

I could see at once that he knew why Germany would win the coming war.

By this time, Helga had got up to introduce Clara, who had been left standing uneasily on the periphery of this ridiculous carry-on. I felt the least I could do was go up and shake her warmly by the hand. Andrew, a little stiffly, also shook hands all round, and we settled down once more to finish our tea.

Hans was neither very tall nor very short. Beneath a forehead of average height, two grey-green eyes looked out at one with an air of peaceful interrogation. The trimmed moustache, below a straight nose, traced a honey-coloured line on his pale features. His lips were colourless and thin, and his chin receded, which was a pity for someone who so obviously liked to present a macho appearance. A faintly mocking smile revealed two rows of excellent white teeth; his slender, almost feminine hands lay motionless on his lap once he had finished saluting and had sat down at the table. He gave me the creeps.

Since the main purpose of the house party was to make music, it was not too hard to avoid controversial topics of conversation, though I once put my foot in it by suggesting that we play a piece by Mendelssohn.

At the end of two days, I knew that Hans was mad. He was amiably, and to some extent contentedly, mad. He was a man adrift from normal human experience. He was one of those terrifying human beings foreign to all normal human behaviour. He didn't seem to be particularly cruel: he was not distinguished, so far as one could tell, by lust or excessive vanity, by overwhelming ambition or by systematic deceitfulness. His qualities were unremarkable — vices and virtues alike. But he seemed to have no centre: such qualities as he possessed simply didn't cohere.

There are men like Hans in the prisons and mental homes all over the world. They are the sort of men who lead slightly dotty lives, make good fathers and husbands, are kind to animals, gentle, well-spoken, absorbed in some mild hobby like wicker-work, but who would quite easily murder their wives because they wished to marry some other girl, and because they flinched at the scandal of upsetting the neighbours by a divorce. Hans was the type of man who delights in pulling the legs off spiders, and exercising whatever small authority he might possess to make life hell for his subordinates. It didn't take long to discover that he believed not only in the pre-eminence of the German race but also in Nordic runes. He held forth at enormous length one evening about them and their hidden secrets. If they could be deciphered, he declared, they would prove to have a close affinity with Japanese ideograms, and this meant that the Japanese, in spite of their oriental appearance, were in fact also Aryans and thus fit allies for Germans. He also firmly believed that a Slav was an animal and must be treated as such — treated much more harshly in fact. His sole aim in life was to make the world a place fit for Germans to live in.

And when it came to animals, I heard him declare that Germans were the only people in the world who had a decent attitude towards them, and so far as human animals were concerned, the Germans would adopt a decent attitude towards them too. But it was a crime against German blood to worry about them. 'If someone comes up to me,' he said one evening at dinner,' and says, "You mustn't use Russian Jews to dig anti-tank ditches because it might kill them," I would reply, "You are the murderer of your own blood, because if the anti-tank ditches aren't dug, German soldiers will die, and they are our own blood." Our concern, our duty is to our people and our blood. We have the moral right and duty to our people to destroy these people, who have always wanted to destroy us.'

On another occasion the conversation turned to blood sports. Hans turned to me and asked if I hunted. I told him I didn't, but that I had nothing particular against it so long as it was the best way of keeping foxes from slaughtering lambs and poultry. I said I hadn't any particular liking for people who hunted, mainly because I found them, on the whole, rather snobby and arrogant. But Hans hotly condemned all blood sports, including fishing, calling them cold-blooded murder of innocent creatures: he was mad, just plain mad.

During the day, the house party tended to split up into pairs. Hans and Helga usually found some reason to go into Kiel to attend to Party business. Hans hardly ever appeared out of uniform, and Helga felt it necessary always to wear 'peasant' costume, which she regarded as *echt deutsch* and the only dress worthy to be worn by a true daughter of the Reich. Andrew and Clara, who had quickly taken a great liking to each other, would take themselves off to a hide in the salt marshes to watch ducks, geese and waders. Manfred and I either went riding in the surrounding countryside, or walking among the sand dunes. But one day it was particularly warm and there was a light breeze, so he suggested that we take the boat and sail over to the island of Pellworm about twelve miles across the broad sea, to look at some Viking ruins.

The yacht lay in a kind of trough in the inlet, which she had dug for herself on the receding tide, so that she was still ringed with water a few inches deep when we got to her. For miles in every direction lay a desert of sand. To the north it touched the horizon, and was only broken by the blue hump of Pellworm and its light-house. To the south, it seemed also to stretch to infinity, but the smoke of a steamer showed where the Elbe estuary lay. Only to the west was its outline broken by any vestiges of the sea. There you could see the white breakers and hear the murmuring hiss of waves. Its colour varied from light fawn, where the highest levels had dried in the wind, to brown or deep violet where it was still wet, and slate-grey where patches of mud soiled its clean surface. Here and there were pools of water, rippled by the wind and speckled by shells and seaweed. And close to us, beginning to bend away north-wards towards the hissing surf, wound the little channel hardly deep enough to float our small boat, In spite of the clear sky, there was something very forlorn about this coast, part, perhaps, of the mel-ancholy which I think most of us felt hovering just below the surface of our lives.

From the west, shelves of water were beginning to spread over the sands, each pushing tongues of spume that met and fused with one another. The yacht, which was grounded when we arrived, began to tremble under the gentle buffeting of the little waves. Then she jerked herself free and her nose swung round and she was drifting broadside to the wind till the anchor checked her. We ran up the sail and started off towards the north.

III

I had been conscious ever since my arrival at Jeven of a certain reticence that had grown up between me and Manfred. Superficially everything seemed much as it had been, but the intervening months since we had parted in Austria had had some indefinable effect on us both. For my part, I had gradually come to realise that my feeling for him was quite different from and much deeper than anything I had ever felt for Michel. On his part, I thought I detected a slight feeling of distrust, and I was forced to ask myself more than once whether he trusted me to go on loving him because of what he was. Sometimes he seemed to bolt away from me like a scared rabbit into its burrow whenever I tried to make an affectionate gesture towards him. At other times, he seemed to forget my very existence — not only me, but everything round him, and to be sunk in some reverie, which obliterated everything but itself.

And yet, when he caught my eye during some piece of music we were playing together, or over the dinner table, the reflective sadness would vanish, to be replaced by that expression of tender humour I had come to love so much when we were in Austria. It seemed, at such moments, as if he'd been suffering some apprehensions on my account — apprehensions of doubt lest our different attitudes to the coming war had interposed themselves to separate us utterly. He seemed to be in need of me as a reassurance for life itself; or was he being driven by the emptiness of his life to find fulfilment in me? If so, I was gradually coming to feel the same need myself. But why was his life so empty? He enjoyed soldiering; he was happy to be part of a highly efficient and well-motivated machine, and although he was clearly not such a fanatical Nazi as Hans, he had told me on more than one occasion how much he liked regimental life and the company of his fellow officers.

But something sinister seemed to have crossed his path: an overmastering fear seemed to be separating him from the warmth of intimacy, and the dam of his emotions seemed on the point of breaking down and engulfing him. It wasn't just the prospect of war, but something far deeper. He seemed to be seeking my help, and though I was willing to give him what help I could, I kept asking myself if it could possibly be enough.

It was very bewildering, because surely he could understand that affection is all a matter of trust, and that I was very fond of him. And yet at times he seemed almost greedy for my love. What did he want? To be taken in my arms and to be kissed; to be trusted with the warmth of my own life; to sleep in my arms as we had slept together in the chalet in Austria? I, certainly, would have given him all of this, and more, if he had suggested it, but in the cirumstances in which we found ourselves, it would have been out of the question. He had not suggested it, and nor had I, partly out of fear of being rebuffed, but mainly because no easy opportunity presented itself.

There had been occasions when I felt that my presence was hurting him; even that we were hurting each other, that we had become timid, yet wanted to talk to each other without the constraints of family and common politeness. He wanted to talk to me alone and at length, I was sure, but had not been able to bring himself to find the right opportunity. At last the opportunity had come, and he had proposed this long sail in order, I felt sure, to unburden himself without fear of interruption. But I had no idea what was on his mind when we sailed out of the inlet, and into the open sea. He set a course for the distant island, and we settled down before a gentle breeze.

'We've got to talk now, Manfred, because we can't go on as we have done since I came here,' I said. 'If I can help you, you must trust me.'

'If I've seemed to distrust *you*,' I went on, 'it's because I'm afraid you'll not let yourself go — I feel it's you who are putting up a certain barrier of distrust between us. You see, I really do care for you very much, but you've not let me put my arms round you without seeming to feel embarrassed. I want you to relax in the knowledge that I genuinely feel like that about you; that you're really safe with me, but you'll never know it till you trust me. You seem afraid to commit yourself. You seem afraid of the deep warmth within you, which urges you to trust me and to love me, and yet you can't.'

I looked at him wondering if I had gone too far, or, on the contrary, if he were trying to force my hand in some subtle way. Distrust and habit were fighting against a real wish to respond positively. Till then we had been talking different languages, but now, when I looked straight into his eyes, I saw sincerity, hope, true affection and love. That was what had been hurting him. I'd been so thoughtless, because 'love' in his language was not 'love' in mine, and it hurt because I'd been misinterpreting what had happened in the chalet, and had seemed to him, since my arrival at Jeven, to have been punishing his simple human need for affection because I didn't recognize it. I suddenly felt sorry for all we had missed: all the understanding and friendship we could have given each other now that time was so short: sorry that my stupid British reticence should have prevented us from communicating with each other sooner.

I lent forward and put my arms round him, and we kissed each other as we had kissed in the chalet, and I knew we had broken through the invisible barrier that had been dividing us, and that he really did care for me as much as I cared for him.

'I've got to talk to you, Tony,' he said, 'while there's still time. Something terrible is about to happen. It's not just the war that's coming; that's only part of it. It's Hans. What d'you think of him?'

I hesitated before answering, afraid to say what I really thought. 'Oh, he's okay,' I said as casually as I could.

'I detest him,' he answered vehemently. 'I can hardly bear to be in the same room as him.'

I was taken aback by the ferocity of this outburst. 'He's obviously a very keen Party member,' I said, 'and Helga seems to be fond of him.'

'That's the trouble. None of us — I mean father and mother and me — none of us trust him an inch. I think father and mother are frightened of him, and I don't blame them. Neither of them is a member of the Party, you know.'

'But you've all known him a long time, haven't you? I thought you were at school together.'

'We were.'

He turned away to make a small adjustment to the sail. 'That's why I hate him so much.'

'Why? What did he do?'

'It's a long story. That's what I've been wanting to tell you ever since you arrived.'

And for the next three hours Manfred told me a tale that not only shocked, but also frightened me.

His parents had sent him to the Haase Gymnasium, a boarding-school in Brandenburg, when he was about thirteen years old, he began. It was a large school, much patronised by families with military and civil service connections. By the way Manfred described it, I formed the picture of a German version of Templars before Dr Santon took it over. Manfred was a little younger than most of the new boys of his year, but not the youngest. The youngest was a boy called Heinrich, a son of one of the noblest, most influential and most conservative families in the country. Everyone else found Heinrich boring and affected, but Manfred said he had liked him. Perhaps the fact that he was a prince had something to do with this dislike, but however that might be, Heinrich was different from the others of his year.

'He was so self-assured,' Manfred went on. 'When he walked, it was with smooth, lithe movements, and with the faintly diffident attitude that you get from being used to walking very erect through a succession of vast, empty rooms.

'I became quite attached to him, and we spent a great deal of time together. He was rather devout, but I wasn't put off by that. I accepted it without a qualm as something rather admirable in him, since it was an attitude so unlike my own.

'In his company I felt rather as though I were in a chapel seeing the daylight through a cloud of incense. But quite suddenly there came a break between us. It was really my fault. One day we began arguing about religion, and I lashed out at him, pouring a great deal of rationalist scorn on him. I suppose I kind of desecrated the delicate framework of his beliefs. We parted angrily, and after that we never spoke to each other again. I was worried that something I might have said or done to *you* had damaged our relationship in a similar fashion. That's why I had to talk to you. In Heinrich's case, I was dimly aware that what I'd done was senseless, and that I'd shattered a subtle relationship. I didn't want that to happen to us. But at the same time, I simply couldn't help it. The break with Heinrich left me with a sort of yearning for something I couldn't quite define until I met you at Templars. But it wasn't only about Heinrich I wanted to tell you, it's about what happened after I broke with him.'

He paused as if uncertain how to go on.

'Not long after we'd quarrelled,' he continued, 'Heinrich's parents took him away from the school, and I then realised how much I'd enjoyed his company, for life suddenly became very empty and boring. Not for long. I soon made other friends, but the two I was closest to were Kurt von Bahlenburg and Hans Streiter. They were three years older than me, and had the reputation of being bullies. On the other hand, they were clever, and at times wild and reckless to the point of madness.

'I suppose I was drawn to them because of my own lack of self-confidence. In contrast to Heinrich they were tough and sturdy. They were good at sport, and I think it was this that attracted me to them, but I was even more impressed by their wildness and daring. I was ambitious, and now and then I tried to beat them at their own game. But somehow, I used to leave off half way. The result was that I had to put up with no end of ridicule and teasing from them, which led me to try all the harder to emulate their rough ways.

'In the third term after Heinrich left, my parents came to take me out at half-term. I wasn't quiet and shy when I was with them alone, but when my mother tried to kiss me goodbye, I tried to stop her, though I'd have liked her to embrace me. I was ashamed because I was being watched by Kurt and Hans, and was frightened they would tease me for being such a baby.

'Hans loved setting people against each other. At school he had got hold of skeleton keys to the attics, and he used to slip away to sit by himself up there reading adventure stories and writing his diary. He once showed it to me: it was filled with plans for the future, and with exact records of the origins of the other boys. Hans's favourite game was to subdue one boy with the help of another, and he revelled in the flattery he got as a result. He kind of extorted favours from them, though it was obvious that his victims — and they really were his victims — were frightened of him, and that they really hated him.

'Hans loved talking about his father, who had disappeared quite suddenly one day. At least that's what he made out. Actually, I now think he's illegitimate. He used to hint that his name wasn't really Streiter. He kept telling us that his mother would one day tell him about some inheritance he'd come into in due course. His diary was also full of plans for coups d'état and things of that sort. His ambition seemed boundless, and he was determined to become an officer in a smart regiment. I didn't take these ambitions very seriously. All the same, Hans was quite capable of putting his ideas into practice, even if only in a small way. He was a tyrant, and quite ruthless towards anyone who opposed him. He changed his supporters constantly, but somehow he always managed to get the majority on his side. That was a great gift. Some time before I came to the school, he had waged a campaign against Kurt von Bahlenburg, and had defeated him. This resulted in Kurt's isolation, although his own capacity for arousing the dislike of those who incurred his displeasure was scarcely less formidable than Hans's. But Kurt lacked Hans's charm and winning ways. Most people distrusted him; they couldn't help suspecting there was something disreputable under-lying his personality. Hans's victory over Kurt had been little more than a matter of luck, and since that time they had found it profitable to join forces. On the whole, all this didn't matter much to me one way or another, but I had a certain diffident respect for them, and sometimes felt the urge to emulate them. I certainly enjoyed their protection, because, of course, I was so much younger than they were. I sometimes felt like making fun of them, for they took themselves and their "politics" so seriously. But I was afraid there might be more truth behind their fantastic notions than I was able to admit to myself. I felt myself kind of between two worlds: one was the solid everyday world of respectable people, in which all that went on was well-ordered and rational, and the other was a world of adventure, full of mystery, blood and thunder. It seemed to me as if one world excluded the other.'

He paused to offer me a cigarette, and to light one himself. 'There was an incident at school involving a boy called Felix,' he went on. 'Felix had got himself involved with a tart in the local town, who started to blackmail him. To begin with, he managed to borrow money from the other boys to pay her, but when they asked for their money back, he was foolish enough to begin pinching it. One day, Kurt found a large sum missing from his locker, and Hans, suspecting Felix, determined to pin the theft on him if he could. He laid a trap for him, caught him red-handed, and forced him to own up. Hans then asked Kurt and me what we thought should be done about Felix. Without thinking, I said, "He's a thief. We should report him and get him expelled." But the others disagreed. "We've got him where we want him," Hans said. "We can do what we like with him. For all I care, you can spit on the little Yid every time you see him. If he rebels, we can soon show him who's boss." "Why are you so keen to put up with him?" I asked. "I'm not," Hans replied. "Have you some other reason for wanting him to be kicked out?" he asked suspiciously. There seemed no point in carrying the argument any further, so I left it at that. Hans then proposed that Felix should be watched — put under surveillance, he called it. His income and expenditure were to be strictly checked, and his relations with the rest of the boys were to depend on permission from his self-appointed guardians, Hans and Kurt.'

'What sort of a boy was Felix?' I asked.

'He was only partly Jewish, not particularly intelligent, bad at games, but he had a pleasing enough manner, and could make himself pleasant enough if he wanted to. Physically, he was a little taller than me, but slighter in build. He was extremely good-looking in a soft sort of way. He had a very smooth complexion, dark, wavy hair and brown eyes. On the whole he wasn't a bit Jewish looking, except for his brown eyes, though his complexion was a bit paler than most of the other boys.'

'Why did he go to the tart in the first place?' I asked.

'Oh, to keep up with the others, I suppose. At least that's what he told Hans and Kurt. He told me he was quite glad when he'd left her. The trouble was, you couldn't wholly believe him, because he tended to boast about his affairs with women a bit too much. At least that's how it seemed to me. I wrote to my parents about this incident soon after Felix had been caught,' Manfred continued, 'and told them I thought he ought to be reported to the headmaster, and perhaps expelled. Rather to my surprise, they took the view that what Kurt and Hans had suggested was really best, and that he should be given a second chance. Of course, they had entirely misunderstood what I had meant, for I knew that Kurt and Hans had no intention of letting Felix have a second chance. I didn't tell my parents why he'd stolen the money, and I suppose they thought that perhaps his parents weren't giving him enough pocket money or something. But I was very surprised that my parents weren't shocked: that they seemed to treat stealing money as something quite usual worried me a lot. Then one day, Kurt took me aside and told me he was sure that Hans was up to something behind our backs, because Felix had paid back the money he'd stolen, and that it wasn't out of his own pocket, but money Hans had lent or given him. He went on to tell me that he was sure that Hans was having an affair with Felix. "Haven't you noticed how uppish Felix has become?" he said. "It's because Hans has promised to look after him as long as he does what Hans wants him to do. They have it off together, I'm sure. Hans has put himself in my power," he went on, "by doing what he's done. His mother's not very well off, you know, so if he gets expelled for having it off with Felix, that'll be the end of his career. If he stays here, he may get somewhere, but not otherwise. Anyway, Hans has never liked me — in fact he used to hate me, and did everything he could to damage me. I think he'd still be glad to get rid of me if he could, only he knows I know too much. Now d'you see what I can do with what I've found out, especially if I have you as a witness."

'I was startled by Kurt's cold ruthlessness. I wasn't all that fond of Hans, but I did like the impudent, carefree way he set about his intrigues. By contrast, I loathed Kurt at that moment, as he stood there grinning at me. I found him utterly repugnant. "What I want to do is torment Felix," he said. I was still a long way from fully understanding precisely what he meant, and my puzzlement must have been evident, for Kurt went on: "You needn't be shocked. It's not as bad as that. To begin with, there's no need to consider Felix's feelings. Whether we decide to torment him or to let him off depends entirely on whether we feel the need for the one or the other. All that stuff about morality and society you brought up before doesn't count. I assume that you wouldn't care one way or the other now." By now I was utterly confused. I didn't like Felix particularly; I thought he'd been an idiot to have got himself involved with the tart in the first place, and a bigger one to steal money from the other boys. He'd been caught red-handed, and at the time I'd thought it would be best if he'd been reported to the headmaster. The head might have taken the same line as my parents, but at any rate, the whole business would have been out of our hands, and that would have been the end of it as far as we were concerned.

'Some days later, Kurt came to my dormitory late at night and whispered to me to join him and Hans in the attic. Felix was coming too, he told me. I was sleepy, and not sure that I wanted to go with him, but my curiosity got the better of me, so I got out of bed, pulled on some clothes and went upstairs. The school attic was a huge, empty space, lit at each end by two round openings. On either side were stacked trunks and broken tables and desks, leaving a narrow passage down the centre. I arrived to find Hans and Kurt sitting behind a table, on which an electric lamp was burning. They told me to bring up a chair and sit down beside them. While I was getting one, the door opened and Felix came in. He was smiling nervously, reminding me of the fixed smiles you see on portraits. Hans told him to stand at attention in front of the table, and Kurt began to recite in a monotonous, hoarse voice the list of his misdemeanours. "Aren't you ashamed?" he asked, when he'd finished.

Felix looked at Hans as if asking for help. Instead, Hans got up and hit him hard in the face, so that he staggered back, tripped over a box that was lying on the floor behind him, and fell down, knocking over the lamp. Kurt and Hans then leapt on him, and began tearing off his clothes. When they'd stripped him naked, they began whipping him with something thin and pliant. I couldn't see what it was, because as Felix had tripped, he'd pulled the lamp wire out its socket, and the attic was plunged into semi-darkness, but it was metal, possibly a sword. It was quite obvious to me that they'd carefully stage-managed this for my benefit to see how I'd react. Felix began to whimper and cry for mercy, and then finally to groan in agony, while the others renewed their attack on him, cursing him and insulting him, and I could hear their heavy, excited breathing as they laid into the unfortunate boy.

'At first, I just sat where I was, but by and by a savage desire gripped me, and I wanted to leap up and join in, but something, I couldn't tell what, held me back. Instead, I just sat there in apparent indifference, and I might have gone on sitting there for an hour, for I was thinking of nothing, my mind a blank. I seemed to be observing myself; it was like looking into an empty space and seeing myself as a vague shadow. Then all of a sudden, I felt again this overwhelming urge to join in. I got up from the chair, which I'd moved round the table in my first impulse to join the others. I was half squatting, and felt an enormous desire to go down on my knees on to the floor, and to flatten my body against the boards.

My eyes felt as if they were growing as large as a fish's, and a wild excitement took hold of me. I had to grasp hold of the table leg beside me in an effort to fight off the craving that was dragging me downwards. The sweat was pouring off me as I strained to hear what the others were doing in the darkness, for it had suddenly gone quiet over there. I could hear Felix groping for his clothes, and moaning softly. I am ashamed to say that when I heard him whimpering, I was filled with an agreeable sensation, a sort of tickling shudder, as if a spider was running up and down my spine, contracting my shoulderblades and pulling my scalp tight as though with sharp claws. I was disconcerted to find that I'd got an erection and had come. I thought back, and though I couldn't remember when this had begun, I know it was when I felt that overwhelming urge to press myself against the floor. I felt dreadfully ashamed of myself, but it was like a tremendous surge of blood going through me, numbing my thought processes, and taking total possession of me.'

Manfred fell silent, lost in the recollection of the scene he had just described. We were approaching the island of Pellworm, with its low line of sandhills, fawn and green in the bright morning sun, at one end of which a little village huddled round the base of a massive, four-square lighthouse. Manfred pointed out our landing place, for the island had no harbour on the south side, and was hedged in by a mile of sand at low water, so we had to run in on the rising tide till we grounded, in order to give ourselves as much time as possible to explore the island before the next high tide would let us cast off for the return voyage. Manfred told me to lay out the anchor, and when she was fast, we climbed overboard and waded ashore.

IV

By the time we had explored the Viking ruins and returned to the yacht, it was once more floating on the high tide. We climbed aboard, and set sail for Jeven.

'The war will come soon,' he said after we had settled down before the breeze. 'I'm sure of it. I'm not afraid of being killed, but I am afraid for my family and for everything I love here.

'The Polish affair will be settled peacefully, I expect. Daladier will come forward as mediator like Chamberlain did last year. The West Wall is impregnable, and you English can't help Poland except by sea. It's unthinkable for us to sit back and watch the persecution of the *Volksdeutsche* without doing something. I firmly believe that the Fuhrer will do all he can to avoid war.'

'I wish I could be as optimistic as you,' I said. 'I suppose it's possible the French or Italians might try to mediate — the Swedes even — but the mood in England has changed completely since last year, and I'm convinced we will go to war over Poland.'

'But how could you do that without France?'

'I don't know, but I'm sure Chamberlain means what he says when he declares the Polish alliance to be sacrosanct.'

'He may make a gesture, I grant you,' said Manfred, 'But I can assure you we will be able to take Poland over completely in a matter of a few weeks if the Russians don't attack us, and even if they do, we would go on to attack Russia, for there are many *Volksdeutsche* there too. When England sees this, she'll know where her true interests lie — in an alliance with us against the Bolsheviks.'

I sighed. 'I would like to believe you're right, but I'm absolutely convinced that you're wrong. Don't let's talk politics; it'll get us nowhere. Tell me why you're so worried about your family.'

'I'm worried for two reasons: if there's a war with England, it will probably be a naval war, and being on the coast, and not far from Kiel, Jeven may be destroyed. But what worries me far more is the threat that Hans poses to us. The SS suspect people like us of disloyalty to Hitler and the Party, and they are right to do so. The army is only waiting for an opportunity to attack the SS; the country can't afford to have two bodies of armed men who hate each other's guts. For the army and for my family, Germany comes first and the Party a long way behind; with people like Hans and, I'm afraid, with Helga, too, the Party comes before everything.'

We were silent for a while. I had the feeling that he'd had other reasons than his dislike of Hans for telling me at such length about his experiences at the Gymnasium. That had happened when he was not yet sixteen, and when he was, no doubt, far less mature — a shy, introverted, clever schoolboy. It was his shyness, his intelligence and his musical talent that had attracted me to him at Templars, but the way he had described Felix — a weak, effeminate, petty criminal — and his ambivalent attitude towards him, made me think this was something he had worried about a great deal, and which he now wanted to talk to me about because there was no one in his family with whom he could discuss it.

It was obvious we were both concerned about the direction of our sexual drive. I recalled that when we were in Austria, he had said that according to the best German psychological opinions all human beings contained masculine and feminine characteristics in varying proportions, and that every human being was potentially homosexual, according to the share of the opposite sexual characteristics in his or her make-up. This was an opinion with which I entirely agreed, but in spite of our passionate encounter on the mountain, and again just now in the boat, neither of us then thought of ourselves as homosexual. Maybe we were not, but there was no doubting the strength of feeling each of us had for the other.

The next day, Manfred had to go into Husum for some reason, I was left behind at Jeven, and Frau von Schrade took the opportunity to talk to me about him. It must have been clear to her that Manfred and I were very close to each other, and I think she wanted to get to know me better, as well as talk to me about her son. She told me that as a boy he was extraordinarily sensitive. His reactions to people around him, she said, to personalities, to moods and to physical characteristics showed an extreme sensibility. Manfred himself, I could remember, had once said how conscious he was of changes in his surroundings, of light and dark, of trees and animals, of favourable and threatening moods in nature and in people. She told me he had always found it hard to express these experiences in words. I said that I could sympathise, because I, too, had found this very difficult. In my own case, I had put this down to the English custom of bottling up feelings and emotions at all times. She asked me if I thought that this worried him. She went even farther, and asked me directly if I had detected anything on this visit to suggest that Manfred was worried or unhappy. I found this hard to answer. I did not feel at liberty to divulge what he had told me the day before about Hans, Kurt and Felix, for I wasn't sure how much he had told his mother. I said he was worried about the coming war, but then we all were.

'Oh, I think it is more than that. He is very fond of you, and the thought that you may be enemies soon is obviously worrying him, but I think there is still more to it,' she said. 'He once told me that when he was younger, his inability to express his feelings worried him a lot. In fact, he told me it almost became an obsession. He said that his teachers didn't appear to notice any of the strange things he was aware of.

'We know he wasn't happy at the Gymnasium,' she said. 'That's why we took him away and sent him to Templars.'

'I don't think it was just that, Frau von Schrade,' I said. 'He told me he used to feel threatened by things like trees in the forest or the garden wall here at Jeven. He said that they seemed to be looking at him. He became so worried about the discrepancy between what he observed all around him and the words available to express what he perceived. He found this especially true in the case of music. He told me once at Templars that he thought he was going mad, but I'm sure he's grown out of that now. In fact, I'm certain he has, and I'm sure you've no cause to worry about him on that score.'

Frau von Schrade thanked me. 'Both his father and I knew he'd had a difficult time before we sent him to England. Your country did him a lot of good, and he returned here much happier than when he went. We were so glad, too, that he met you again in Austria. That was a very happy time for him.'

A few days later, Manfred returned to the topic of Felix, Hans and Kurt.

'When Felix was caught stealing, I was forced to recognise that emotion and abnormality existed outside as well as within myself,' he said. 'I'm still obsessed by my incapacity at that time to take action independent of Hans and Kurt. At first I was drawn to Kurt, but I've since come to realise that he hid his evil intentions behind a facade of quasi-philosophical nonsense. I got absolutely no help from him at all.

'I then turned to one of the masters, but he wasn't able to offer me any immediate solutions. I didn't, of course, tell him anything about Felix and his stealing, but only about my problem of perception and expression.'

'What did he suggest?' I asked.

'Oh, he gave me a copy of Kant's *Critique of Pure Reason*.'

'Heavens,' I said, laughing. 'That must have been tough going.'

'It was. I couldn't understand most of it.'

'I'm not surprised.'

'What I really needed was someone to help me understand Felix's irrational behaviour. I'd become morbidly fascinated by him. That's why my first reaction had been to report him and get him expelled. It only gradually dawned on me that my indignant reaction was a defence not just against Felix, but against myself. Felix became in an odd way the embodiment of all the shameful thoughts and emotions which, at various times, had passed through my own mind. That's why I wanted so much to study him, and, of course, in the end it led to my emotional relationship with him. I almost persuaded myself that my own problems would be solved if I lived like him from one impulsive act to another. But I soon realised I couldn't. After a time my personal involvement lessened and was replaced by something diametrically opposite. In the end, the sight of Felix's scarred body forced me to take positive action to save him from Hans and Kurt.

'Felix was really a very weak character,' he went on after a moment's reflection. 'Very, how d'you say in English? unreflective. For a time, I found him emotionally fascinating, and I was tempted to give up all my questionings and live from day to day like he did. I thought that if I did so, all my own perplexities and difficulties would vanish.'

Manfred's relationship with his family interested me greatly. He was clearly very fond of his mother, but it didn't seem to be a very easy relationship, for she gave me the impression of being nervy and temperamental. This, of course, could easily be explained by the unwelcome attention Hans was paying to her daughter, Helga. In England, it would have been natural for a parent to express his or her disapproval of a young man they didn't like. This was something that happened every day. But English parents had no need to fear that such disapproval might land them in a concentration camp. It was as clear as daylight to me that both Frau von Schrade and her husband detested and feared Hans; and not without reason as I now knew. Manfred's father was a good deal more reserved than he might otherwise have been. He solved this domestic difficulty — at least during the short time I was a guest in his house, and, no doubt, at other times too — by busying himself all day on the farm. In fact, I only met him at mealtimes and when we played music in the evenings. He was obviously a sensitive man, and, like his wife, an excellent musician. Manfred spoke admiringly of him, and I felt sure that he respected him greatly. Between Manfred and his sister there seemed to be a coolness, on account of her infatuation with Hans.

I asked Manfred if he had visited the prostitute who'd blackmailed Felix, and he said that he had been a couple of times with Kurt. He said he'd felt dreadfully guilty on both occasions, partly because he was ashamed of what his parents would have thought if they had seen him in her dirty room. In his mind he regarded his parents as models of propriety, and his mother, especially, as a being above earthly passions. But when the tart insinuated that his own mother was a creature of flesh and blood, a woman like her, not an angel from heaven, he was deeply shocked.

'I remember occasions when my parents were walking together in the garden at Jeven,' he told me. 'They were laughing at something, and I saw my father take my mother in his arms and kiss her passionately. I then realised that they too must have experienced love and sex, in spite of their outward decorum. In an odd way this knowledge made me feel excluded from their relationship with one another, and I felt that my parents, particularly my mother, were betraying me, just as I, by visiting a prostitute, was betraying them.'

This vague suspicion that his parents and all members of their highly respectable society must experience passions just like he did, was confirmed by Felix's theft. His mother's letter in reply to the one in which he'd told her about it, and which had shocked him at the time, was further confirmation of his suspicion. He came to realise that there are no such things as absolute standards.

The realisation that his mother was a woman just like any other coincided with his involvement in the intrigues of Kurt and Hans.

The certainty that Felix, one of his schoolfellows, was a common thief undermined his already fragile view of the world.

'When I first went to that school,' he told me, 'I experienced an almost schizophrenic feeling of emptiness and lack of contact with people. Whereas most children are usually too involved in sport and things like that to worry much about other people and their lives, except insofar as they impinge on their own, I derived support from the belief that other people's behaviour was correct, and therefore to be relied on. When I learnt, within a short space of time, that my mother and that tart had much in common, and that a boy who shared my life at school was a criminal, my sense of security was shattered.'

Manfred's loneliness was exacerbated by the fact that the school was run on military lines. None of the teachers, who were mostly old soldiers, nor the chaplain, nor his parents, seemed to understand or sympathise with his wish to read music; consequently he was driven more and more into himself. Although both his parents and sister were very musical, his father discouraged him from thinking of music as a career, pointing out very firmly that he came of a military family, and that he should go into the army and become a regular soldier himself. This, he explained, was one reason why he took up with Kurt and Hans in the first place.

'But from time to time,' he said, 'my true interests reasserted themselves, and left me each time with the feeling that I'd done something useless and ridiculous. There was a constant conflict between my private inclinations and the rational ethos of the school, This resulted in my lack of confidence, which wasn't restored to any extent till I came to Templars.

'Take music, for example. I found it ridiculous to attempt to explain a given piece by means of words and ideas. I could understand how music could illustrate ideas, emotions, even concrete things such as the waves crashing against the rock in Mendelssohn's Hebrides Overture, but not the other way about. In other words, I can only convey my impressions inexactly. And yet the certainty of understanding what the composer intends to convey is indescribably strong. It's as if there's something inside me to whom the music speaks, and that my real self which belongs to me only grasps the shadow of this other being. I feel as if I am literally split in two, and this worries me.'

This was an experience I, too, could share with Manfred. One evening, just before I returned home to England, someone suggested playing Schubert's String Quintet in C major. Andrew and Clara, as the other string players, joined Manfred and his parents, leaving Hans, Helga and me as audience.

The slow movement of Schubert's posthumous string quintet is arguably the most sublime piece of music ever written. Arguably because words like 'sublime' are subjective and mean different things to different people. It begins in the key of E and is in twelve-eight time. This makes each bar enormously long. The melody is given to the inner instruments, the second violin, viola and first cello, while the accompaniment is shared by the first violin and second cello, the latter playing the first, sixth, seventh and twelfth beats pizzicato, and the former the third, fourth, eighth, ninth, tenth and eleventh legato. This gives to the music an exquisite poignancy that no words can describe. After twenty-eight bars a passage of frenetic anger breaks in, and though the time doesn't change from the twelve-eight rhythm, the rushing semi-quaver triplets played by the second cello in alternation with the second violin and viola, give the movement a sense of furious urgency. This middle section is followed by a return to the key of E major, and eventually to the first, poignant theme, by way of a passage which calls to my mind that transition to calm after a bout of angry sobbing, and in turn gives way to the painful melancholy that provoked the spasm in the first place.

Even in normal circumstances, sitting at home by the fire on a winter's evening this music can reduce me to tears. On that occasion at Jeven, with the war less than two months away and the near certainty I would never see Manfred again, coupled with the anger I felt towards Hans and Helga, sitting there in their ridiculous uniforms representing everything I found so distasteful in the German people — cruelty, stupidity, arrogance, sentimentality — was too much for me. To think that Germany could produce people like them, and at the same time music as sublime as Schubert's, was appalling, and I found myself sobbing. As I dabbed my eyes, I caught sight of Hans nudging Helga; their contempt said it all.

I had last heard this music at Drachenfels a few days after Manfred and I had declared our love for each other. He was playing the same part then as tonight, and I was utterly overwhelmed by it. When something like this is shared, as it was at Drachenfels and at Jeven, with the person one loves, it is mystical. I felt that Schubert's music was a requiem for the death of civilisation, a defiant outburst of anger against the insanity and the cruelty that had already begun to consume the German soul, and that was epitomised in that room by the black-uniformed, contemptuous figure of Hans Streiter, and I was certain that Manfred felt just as I did.

This feeling that words were inadequate to express what has been perceived was the cause of both Manfred's and my confusion. It had affected us both never more profoundly than during our night together in the mountain chalet in Austria. I had told Manfred in a letter after we'd parted in Austria, that Michel and I had paid a second visit to the Hawkspur camp.

'I was missing you so much,' I wrote, 'because I thought we might never see each other again. I was so lonely, and when Michel wrote to say that he wanted to spend another month in England, suggesting we both go there again to help out, I agreed, because I hoped that doing so would make me forget my loneliness.

'I never regarded my friendship for Michel as anything like my affection for you. I found him intellectually and physically attractive at school, but he had made it plain that my dog-like devotion to him was embarrassing. I went through a period last spring of feeling that, apart from you, no one really cared for me; that I could go to hell by accident and no one would try to stop me. I felt that things were going wrong, and I thought that Michel could help me. But at the same time, it seemed stupid to ask him when I really knew what was the matter all the time. And, of course, this was exactly his reaction. "Since you know what's wrong," he said when I brought the subject up, "why the hell don't you put it right?" But I couldn't, because although I was missing you dreadfully, I didn't realise fully just why.

'We had some long, strained talks, but they were never really useful because they invariably ended in him being sorry for me, and me promising to do this, that and the other, and he suppressing a suspicion that this was all a complete waste of time. At the end of them he usually felt pretty weary and glad to compromise. I forced myself to be reasonable, so that we ended by acting out parts together.

'Sometimes, Michel would be in a disagreeable mood, when I felt I needed cheering up. I would catch his eye and smile, but he would look away and I felt that at that moment he hated me. He just wouldn't or couldn't make the effort to be friendly. Then someone else would turn up and make some flippant remark, so that Michel would hop out of bed and scuffle with him, grinning and hooting with laughter.

'It went on like that day after day. He was clearly keeping me at arm's length, not wanting to get involved in arguments and explanations. No doubt I looked, as I felt, very forlorn and uncared for.'

So long as I had been unable to solve the basic problem of my sexuality I did not know who I was or what I was. My inability to reconcile these two sides of my life — and I felt this was something I shared with Manfred — was tearing us apart. Just as we found it impossible to put into words the effect Schubert's music had upon us, so were we equally unable to put into words what we had felt for each other that night on the mountain and ever since. But just as we knew the reality, the certainty, the profundity of the one, so we knew it also of the other.

During those last few days at Jeven, Manfred kept returning time and again to the schoolboy incident, which still seemed to haunt him. We both knew that time was very short, and he felt the urgent need, I am sure, to relieve himself of the burden of the confusion he had suffered as a consequence of it, just as I felt compelled to tell him about Michel. He told me that his failure to defend Felix against Hans and Kurt, or to warn him sooner than he did, was an act of moral ambiguity, almost an endorsement of their sadistic behaviour.

On reflection, I put this down to the fact that Manfred, with a finely tuned mind aware of all possibilities, took action only when he was convinced it was necessary. In his failure to act sooner, he was no different from Hamlet. These ambiguities and hesitancies only served to make us more united in our feeling for one another. In their different ways, Manfred's entanglement with Felix, Kurt and Hans, and my infatuation for Michel, were cathartic — stepping stones to self-knowledge, stages on that path of life we had now set out upon together. The admission that he had been sexually aroused by Felix's ill-treatment worried him greatly.

'There is something dark in me,' he said one day,' something I couldn't fathom with thought, but which was my life all the same. But when Felix confessed to the headmaster that what I had told him was true, there was a general enquiry into what had been going on. I was interrogated by the headmaster, of course, because everyone knew I was a friend of Hans and Kurt. But by then I was no longer confused. All the same, I don't think any of them really understood why I had become involved, or my reasoning. I just told them that some things can't be put into words: they just manifest themselves; they are mystical. What is mystical can't be approached by means of the intellect, but only through emotion, stillness and the arts.'

The turning-point came, he said, when he was able to take action independent of Kurt and Hans to help Felix. This had nothing to do with his lust for the boy.

'My long hesitation before I did act,' he said, 'might be regarded as selfish, I suppose, or cowardly, but it stemmed from my lack of confidence. I would never have had the courage to assert myself against Kurt and Hans at the start, and I must admit that fear of what they might do to me played a part in my motivation when I finally plucked up courage to warn Felix and report the whole business.

'At about the same time I had an overwhelming longing to return home, although previously my feelings towards my parents had not been very warm. All I wanted after the cataclysmic events at school was to seek the peaceful security of Jeven. My parents realised that I was unhappy and needed a change, which is the main reason they sent me to Templars for a year.

'To begin with, I saw myself as having no character of my own at all, so I looked for support to Kurt and Hans because they were older and seemed to have stronger personalities than mine. At first I thought Hans was uncomplicated: but I soon found out that he was a brutal sadist. Kurt's character is more complex: he used to distort words and ideas, and tried to dominate me and the others by intellectual means before assaulting them physically. He thought he was cleverer than Hans and me, and that he was being coldly rational, but of course he was anything but. He was a fanatic, though he pretended to be a profound thinker. Hans, on the other hand, was not a fanatic then. He's only become one since he joined the SS. Both of them were — are — cruel sadists, and both of them twist the truth. Both of them will go far in the Party.

'The trouble with Felix was that he was spineless. He followed his every impulse, never stopped to reflect, and was constantly at the mercy of stronger personalities. I'm afraid he was typical of a great many of my countrymen today. Kurt was a snake, Felix was a worm, but Hans is a monster.'

Throughout my stay at Jeven, the press had been full of Polish atrocity stories, and of German claims on Danzig. It was plain that the war would begin before the summer was out. I took leave of Manfred's family with a heavy heart the day before he was due to rejoin his regiment. He drove me to Flensburg to catch the train for

Esbjerg, where I was to embark for home. The countryside through which we drove could not have looked more peaceful, and it was hard to believe that only a few hundred miles to the east, the German army was already massing for its attack to 'liberate' Danzig. Neither of us felt much like talking; we both knew that in a few weeks' time we could be dead; he in Poland and I from German bombs in England.

'Let's try to keep in touch,' I said. 'We can at least send each other messages through Clara Edelstedt. If we say we've been playing the Schubert Quintet, that'll mean that we're alive and well. If we say we've been playing the slow movement only, it'll mean that we're ill, wounded or a POW. In any case, we'll try to write to each other once a month as long as we can.'

Just before we got into Flensburg, Manfred stopped the car in a little wood, and got out. I followed him along a track for a few yards till we were out of sight of the road.

He turned to face me, and opening his arms we embraced each other.

'You know how the old German knights used to swear a Blutbruderschaft?' he said.

'They made a little wound in their arms, and rubbed each other's blood into the cut,' I replied.

'Yes! And swore to be true to each other, of one blood, all their lives. That's what we should do now. We must swear to love each other, you and I, implicitly and perfectly and finally, with no thought of ever going back on it.'

He took a penknife out of his pocket, opened the blade and made a small incision in the palm of his right hand. Handing the knife to me, I did the same, and we placed our two palms together.

'Say after me: "Ich seh in dir den Gott/Den schauernd ich erkannt/Dem meine Andacht gilt."'

'I'll say it to you in English. "I see in you the God/whom I recognise with awe/to whom I owe all devotion."'

We kissed each other again, and I felt the tears starting to my eyes as I broke away from him. 'We must be going, or I'll miss the train,' I said, not knowing what else to say, my heart so full. I looked at Manfred, whose eyes, too, were glistening with tears. 'Auf wiedersehen, mein lieber Freund.'

'Ja; auf wiedersehen. Nicht Adieu. We *shall* meet again. I just know it. We shall. This cannot be "Goodbye".'

Our eyes met again. Manfred's were suffused now with warm

light and with intense love. I looked back as out of a darkness, into which I was about to plunge.

We got back into the car without another word. He dropped me at the station, and I took my pack out of the car. He did not get out. I came round to the driver's window, and put my hand in to shake his. 'Auf wiedersehen, mein lieber.'

'Auf wiedersehen, Tony.'

V

The new academic year was due to begin in October, but by the time I returned from Jeven it was clear that we were on the verge of war. I had to decide whether to return to Cambridge for my second year, or to start at once to train as an ambulanceman. Everyone tried to persuade me to return, but I knew I would be called up as soon as I reached twenty in November, and though I could have got a postponement to finish my course, having made up my mind to object, I wanted to get through the Tribunal as quickly as possible so that I could plan what to do next. I proposed to seek exemption so that I could choose the kind of work I wanted to do, but to judge by the fate of objectors in the last war, there was a strong possibility I would be sent to prison if I refused to do as the Tribunal ordered. With such uncertainty hanging over me, I felt it would be impossible to settle down to serious work.

Germany invaded Poland on September 1st, 1939, but Britain didn't declare war at once. The appeasers in Britain and France still clung to the hope that the clock could be turned back. For a few brief hours it looked as if Manfred was right when he had said that Daladier would mediate. It is fashionable nowadays to say that the politicians' willingness to grasp this illusory hope did them no credit. But it is fairer to see in their reluctance to declare war evidence of a fear of war, even though a prompt declaration might conceivably have precipitated a coup against Hitler.

The men who made up the governments of France and Britain remembered all too vividly the previous bloodletting. Anyone over forty remembered Europe as it was before July 1914, even though their memories were highly selective. They remembered easy, calm days, the certainties, the expectancy, their youth and their ambitions. They forgot the social strife, the strikes, the violence in the streets , the poverty, the disease and the overcrowded slums.

117

The differences which so occupied the telephone lines between London and Paris during September 2nd and 3rd amounted simply to fear of war, fear of bolshevism, memories of slaughter and the hatreds of 1914-18, concern for a Europe which was coming to an end, a social order which a new war would certainly destroy, and a divided political society in both countries.

But society in Britain was far less divided than in France. In Britain, we anticipated the war would begin with massive aerial bombing, the wholesale use of gas and the destruction by fire of our cities. I suppose that those who lived in cities took comfort from the air-raid precautions, the issue of gas masks and Anderson shelters, but we who lived in the country feared that we would be overrun by people fleeing from the holocaust over London.

During the night of September 2nd/3rd the hitherto peerless summer weather was broken by a massive thunderstorm. It was, indeed, as if the gods were taking part in the affairs of men. Sunday the 3rd was another beautiful September day, calm, peaceful, without a cloud in the sky, the air fresh and clean, the roads washed free of dirt after the overnight cloudbursts. The Sunday papers were filled with war news, reports of savage fighting in Poland intermingled with admonitions to carry gas masks everywhere, advice on what to do in the event of an air-raid warning, as well as statements about the rationing of meat, butter, cooking fat and sugar, and warnings against panic buying, which many people ignored. I decided to go for a ride to the next village to visit a friend of mother's who was organising courses of first aid and home nursing, to ask if I could join one of them before my call-up papers came. I rode down a lane that led to nearby woods, dismounted and tethered my horse to a tree at the far edge of it and lay down in the grass to think.

This was a place I often came to on horseback, for it was open downland, and I could canter and gallop across it for more than a mile in either direction. In front of me stretched the broad fields of Buckinghamshire beneath the Chilterns, serene and untroubled, their patchwork of golden stubble and new-ploughed land vanishing into the haze towards Oxford. I closed my eyes against the glare of the sun, and an immense tide of melancholy swept over me as I took out of my wallet the photograph of Manfred and me sitting arm in arm on the steps in front of the main building at Templars. I turned it over to read for the thousandth time what he had written on the back: 'Meinen ersten englischen Kamaraden, Anthony Kildwick, zum andenken. Manfred von Schrade. 1936.'

Where was he now? In a tank rolling across the plains of Poland, no doubt. What was he thinking? Was he exulting in Hitler's stand in defence of defenceless Danzig? Or was he worried lest this war might end in yet another defeat for Germany? At best he could say that England was not yet at war with Germany; and would never be, for that was what Ribbentrop and Goebbels had been telling Germans ever since the crisis blew up. But he would soon be bitterly deceived. Would he then begin to hate me as an enemy? Would he then be able to think of me as his blood-brother, or rather as his first English enemy?

As I lay in the sunshine with the larks singing unconcernedly overhead, I felt that my heart would break if he were to be killed. He was my soul-mate, my first love: far, far more dear to me than just my first German comrade. He had said that I was his heart's desire, his friend for ever, but could he really mean that now? Did he ever think of that night together in the alpine hut, or that recent sail to Pellworm, when we had joined our bodies together and he had then unburdened his soul to me, as a kind of mystical union? Or had the changed circumstances changed him? We were now enemies, or would be before the day was out, and if we ever met in battle, it would be our duty to kill each other.

A gentle breeze stirred the trees behind me, and faintly, across the plain from the direction of Aylesbury, I heard the distant wailing of an air-raid siren; the British ultimatum must have been rejected, and we were at war. Just then a cloud passed in front of the sun; the sunshine was blotted out of my life. I remounted and rode down to the village, tethered my horse, and knocked on Mrs White's door to ask if I might enrol with her group to learn how to dress wounds.

At the end of November I had a letter from Clara Edelstedt enclosing one from Manfred, which he had written in the early weeks of the war from Poland. It reached me through her uncle, an attaché at the Swedish embassy, and had come over uncensored in the diplomatic bag. Though the letter was addressed to Clara, she knew it was intended for me.

Manfred began by describing his regiment's thrust into Poland during the first two weeks of the war, and his reaction to the country and its people. 'One day we were thirsty and wanted to wash,' he wrote. 'We went to a house in this village near Krakow, and got some milk fresh from the cow. It was marvellous! The farmer's wife who was milking it hadn't any bread, so I gave her some of ours.

She didn't want to take it at first, and I couldn't understand why. Then, one of my men who spoke a little Polish, told me that the Poles had been told that any food we offered them would be poisoned. To show her this wasn't true, I ate a slice in front of her before she could be reassured. A few days later, we heard that Goering had spoken on the radio and said the war would be over in three or four weeks at most.'

News of England's declaration of war didn't reach Manfred until the middle of September, and when it did, he'd considered it nonsense. 'The Poles are a cowardly lot,' he continued. 'Seven of our soldiers were set upon by an entire village, their eyes were gouged out and they were castrated. This, luckily, didn't happen to men of my unit, but to those of a neighbouring one up the line. If this is true, and an armed civilian crosses our path, I swear we'll cut his head off with our own hands. I'm very much afraid that the Poles really are savages.

'There are homeless families everywhere,' he went on. 'It's all the fault of the Polish government for having called down on these miserable people this distress and misery. We're not fighting just for our rights alone, we're fighting for the poor Polish people too, from whom the ruling clique have withheld any sort of civilisation and culture. You just have to look at the houses the peasants have to live in: they're no better than pigsties, so it's now up to us to free these people from their wretched conditions. Under our leadership we can make their lot a much happier one.'

Manfred's letter depressed me. Although I was glad to have news of him, I was depressed to read how his outlook seemed to have been coloured by Nazi propaganda. It was, I supposed, quite inevitable that he would see the attack on Poland very differently from me, but when he had written the letter, there must have appeared to him at least a chance that the war would end with the conquest of Poland. This belief would have been fortified by the long period of military inactivity that followed for the next six months.

But his letter only served to increase my sense of loneliness. I longed to be able to see and talk to him. I felt our separation desperately, and longed for his presence; it was agonising. But the worst of it was the inability to talk about him to my family or friends without revealing the truth about our relationship; it wasn't their concern, and they would have been shocked if they had understood its true nature. There was nobody who cared about my loss; and I knew nobody who could break through my loneliness and drag me back into the mainstream of life again. I hoped that Manfred could guess how I felt, but that was unrealistic. Was he missing me as much as I was missing him, or had his enthusiastic involvement in the war totally taken him over so that he had no time to think about being lonely, for he was surrounded by his comrades and was taking part in a triumphant advance.

Nobody really cared; I could go to hell by accident, and nobody would try to stop me. But was my missing Manfred so unnatural? If he did still think of me as his Blutbruder, would he still think the same when the war ended? I missed him so much, and longed for the warmth of his affection. My feeling of loss was worst at night, when I woke suddenly, thinking of him, and aware I had been dreaming of him and had an erection; aware that my body was an unused machine that was never alive without him. To love somebody who isn't there to love you, who may never be there again, can easily become a neurosis. But I couldn't stop loving him just like turning off a tap; I could never desert him, but, oh God! if only I could have told him this at Jeven.

I scolded myself for behaving like a child; for feeling guilty. I was sick of the strain of keeping up appearances, of my own fake laughter. On the one hand, I wanted desperately to be a man in my own right, and on the other to enjoy the warmth of Manfred's love. I told myself that these two desires did not conflict; that they were part of each other, though I couldn't then tell how. I longed for his life to be included in mine. I had never felt so barren, such an utter failure, so completely empty.

Although I still held firmly to my pacifist beliefs, I did not feel myself to be committed to them heart and soul, as I was sure that Manfred felt committed to his soldiering. The triumphant Polish campaign would have strengthened rather than weakened his faith in Hitler. His letter had shown that clearly enough, unless he had written it in the knowledge that anything else he had said in it would have been censored and have placed his loyalty to the regime under suspicion. At the very least, he was achieving his patriotic goal, convinced of the rectitude of what he was doing. To rejoice in Germany's triumph did not mean he rejoiced in Hitler's political philosophy, but Hitler's successes would make it all the harder to fight against it, and he would be obliged to pass himself off as a devoted admirer of the regime. He might have lost his sense of direction and allowed himself to be influenced by external events, and to expect these events to provide solutions, which he didn't think he could discover on his own. The regime had been immensely successful and it was impossible to see how the army could carry out a revolt against it. As I had said to him on more than one occasion, the ultimate battle would be a spiritual one. Christians had fundamental ideas in common. Only governments were at odds with one another: Christians were not.

Not long before I had received Manfred's letter, I had also had one from Michel. He had written it within a month of the outbreak of war: 'So this is it,' the letter had begun. 'We're at war. I'm not going to pretend to you that it is anything other than an utter disaster — from the purely material point of view it would be merely trite to say that. But it is without doubt a dreadful calamity — the calamity of calamities, because it is a terrible step backwards, a setback in the progress of the human spirit, a progress that is already too slow, and which can only be achieved in peace.

'War is no more than the rule of force — he who commends force denies reason, and he who denies reason denies the spirit. Historically, we have every justification to carp at this war; it is nothing less than the outcome of the mishandling of an ill-conceived treaty. It was, alas, inevitable. If you look at it from the point of view of the belligerents, it is due to the bellicose docility of the Germans, the sentimentality and traditional blindness of English support of Germany in 1920, and of unshakeable obstinacy.

'And just look at Hitler. Is he mad? Has he made a frightful mistake? Has he counted the cost of what he has set in train? It makes me shudder to think that one individual can be responsible for the unhappiness and misery of millions of Frenchmen, Britons, Germans and Poles, especially of Germans, whose well-being he claims to be promoting.

'As I see it, we're in the position of a man, who has attacked another because he's been robbed, yet we are within our rights, because everyone has the right to defend his property. In other words, we are only fighting to defend our interests, not our ideals, because our ideals are pacific and against war.

'I love France, but I also love Germans, though I wouldn't want to live in Germany. Here we have all we want to eat and drink, and we can say what we think. In other words, we live comfortably, and we enjoy liberty. These are the essential conditions for the favourable development of thought. I don't know what to think.'

There was little I could do now, except wait for my summons to appear before the Conscientious Objectors Tribunal.

* * *

My instructions, when they came, were to report to the Conscientious Objectors' Tribunal at Southwark in mid January, 1940. Most pacifists were basing their objections on religious grounds, but political objections, although regarded with suspicion were respected by the more enlightened tribunals when it was clear that they were sincerely held. Every objector was allowed to call a witness to speak on his behalf, and to produce two or three character references to show his adherence to a church or pacifist group. More often than not these witnesses were clergymen, though schoolmasters and tutors often spoke on behalf of their students. Long-standing members of the Plymouth Brethren, Jehovah's Witnesses and Quakers were almost always granted exemption, and many of them did valiant work as air-raid wardens, ambulancemen and as human guinea-pigs for medical research.

The tribunal sat in a large hall in the Borough not far from Guys' Hospital. The day I appeared before it there were about twenty objectors, none of whom I knew. A representative of the Peace Pledge Union and another of the Communist Party of Great Britain were standing outside the door distributing pamphlets and offering to speak on behalf of those who had not brought someone with them to do so. I sat down by myself towards the back of the hall, and waited for the proceedings to begin. There were five members of the tribunal, all of them men in their late fifties or sixties, who had probably fought in the last war. Two of them looked as if they suffered from high blood pressure, and one seemed to have an obsession with cleanliness, for he took a yellow duster from his brief-case, and wiped his chair before sitting down. In front of the dais there were sundry officials and clerks sitting at a long, green baize table taking notes. The usher, having told us to be 'upstanding' (why, I wondered, couldn't he have told us to 'stand up?') then told us not to be downsitting but to sit down, which struck me as singularly illogical. When we, like sheep, had all obeyed, he called the name of the first objector.

He was a seedy looking youth with a pinched, earnest expression and steel-rimmed spectacles. His objection was to taking part in a capitalist war against the workers of Germany, and now that

Russia had allied herself with Hitler, this enabled the Polish working class in that part of the country occupied by the Red Army to throw off their shackles. He appeared to have a particular animus against the Radziwills and another aristocratic Polish family, whose name I didn't catch. He then called his witness, who turned out to be the young woman who had been handing out leaflets for the CPGB. The chairman asked her if a community should not defend itself, to which she replied that we in Britain were not a community, for we were divided into two parts. 'But,' protested the chairman, 'if this war was of benefit to the common people, would you support it?' 'It isn't for their benefit.' 'Well, let me put my question another way; would it be worthwhile defending an ideal democracy?' 'Socialism is international, and if a socialist state started to defend itself it would no longer be able to retain its socialism.'

Turning to the applicant he asked, 'Is your objection only against this particular war?' 'No, it is to all wars,' whereupon he launched into a long diatribe about the exploitation of the workers in France and Britain. It was their duty to stop this crazy war before it got crazier. It wasn't clear where Hitler came into all this, or whether we were supposed to be at war with him, or with our ally Stalin. But since the two of them were now such chums, I suppose it didn't matter very much. After about ten minutes of this the member of the tribunal with high blood pressure appeared to be in acute danger of cardiac arrest, and to prevent what would certainly have been an awkward situation if he had succumbed, the chairman conferred with the other members, and after we had been told once more to be upstanding, they withdrew for private consultation.

After a few minutes they came back, and refused him the unconditional exemption he had asked for, telling him to go and work on the land or in forestry. He and his girlfriend retired muttering about the impossibility of getting justice from a capitalist society.

The next applicant was a Jehovah's Witness with a hot line to God, by whom he had been told that the End was nigh, and that he had better do something to save his soul while the going was good. God had told him to have no truck with this bloody war, which displeased the tribunal greatly. His application for unconditional exemption was likewise dismissed, and he was sentenced to become a coal miner.

The third objector was a student from the London School of Economics, who delivered a lecture on imperialism as the cause of war — he was probably writing a thesis on the subject — basing his case on the iniquitous exploitation of the natives of India, Kenya and Brazil. We were left in some doubt about the status of these unfortunate Brazilians within the British Empire, for no one knew that we had annexed Brazil. There was a good deal about vested interests and the City of London, which elicited applause from the audience and a harsh rebuke from the bench. He was shocked by Germany's treatment of the Jews, but what about our exercise of British power in Palestine? Why were we in Palestine anyway? and what about the Amritsar massacre?

It took no time at all for the bench to refuse him unconditional exemption, and if the cardiac gentleman could have had his way, he would doubtless have been despatched to a firing squad.

Number four began by stating the obvious: 'I belong to the youth of Britain,' he declared, which none of us could deny. He had no vote, yet the young, by which one felt he meant himself alone, were the innovators in society. Youth was the future; the young mind was open to sane ideas, and the initiative of the young, their faith in life gave them the ability and the energy not only to think (this went down very badly) but to act (which went down worse). Youth should be on the side of life not death. To build a peaceful world in which abundant life is the first consideration, was youth's proper function. His choice was not to range himself on the side of death and destruction, but to serve the future of life by turning the tide of war and offering himself to the service of peace. The chairman asked how he proposed to achieve all this, to which he replied that he wanted to educate the British public and change its morality. What was needed was more mentally alive people (further signs of cardiac arrest). Britain would not be truly great until it saw itself as others saw it, and to reach this happy state, it had to acknowledge its own shortcomings, and then act courageously to rectify them. The cause of the present conflict was Britain's policy of imperialism and nationalism, and when it saw clearly that there were just as many injustices in our national policy as in anybody else's (meaning by implication Hitler's) then, and only then, would there be any chance of making peace.

All this proved too much for the gentleman with the cleanliness phobia. His voice ringing with indignation, he demanded to know if the applicant would stand by and see his mother and sister raped, to which he replied that he would.

'This is disgraceful,' shouted the clean man. 'Don't you realise that people are risking their lives to defend you?' 'Yes I do. They're dupes.' This was the last straw — exemption refused.

Next to appear was a languid young man in maroon pants. In those days of grey flannels, maroon pants indicated only two things — either that you were a member of the Dragoon Guards or you were a pansy, and he was clearly not a dragoon. Even the Jehovah's Witness and the champions of the working class, who had stayed behind, perhaps in the hope of making a few converts, showed signs of siding with the Establishment. Since it was clear to them that this young man would not be a credit to either movement, they felt safe to show a glimmer of sympathy for the tribunal.

When asked his profession, the young man declared that he was a thurifer, which foxed the nonconformists and atheists, and embarrassed the Anglo- and Roman Catholics, especially when he added that he was also a verger, and ran a scout troop. After objecting to both military and ARP service, he said he wanted to undertake youth work, which produced a manifestation of outrage on the tribunal's part marvellous to behold. Like the Jehovah's Witness he was sent to work in the mines.

We then adjourned for lunch. I reckoned that if the tribunal were fortifying themselves with strong drink, I might as well do the same, so I went and had two double Scotches and a beef sandwich in a nearby pub. After we resumed, the first objector to appear looked like a truck driver, and said he was a Plymouth Brother, and wanted to work on the land. He was supported by a much older, red-faced man, who said he was the young man's uncle, and that he was willing to take him on his farm. This went down well, and, he was granted exemption on condition he worked in agriculture.

I was called next. 'You are Arthur Anthony Kildwick?' 'Yes.' 'You were born at Wraysby on November 21st, 1919?' 'Yes.' 'You were educated at Templars and at St Sergius' College, Cambridge?' 'Yes.' 'You are a student of modern languages?' 'Yes.'

I explained that I had not yet taken my degree, having been up for one year only, but that I was currently training in first aid and home nursing with the local Women's Voluntary Service, as this was the only organisation that would teach me. 'Why do you object to joining the forces?' 'Because I believe the war to be the wrong solution to current international problems.' 'Do you not think it wrong for a young man in your situation to opt out of the forces while the rest of your contemporaries are risking their lives for their country?' 'I have no objection to risking my life, and I am not seeking exemption on that account.'

I could feel myself getting angry at the snide way the last question had been put to me by a member of the tribunal, who up to that point, had not opened his mouth.

'Would you defend yourself from attack?' 'Certainly, if it were a personal attack.' 'Then why do you object to joining the forces?' the same member of the bench asked with some asperity.

This provoked a round of applause from the audience which was sternly silenced by the chairman. Taking up the questioning, he said: 'You have just told us that you have no objection to risking your life and that you are training in first aid and home nursing; why do you not join the RAMC?' 'Because as a conscript I cannot choose the arm of the service I might wish to join, and as I am not a medical student, there can be no guarantee that I would be accepted by the RAMC. Furthermore, I would be required to kill people in an emergency.'

This was a bad slip, for they took me up on my answer to the earlier question about defending myself, and tried to make out that I was being illogical. But I stood my ground.

'What are your religious beliefs?' one of them asked. As briefly as I could I told them, adding, almost as an afterthought, that I was proposing, if they granted me exemption, to join some fellow students to form an ambulance unit, and that once we had trained ourselves, we would offer our services either as a body, or individually, to whomever could make use of us.

They put their heads together, and the chairman began writing something on a sheet of paper, which he folded and placed in an envelope. He handed it to the clerk with a whispered instruction. 'Exemption granted on condition you undertake ambulance work. Next please.'

I turned to leave the witness stand, and made for my seat at the back of the hall, where I had left my coat and hat. As I was walking down the aisle the audience clapped, and while I was putting on my coat, the clerk came up and handed me the note the chairman had written. It was all extremely embarrassing, most of all the note that had just been handed to me. I stuffed it unopened into my coat pocket, and left the hall as quickly as I could. Once outside I found that I wanted desperately to pee, and when I got to the gents, I took out the envelope, slit it open and read the note. 'You must be Doris de Vergy's son. I knew your uncle, Anthony Tynron, I hope your ambulance unit does well.'

Sickened, I crumpled the note and flushed it down the loo. If that was why I'd been granted exemption, I would rather have gone to prison.

VI

Once I had gained exemption, I became the prey of grave doubts. I kept thinking of Manfred and Hans, both so patriotic and keen to serve their country honourably in what they, and millions of Germans, thought of as a just cause — the liberation of their fellow Germans from foreign oppression. This was not an ignoble aim, and contrary to what many people in England believed, most Germans were not thirsting for war. In spite of all the propaganda to which they had been subjected, they did not appear to bear me, an Englishman, or my country, any ill will. If, on the other hand, only half of what the Poles were alleged to have been doing to those Germans who'd been stranded on the wrong side of the frontier by the Treaty of Versailles was true, it was only natural that they should wish to rescue them, and reunite them with the rest of Germany.

But was it all true? Having heard Hans and Helga seriously asserting that *all* Poles, *all* Jews, *all* Slavs were no more than human animals, only one degree superior to apes, I could not but suspect that at the very least such oppression as the Danzigers and other Germans were said to be suffering was grossly exaggerated. I was certainly left in no doubt that the elite cadres of the Nazi Party, the SS, the SA and the Gestapo were thoroughly evil and disreputable, and that there was a world of difference between Manfred and his parents on the one hand, and Hans, Helga and their like on the other.

But above all else, I was singularly fortunate to be British. The provisions the government had made for conscience were enlightened, and, where sincerely applied, as in my case, no one could complain that they were in the least oppressive. Among my family and friends, I was tolerated, and the press seemed, on the whole, to grant a similar toleration to those who had thought deeply on the ultimate consequences of their stand and the implications of their resistance to war. Men and women well-known for their pacifist views had been allowed — and were still allowed — to lecture and to write with full freedom of speech. As for pacifists themselves, they came in many shapes and sizes, but they could not be accused of dragooning consciences. There was no pacifist party line, no programme of action, no demanding creed or dogma. The contrast with what I had just experienced at Jeven in the persons of Hans and Helga could not be greater. A system, whether Nazi or communist, which was based on mass meetings, torchlight processions, card votes and executive decisions can never tolerate the conscientious objector.

There was a popular idea once that all COs were left-wing, middle-class intellectuals, teachers, writers or academics. It was certainly the case that the twenty or so undergraduates who volunteered to form the Universities Ambulance Unit in 1940 were middle-class, and of independent means — or rather their parents were. But taking the country as a whole, there was a slight preponderance of white-collar workers, though the lists that have survived show that COs included policemen, artisans, clerks, civil servants and unemployed. My encounter with Hans Streiter had made me extremely proud to be a citizen of a country that tolerated my unorthodoxy.

Just before I went to Germany in June 1939, I had been in contact with Kenneth Powell, an Oxford undergraduate, whom I had met very briefly three years before during my sojourn with Michel at Hawkspur Camp. Kenneth had been in contact with the Friends' Ambulance Unit to ask what plans they had to recruit volunteers, who, though pacifist, were not Quakers. They had none, he told me, so together we decided to form our own unit. It was to be independent of both the Peace Pledge Union and the Fellowship of Reconciliation, and would be open to any pacifist students, regardless of whether or not they had been through their Tribunals, and regardless of their religious or political beliefs. It was to be unpaid, so every volunteer had to be responsible for his own support. As soon as war broke out, Kenneth asked David, when he heard that Hawkspur was to be closed down for the duration, if we could have it to train in. He offered to let us have it free of charge for the summer of 1940, and with his help and some money from other sympathisers we were able to raise enough to pay for the board and lodging of twenty-five volunteers.

We were an odd bunch. There was Desmond, who later became a well-known Christian scholar and Arabist, but at that time was a fanatical Nazi. While most of us watched the Battle of Britain dog-fights with a degree of patriotism, he would shout encouragement to the Messerschmidt pilots, jumping up and down whenever they shot down a Spitfire.

While I was at Jeven, I had told Andrew Dahl of our plans, and had persuaded him to become our medical instructor. Andrew was a raw, bony individual, and I had not found him easy to know, for he seemed to have a chip on his shoulder when in the company of gilded Oxbridge youth. He was also that uncompromising sort of rebel who refuses to pay taxes or eat imported food, because it had had to be brought in by men who were risking their lives at sea. His diet was consequently pretty meagre. He didn't like any of us very much, because we seemed to him to be taking our pacifism too light-heartedly. He also objected to some of us peeing on a patch of nettles outside the bunk-house, because our urine, if properly directed, would have helped the compost heap to do better whatever it is that compost heaps are supposed to do, and nettles if plucked young are an excellent source of vitamin C.

Hubert, a rotund convert to Rome, known to some as the 'pansy hippo', was heard to murmur at Andrew's protest:

'Consider the nettles how they grow;
they toil not, neither do they spin;
but I tell you that Solomon in all his glory
was not besprayed like one of these.'

Hubert's attraction to Rome was much stimulated by his delight in ceremonial and watered silk. He had a brilliant mind and a voice like Robert Morley. He would begin an argument on almost any topic with the statement: 'Speaking as an *extreme* sacramentalist...' He had a passion for the music of Gustav Mahler, then little heard in England. He had brought with him a recording of the Ninth Symphony, which he would play on his wind-up portable at least once a week. Considering that this work occupied thirty-two sides of 78 rpm discs, to play it was in itself an act of considerable devotion. He died soon after the war after falling off his bicycle in the High at Oxford.

Not long after the war I bumped into Charles, who had by then become a young professor of history. 'The Universities Ambulance Unit,' he told me, 'did more for my intellectual education than any other episode of my youth. At Oxford I used to go around with Peter, who was one of a group of Christian-socialist philosophers. I liked him more than he liked me. He's become an authority on Plato. He taught me to drive out of sheer good nature. He had, I remember, a 1928 Hillman Minx that had to be cranked by hand. That was the first time I heard an educated man say "fuck". I was awestruck.'

'You were a friend of Dennis, too, weren't you?' I asked.

'Yes, I was. He later lectured on politics at Oxford. He was murdered in Turkey some years ago, did you know? I think the motive was robbery, but no one was quite sure.' I thought that I could make a better guess than Charles, who was certainly unaware of Dennis's extreme promiscuity and love of rough trade.

'Did you know that Kenneth Powell went to be a porter at Guy's Hospital when we wound up the UAU?' Charles went on. 'He's become a professor of urology, I believe. He had an inexplicable affection for me, but his teasing used to frighten me. He gave me a copy of Plato's *Dialogues* which I still treasure without liking the contents. How Plato haunted that little world,' he added wistfully. 'Very sinister....' Obviously he had no idea why Kenneth had been so inexplicably affectionate, but I had: Charles was quite the most handsome of a very good-looking lot of guys, and Kenneth — well, Kenneth and Dennis were insatiable.

'D'you remember when Kenneth told us that he suspected Andrew of being a German spy?'

'That was because his father was German,' I said.

I remembered the incident vividly. Andrew used to get up very early to go birdwatching. One weekend he disappeared and Kenneth told us he'd been taken away by the police, who'd discovered that his ornithology was a cover, and that he'd been photographing military installations. I didn't seriously believe this at the time, for I knew he had been behaving in much the same way at Jeven. He could have been a double agent, I thought — he was certainly eccentric enough. The reaction of the others to this news was interesting. Some suggested that we should issue a statement on behalf of the Unit, and hand it to the police dissociating ourselves publicly from Andrew's alleged nefarious activities. But this wasn't the only time we were suspected of spying. One day we had gone on a route march to see some medieval ruins in a nearby village, and one of us had taken a picture of them with his Box Brownie. He'd hardly had time to click his shutter before a Home Guard swooped down and marched us all off, docile as sheep, to the nearest police station, where the film was solemnly taken from the camera and exposed.

On the Monday, when Andrew had not reappeared, speculation reached boiling point. That afternoon, he walked into the camp with his normal look of aggressive humility and announced that his wife, of whom we had not heard a word, had had a baby. None of us quite believed him.

Harry, who had spent some time in India sitting at the feet of a guru in an ashram, had been at Harrow with Nol and Torquil. Torquil rode a motorbike, was extremely good-looking, very promiscuous, very sophisticated and a heavy smoker. He maintained that smoking was nourishing. Nol, who later became a judge, nearly died of terror at the home nursing exam because he thought he'd bound his patient's tourniquet so tight that he'd get gangrene. Nol used to tease Harry about his devotion to gurus. He could be heard singing while he washed up, a little ditty he'd composed which went:

For I believe in ashrams, the ashrams must go on

As long as there are other people's goods to live upon.

The local inhabitants had come to look upon the occupants of Hawkspur Camp with suspicion and mild hostility. For the most part, our predecessors, the delinquents, who had been removed to Borstals on the outbreak of war, had behaved themselves reasonably well. With our arrival, the neighbours began to wag their heads and tut-tut about the 'goin's on down the lane'. A rumour was put about that we were naturists, which had arisen, no doubt, from the fact that during the hot summer of 1940 most of us went about very scantily clad. One day, returning to camp with the rations, I surprised a small knot of locals peeking through the hedge hoping, I'm sure, to see something rude or nude. It has to be said that both pacifists and delinquents were better behaved than the incipient priests from the local theological seminary, who refused to acknowledge their illegitimate offspring. But, to be fair, the proportion of gay pacifists was almost certainly larger than the proportion of gay incipient priests.

As our training came towards its end, we began to think about our future employment. Some joined the Friends Ambulance Unit, but five of us offered ourselves to the Imperial Volunteer Ambulance Corps (IVAC). This rather dotty enterprise was staffed by a mixture of First World War veterans, debutantes and young men unfit for military service. It had originally been formed to serve with the French army, but owing to the speed with which France had collapsed, it never left the country. Its female drivers joined the ATS, and the organisers were left with twenty-five brand new ambulances and no one to drive them, so it was decided to advertise for men too old for military service and those who for one reason or another were exempt.

* * *

The Arthur Anthony Kildwick who joined IVAC was different from the young man who left it a year later; almost unrecognisable from the chap who joined the army in the summer of 1941. That Tony was gauche, priggish and naif; longing to love and be loved; wanting to conform and to reject the rebellious stand he had taken. He looked forward to donning his IVAC uniform, for it made him look like a soldier. He knew that by doing this, rather than joining the totally civilian FAU, he could silence his critics. After all, it was outward appearances, not inner motives, which counted then. In a uniform which was more or less indistinguishable from a French officer's service dress, he could be mistaken for one of the many Allied servicemen who then thronged the streets of London.

I was prepared to make sacrifices for my ideals: I was still enough of an optimist to believe that pacifism was the practical answer to Hitler, Stalin and Mussolini. If I, and those who thought like me, did not take a stand, there would be no point in having any ideals at all. But that had been back in January during the phoney war, when there was still a faint chance that peace could be restored after the rape of Poland. By late summer all that had changed.

What at the beginning of the year might have looked like courage, now looked like cowardly naivety. The war had hotted up by the summer of 1940; IVAC might well have been sent to Greece, which had been invaded by the Italians in October, and I was prepared to risk my life if it were. Failing an overseas posting, I was ready to go wherever I might be sent in England. So kitted out as an officer and a gentleman (paid for by a much-relieved father, who now felt sure that I had 'come up trumps') I reported to Hemscott Hall, a large mansion on the Northumberland coast which had been handed to the corps by a well-wisher to be its operational HQ. *That* Tony Kildwick thought he'd found the ideal solution: everyone seemed content — at least for a week or two...

It was early in November 1940 when I drove up to Hemscott in my red MG, and, as I always do once I've got past Doncaster, I felt I was coming home. There is something about the North of England for those who have the good fortune to have been born there that makes them terrible chauvinists. It is a masculine country; its ugliness and its beauty are as uncompromising as the people who live there. You know where you stand: spades are spades and shovels are shovels. I was happy; I was coming home after too long away. I felt safe here.

The big house seemed deserted when I arrived and parked my car on the broad sweep of gravel in front of a fine Palladian portico. I took my briefcase out of the back, went up to the front door, and rang the bell. There was a longish pause before it was opened by a wizened old man in a green baize apron, whom I took to be the butler. He bade me come in, and showed me into what had once been the drawing-room, but which was now furnished with government issue furniture as a mess.

'If you'll be good enough to wait here, sir, I'll go and see if Mr Cuttlance is about. He'll show you to your room.' Whereupon he went out leaving me by myself. I didn't have long to wait before the door opened, and an extremely handsome man of about forty came in. He had a mass of wiry, grey hair, fine brown eyes and a small, well-cut moustache; the sort of man you could not mistake for anything but an upper-class English officer.

In addition to the British War and Victory medals, he wore the ribbons of the DSO and MC on the breast of his tunic. He was wearing the IVAC uniform with riding breeches and field boots, and was carrying a file of papers under his arm. He walked with a slight limp, and his right hand was bandaged. Coming towards me with a welcoming smile, his left hand outstretched, he said, 'I'm Jack Cuttlance. Please forgive my left hand, I stupidly spilt some boiling water over myself this morning, and got badly scalded. Welcome to the madhouse! So glad to see you. You're the first to arrive; come by car?'

'Yes,' I said introducing myself. 'The others are coming up tomorrow.'

'Huge relief to see you. The unit's almost falling apart for lack of drivers. It'll be great to have you all to relieve the pressure a bit.' He said this in a way that suggested just the faintest hint of criticism. 'If you'd like to get your things,' he went on, 'I'll show you your room. You'll be next to me; it's the last of the small rooms, and I guess you'd rather be on your own than with three or four others.'

I thanked him and said that I would. We went out to the car, unloaded my valise, with its sleeping bag, pillow and camp-bed, then my suitcase, and I followed him into the house and up a grand staircase to a gallery beneath a dome.

'I hope you realise you've joined a crazy outfit,' he said as I began to unpack the valise and set up my camp-bed. 'You've no idea what you're in for.'

'I only know what they told us in London.'

'The trouble is that no one quite knows what to do with us. Lambourne — he's in command — is having a meeting with the RAMC people at Northern Command today, and he hopes to work out something with them. He won't be back until the day after tomorrow, so we won't have any news till then. All the others have gone into Newcastle with the ambulances,' he added. 'The silly buggers at Ford's sent them up without blackout masks for the headlamps and no brackets for the stretchers. They should be back for dinner.'

He went on to tell me that a vehicle maintenance course had been arranged with the Ford agents, and that we would be spending a lot of time there.

'How long have you been here?' I asked.

'I got here last week. I came up with Lambourne and Hassell as an advance party. I'm supposed to be responsible for catering and billeting. Needless to say, those idiots in the London office had done bugger all. They've all had their knickers in a twist since the fall of France and the change of plans. Lambourne and I more or less waded in and took command.

'The original commandant was a Frenchman. He's disappeared in the chaos. There was no one else in England, except a lot of hysterical women drivers, who hadn't a clue what to do. We got rid of them, and decided to start afresh.' He paused: 'I must say, I'm glad to see you're not another geriatric. Talk about the halt, the maimed and the blind, that's us.'

I'd finished the little unpacking I had to do and stood up.

'Like a drink now?' he asked.

I said I'd like nothing better, and we went downstairs to the mess. Jack went over to a trestle table which was standing at one end of the room, on which glasses and drinks were set out.

'I'm afraid we haven't much on offer yet,' he said. 'Sherry? Gin? No tonic. Scotch, beer, and that's about it.'

'I'll have a sherry, please.'

'Fine! You haven't taken to this filthy gin and sherry people are drinking now that you can't get decent vermouth, have you? It's veritable gut-rot.'

He poured a couple of glasses, and we brought them over to the chairs by the fireplace and sat down.

'I'll get Bachelor to light the fire. It gets cold here now in the evenings. No central heating, of course, but the Kirkharles very kindly left us a cellar full of coal. They've been awfully decent and helpful. Nothing too much trouble. And leaving old Bachelor and their cook here has made life a damn sight easier for me, I can tell you.'

He stretched out and pulled an old-fashioned bellrope, which operated a wire to the kitchen regions below. I heard it tinkling in the distance, and a few moments later the old man who had met me came in.

'Oh Bachelor, could you please light a fire for us, and, by the way, Mr Kildwick is the only extra for dinner tonight. Please tell cook. The others won't be here till tomorrow.'

'How many of us are there?' I asked after Bachelor had left the room.

'Only seventeen at present. With you and your lot we shall be twenty-one. There are four or five in London still, and I believe a couple are coming down from Scotland as soon as they can settle their affairs there.'

In retrospect there seems to be only one way of describing Jack Cuttlance: he was glamorous. He possessed that power of investing the most trivial actions with a glow of desirability. Whatever he said or did, I felt it was what I wished I had said or done myself. He could transmute the ordinary into the extraordinary, the prosaic into the delectable. It was something quite independent of sex and more fundamental than imagination or personality. If glamour is a kind of magic, Jack Cuttlance possessed it in great measure. It had something to do with our respective ages and experience, of course. Maybe you have to be a certain age before you become glamorous, or perhaps people can only detect glamour in those older than themselves. To appreciate it, you must be content and enchanted by it. Jack became the first close friend I had who was much older than myself, and I was captivated by him.

He had been seventeen when the first war ended, but had pretended to be older and run away from school to join up eight months before the armistice. He won his MC within a month of going into the trenches, and his DSO saving the life of a fellow officer, Stanley Moore, during the last week of the war, just before his eighteenth birthday. When the war ended, Stanley, who was ten years his senior, invited Jack to live with him, and they had lived together ever since. Stanley taught at a public school in Buckinghamshire and Jack, after going to the Slade, became an interior designer. He had been highly successful and photos of the houses he had done up were regularly featured in *Country Life* and the *Tatler*. He had also made something of a reputation as a stage designer, and had had numerous successes in London and New York. All that, of course, had come to an end with the war. He and Stanley had shut up their little house in St John's Wood, and moved to their cottage near Stanley's school.

Stanley, of course, was in a reserved occupation, and in any case, too old for military service. Jack, who had been wounded in the first war, was not the sort of man to sit idly by, and had volunteered to join IVAC when it was first started early in 1940. By rights he should have commanded it, but preferred to take second place to Hugh Lambourne, who had joined at the same time.

Just then a vehicle drew up outside, soon followed by several more. 'Here they are. Earlier than I expected,' said Jack, and by and by my new colleagues drifted into the mess in ones and twos. Most of them were men of about Jack's age or a little older, men who had been too young for the first war but too old, as yet, for this one. There were several in their late fifties, one of whom had fought in the Boer War, and there were also a few my own age. These young men were all unfit for military service. The Corps secretary, for example, was about twenty-five, and had lost an arm in a car crash; the Transport Officer had lost a foot from frostbite on a mountaineering expedition in the Himalayas; the Quarter-Master was deaf in one ear from a mastoid operation that had gone wrong, and the Training Officer had a glass eye. For the first time in my life I began to feel over-endowed. Despite the ravages of age and misadventure, they were all fit and capable of doing the jobs allocated to them. They all seemed pleased to see me, and extended an equally warm welcome to the other UAU men when they turned up next day.

As a result of Lambourne's visit to Northern Command, we were to spend the next two or three weeks on a driving and vehicle maintenance course, and those who had not already done so were to be trained in first aid. After that we were to be attached to army field hospitals along the coast from Berwick to Whitby.

The driving and maintenance courses were great fun. We were taken to a large patch of concrete behind a bus station in Newcastle, which had been sprayed with grease and oil, and taught how to control skids, and how to stop dead at forty miles an hour without killing ourselves or our patients.

It must have been about six weeks after our arrival at Hemscott Hall that the dreadful fact that the five of us were conchies leaked out. Someone had casually mentioned his Tribunal and exemption from military service, not because we were medically unfit, but because of conscience, which came as a shock to some of our more conventional colleagues.

When we had been engaged, no one had asked if we were pacifists, so none of us had mentioned the fact. Perhaps we ought to have, but we had all taken it for granted that, as we were free to volunteer for ambulance work, it hadn't seemed relevant or necessary to say why. So far as I was concerned, I had made no secret to Jack of the fact that I was an objector, and he had expressed neither dismay nor surprise at this revelation.

A meeting was called at which we were accused of being a bunch of shirkers by a pompous little man who had taken a great dislike to some of us. Jack retaliated by asking him if he considered the job he was doing in IVAC was shirking, whereupon he lost his temper and resigned, much to the relief of us all. As Jack pointed out on our behalf, we had joined in good faith; we were doing a good job; and the Corps needed our services. And so, with a certain reluctance on the part of one or two of the others, we were allowed to stay on.

Throughout this unpleasant experience, Jack Cuttlance was a staunch friend and supporter. Noticing how upset I was — for it was I who had negotiated our acceptance into the Corps — he went out of his way to be friendly, a kindness I had not expected, but for which I was very grateful. My feeling for him began to change from friendship to affection.

Not long after this row, we were split into small groups, and attached to field hospitals along the north-east coast. Jack asked me if I would care to be in his group, and four of us, manning two ambulances to give a round-the-clock service, were allocated to a sector near Berwick. Our duties were not onerous, consisting of ferrying soldiers from their units to the local hospital and back for injections, vaccinations and dental treatment. The invasion scare had passed, and the army had settled down to training and coastal defence duties, from which few casualties were expected.

The winter of 1940-41 was one of the coldest on record, and nowhere colder than on the Northumberland coast. Jack and I were lucky to have found comfortable digs in a big, Victorian house belonging to a motherly spinster, who was only too pleased to look after us as best she could. We divided our time to suit ourselves, and because there was so little to do beyond the daily routine runs between the units we were servicing and the medical centres and general hospital, we were thrown on each other's company a great deal. There was no chance of Christmas leave, so Jack asked our landlady if she would mind if Stanley came to join us for the holiday when his term ended. She agreed, and we planned a Christmas party for the friends we had met locally, and to whom we owed hospitality.

Snow fell heavily the week before Christmas, but it did not seem bad enough for Stanley to change his plan to drive north. Between the three of us we had scraped together enough petrol coupons for his trip, and we awaited his arrival eagerly. About an hour before we were expecting him, a wire came to say that he had skidded and crashed the car. He had broken both his legs, been concussed and was in hospital in York. When Jack phoned, he was told Stanley was worse than was at first believed, for there had been abdominal injuries as well, and his condition had deteriorated since the telegram had been sent. I offered to hold the fort while Jack went down to York, but the hospital said there was little point, as Stanley was still unconscious, and until he had regained consciousness there was nothing Jack could do.

That night, it was my turn for duty, and as usual on such occasions, I slept in my clothes in the sitting room in case an ambulance was needed urgently. During the early hours we were all awoken by a shattering explosion, and the sound of breaking glass. There had been no air-raid warning, and though we listened for the sound of aircraft, we could hear nothing. Almost at once the phone rang; it was the MO. 'Get up here as quickly as you can,' he shouted, 'the place is in a bloody shambles.'

The explosion we had heard was one of our own mines. It had been accidentally detonated by a beach patrol, which had missed its way in the dark and the blizzard, and strayed into one of the minefields which protected that stretch of the coast. One man had been killed outright, and another had a foot blown off. Several others had been wounded less seriously.

Jack, who had been wakened by the explosion, came downstairs just as the MO rang off, and volunteered to come with me, but there was no time for him to get dressed, and the delay would have been too much. As it was, it took me nearly twenty minutes to get the ambulance started and drive it up to the casualty clearing station — a journey that normally took less than five minutes. The accident had occurred some way from the CCS on a lonely and

139

inaccessible part of the beach, too far from the road for the ambulance to reach. When I finally arrived, they were bringing in the wounded. It was my first sight of blood and carnage. Till then I had worried lest the sight of blood and wounds might cause me to faint, but I was gratified to find that I could observe it all with surprising detachment.

The dead man was a corporal of about my own age, whom Jack and I had got to know quite well. Now, only half his head remained, and his brains were spilling out from a gaping hole in his skull. The other half of his face and head were hardly damaged, and one blue eye stared up in startled surprise from under a lock of fair hair. The whole of the right side of his body had been torn away from shoulder to waist, and his greatcoat and battledress blouse were mingled with what remained of his guts. His injuries were so frightful as to seem surreal, and I had no feeling of terror or even sympathy, they were so unlike anything I had ever seen or dreamt of. A second man was brought in as I arrived, still conscious and screaming in agony. His left leg had taken the brunt of the explosion, and a footless stump stuck out from the end of his trousers. They laid him down on a stretcher in the snow to give him a shot of morphia. We wrapped him up and put the stretcher in the ambulance, and while we were doing this, others were brought in, one of them whimpering like an animal that has been kicked.

The hospital was five miles away, and it was snowing so hard that I could only see a few yards in front of me. We kept sticking in drifts and having to dig ourselves out. All the time, I could hear the injured man groaning, which made these delays seen even more frustrating. God knows how long it took — it seemed endless, but we eventually made it just as it was beginning to get light.

When I finally got back to our digs, Jack was finishing his breakfast. I must have looked pretty ghastly, for as I came into the room, he got up and hurried towards me.

'Steady on, old chap. You'll be okay. Come on; sit down,' he said kindly, 'I'll get you a stiff drink,' and then I must have passed out, for the next I remember was lying on the sofa with Jack standing over me looking grave. At least I hadn't passed out while I was on duty, was the only thought in my head. I had remained cool and done what was expected of me, which was gratifying.

This was the only 'active' service we saw. As the winter wore on, and the inactivity continued, it became increasingly clear to both Jack and myself that we were really wasting our time. The Royal

Army Medical Corps was by now furnished with its own ambulances, driven by servicemen, and ours were becoming redundant. After Stanley's accident, which left him severely crippled, Jack was faced with a difficult conflict of duties. When Stanley came out of hospital, who was there except Jack to take care of him? My own dilemma was of a different nature. Jack and I discussed it at length, and came to the conclusion that our position was becoming highly anomalous, and increasingly superfluous. Stanley should be out of hospital by the beginning of May, perhaps sooner, so Jack told Lambourne he would continue to serve in IVAC until Stanley was discharged, after which he must leave. I decided I would stay as long as Jack, and leave as soon thereafter as I could. What I should do next was another matter. I had, in fact, very little choice. I had obtained exemption to do ambulance work, so I could apply to join the FAU, or I could take a chance, join the army and hope to get into the RAMC.

The events of the spring of 1941 helped me to make up my mind. It was clear by now that the war was going to last a long time. It was equally clear that pacifism of the kind I believed in was not going to stop Hitler. Unlike the first war, we were up against something far more evil than anything the Kaiser had stood for. But above all, every mouthful I ate, every gallon of petrol I put in my car, practically every piece of clothing I put on my back, had reached me through the efforts of people who were risking their lives on land and sea. Besides, I was young and healthy; I could no longer afford the luxury of ideals, which, in order to follow them, depended in the final analysis on other people's willingness to make sacrifices for the community to which I belonged. Jack argued that this was no reason for abandoning one's ideals, and pointed to monks who did nothing but pray, yet who equally depended on others for their subsistence. To which I could only reply that I was no monk and didn't believe in the efficacy of prayer to defeat Hitler.

My change of view came about slowly and reluctantly, but once I had accepted it, I found myself for the first time since I became a pacifist, no longer a member of a minority. It was clear that I must join the struggle against Hitler, but not against the German people. Manfred had made me realise the nature of the dilemma that faced decent, patriotic Germans who, while feeling that the defence of their country, the righting of injustice, and the preservation of all that was best in German culture were laudable aims, were nonetheless appalled by what Hitler and his thugs were doing, not only to their fellow Germans, but to the nations they had overrun. My visit to Jeven before the war had done more than I cared to admit to shake my certainty that pacifism was, in the present context, morally defensible.

One evening after dinner, Herr von Schrade had so far thrown discretion to the winds as to criticise the Nazis in front of Andrew, Clara and me. He had done so simply because Hans and Helga had gone into Kiel to a Party function, and he felt able to speak freely in front of his foreign guests. He told us that the SS were devoting themselves exclusively to the task of winning the physical power upon which Hitler rested. But Hitler had sold his old friends, Röhm and the Brownshirts, to the generals, and the generals had sold themselves to Hitler in 1934.

'Where we made the most terrible mistake,' he had said, 'was in regarding Hitler as a distasteful necessity we could get rid of in due course. When Röhm was killed, I remember General von Fritsch saying to me that the army had won. He was desperately mistaken, for he failed to see that by allowing the SS and the Gestapo to break the power of the Brownshirts, they had put themselves in a position to dominate the army. Less than two years later, every individual was debarred from appeal to the law as traditionally understood, and the judiciary was forbidden to re-examine the decisions of the Gestapo. Every means adopted to carry out Hitler's will was considered legal after that, even if it might conflict with existing laws and statutes. That was the end of liberty in our country,' he concluded.

What Herr von Schrade had said at Jeven had sown doubts in my mind which at last had become certainties: I now knew what it was I was prepared to fight against. If public morality could compromise in this way, not just in Germany, but in any state, who was I to stand against it? When a regime becomes too brutal, then its brutality becomes a factor of disorder. If it orders its police to kill its opponents, it has failed because it has increased the disorder, not diminished it, and by abstaining, I became an accomplice by default. If I were to stand by, knowing what I then knew about the Nazis; knowing that millions of innocent people were being liquidated as an act of deliberate policy, quite apart from those who were being killed by the war itself, then I was in some sense participating in such outrages. I had been granted the inestimable good fortune to be the citizen of a country that, in a time of great danger, was willing to acknowledge that I had a right to abstain if my conscience so dictated, so was I not obliged to defend that liberty? My good fortune seemed to me to be all the greater when I compared my position with that of Manfred and his family.

But had I been more than usually lucky? Had I been granted exemption because I was 'Doris de Vergy's son'? because I spoke with the right accent? because I knew the right people? How much of my liberty was due to privilege? I knew of several young, sincere objectors who had been sent to prison; was my exemption granted because I had appeared to the Tribunal to want to compromise? And what difference would it now make if, instead of joining the army, I went to Bermondsey and worked with my former colleagues of the UAU? Upbringing, education and religion had all tended to make me a pacifist — everything except temperament. And so on June 10th, 1941, I enlisted at Edinburgh, and when he heard what I had done, Jack urged me to join the Intelligence Corps. I took his advice and was accepted.

VII

Three weeks later I was posted to the Queen's Regiment for basic infantry training. It would be hard to imagine a less soldierly bunch than the Intelligence Corps platoon which assembled at Hambledown Barracks that Saturday in July, 1941. After reporting, we were free to go into town on condition that we got back to barracks by nine. The first sight of the hut we were to spend the next two months in was discouraging, but not much worse than the dormitory at Templars when I first went there.

Next morning they paraded us to draw our kit. From an early hour we hung about nervously, scared of losing our identities with our civilian clothes. Shambolically we fell into two ranks and shuffled off to the Quarter-Master's stores to be issued with knife, fork, spoon, mess-tin, boot-cleaning outfit, button-stick, brass polish and a hail of clothing flung at us by half a dozen bored storemen.

Throughout this ceremony the QM intoned a dull litany — underpants, pairs, three; socks, woollen, pairs, four; shirts, khaki, two; battle-dress trousers... and on and on until we lost count of what we had got, and what we should have. It struck me as odd that the army was apparently unaware that we came in different shapes and sizes, for uniforms came in large, medium and small only. We were given what most nearly approximated to our shape.

We stuffed our kitbags and hefted them on to our shoulders,

draped battledress blouses and trousers, together with great-coat and denims over one arm, and thus encumbered we were chivvied to the boot store, where we tried on as many as we could grab of the hundreds of pairs lying on the floor. At last I found two pairs which fitted fairly well, though they were as stiff as iron and weighed a ton. The boot man hung them round our necks by their laces, and thus accoutred we staggered back across the barrack square to our hut.

There, once we had divested ourselves of our civilian clothes and packed them in the suitcases we had brought with us, we took them back to the QM stores to be sent home. After this we were squadded and marched off to our hut once more to be indoctrinated into our rights as citizen soldiers. We could get redress for any griev-ances, we were told, but it was made abundantly clear that the rem-edy was likely to be worse than the grievance. We could apply for leave if our wives proved unfaithful, but not if they were about to give birth; what the army was about to teach us would come in useful when we returned to civvy street; last and most important, our rifle was our best friend, better even than our mother.

Sergeant John Ainscough, for that was his name, was assisted at this ceremony by Corporal Andy Wilkinson. It was clear that they viewed us with distaste, for we were not the usual run of infan-try recruit, and they weren't quite sure how to deal with us. I have to confess we were an odd lot. We ranged in age from nineteen to forty, and in profession from student (me) by way of the rag trade, David Allen, the law, Morgan Lear, and the groves of academe, John Pollard, to the personal assistant of the Lord Lyon King of Arms, David Batson, and the police, Alastair Ross.

We lived in a hut which was small for twenty-five of us. A row of beds down each wall; two or three tables with narrow wooden forms either side of them, in the gangway between, two cast-iron coke stoves, known for some unaccountable reason as tortoises. In the middle of each end was a door, one of which gave on to the asphalt parade ground, the other to what the army called latrines and ablutions, which most of us thought of as toilets and baths, or as loos and showers. The hut was designed for the peacetime occu-pation of sixteen men, so that our beds, which twanged like ill-tuned harps when we sat or lay on them, were less than an arm's length apart, divided one from the other by an open-fronted locker, in which we kept our few personal belongings. Consequently we all slept badly at first, for the grunts, farts and snoring of one's neighbours seemed as if they came from one's own bed. Some slept badly because they had never slept in a dormitory before; others because they found the mattresses, known as biscuits, hideously hard. You couldn't turn over without groaning and half waking to ease your aching hips. The nights were therefore never quiet.

My bed was at the end of the row, and next to me slept Sam Barker. Sam's father was a policeman, who had taught him to ride a motorbike, which had earned him a place in the Field Security Police, to which the majority of us would probably be sent when our basic training was finished.

Sgt Ainscough, trim and straight, had been with the regiment in India, and was hesitant at first of giving orders to men who might be less obedient than sepoys: but this hesitation didn't last long. That first day passed with much lolling about once we had changed our kit. Breakfast had been eatable but stodgy; supper was sickening but ample. Testing and examination had gone on intermittently all day, and included the writing of a short essay to see if we were literate. Since the army authorities knew that we were all destined for the Intelligence Corps this seemed a trifle superfluous; we never heard if any of us had failed or passed. Later we were marched off to the barber for our short-back-and-sides haircut. Like Noah's animals we went in two by two, where the barbers, in a hurry, ran their clippers up our sideburns, a couple of inches above our ears, round the back and round the other side, achieving in less than five minutes, and at no expense, what a hairdresser today would make a skinhead pay a fortune for. Then it was back to the hut to stow our kit in accordance with regimental regulations, and begin the soul-destroying jobs of shining stubbornly greasy boots with polish, spit and toothbrush handle, blancoing web equipment and shining tarnished brasses. Cpl Wilkinson was an artist in dress- and kit-folding. None of us in half an hour could ever square our beds as well as he did in five minutes.

Throw together twenty-five strangers from every class of society; shut them for a couple of days in a hut designed for sixteen; subject them to harsh discipline; tire them out with boring, dirty, senseless chores, and one quickly finds that all men are equal in the sight of NCOs as well as of God. Though we were all destined for the Intelligence Corps, we were by no means all Cambridge intellectuals. Far from it. We may have been raw, too independent-minded, too keen to escape our infantry training for the work we had volunteered to do — and all our platoon were volunteers, not conscripts — to care about Guards-standard drill. We were content if we managed to scrape through each day unharmed.

The Intelligence Corps, like any other, needed its clerks, despatch-riders, mechanics and administrators, and though the number of men with academic qualifications was larger than in an average infantry platoon, those of us who had such pretensions were only six out of a total of twenty-five. Guard duty was a chance to get to know one's fellows. It meant an hour on and an hour off duty from eight in the evening till eight the next morning. We were never put on daytime guard duty either because we were too scruffy or because the daytime was supposed to be devoted to training, and only trained soldiers could be spared during the day.

But during the still watches of the night we just stood and chatted to each other. I was on guard duty only once, and my companion was Sam Barker. It wasn't too bad a night to begin with, but by four it had grown very cold. We spent much time discussing the merits of various makes of motorbike and our lives in Wraysby and Liverpool. We might have been born and bred on different planets, so different were our circumstances. As we walked up and down, the chill of the pavement seeped through the soles of our boots; the mist rose from the the valley, gradually enveloping the outline of the town below, its roofs glistening in the moonlight. Our greatcoats became grey with hoar frost, and a longing for sleep began to creep over us. When relief came we went back into the guard-room, whose hot, frowsty air embraced us even if the acrid smell of stubbed-out Woodbines made us gasp and choke at first. Cpl Wilkinson pushed mugs of cocoa towards us to thaw us out. I don't remember ever tasting better, not even in the most expensive Viennese cafés.

He and the other sentries were talking about the girls they had been with on their last day out of barracks. One of them said there was a good brothel in town and recommended those of us who hadn't yet patronised it to do so as soon as we got the chance, which would be tomorrow, for one always got the day off after night guard duty. Sam suggested we go together. I agreed, a trifle reluctantly, perhaps, not wanting to appear stand-offish.

The brothel turned out to be a sleazy house in a back street near the cathedral. Two girls were lounging against some nearby railings when we turned up — the standard of attraction was not, I thought, very high. Sam, who already knew his way about, took one, I the other, and we went inside to get down to business at once. Sam went up to the first-floor back, while I was led down a passage to a room near the kitchen redolent of stewed cabbage.

'Pound first, dearie,' she said as she sat down on the bed, taking a lipsticked cigarette out of her mouth, and stubbing it in an overflowing ashtray. I struggled to get my wallet out of the inside pocket of my battledress blouse, while she looked me up and down with ill-disguised contempt. I handed her the note — almost a week's pay — which she stuck down the front of her inadequate, artificial-silk corsage. Pulling her skirt up round her capacious abdomen, she revealed a pair of mottled thighs above black net stockings. I could see no sign of the 'dainty pink flesh' that Michel's book had gone on about, and I was certainly not reminded of the 'ripe, luscious pulp of some exotic fruit'. I became rapidly discouraged.

'Just let me get the thingummy, ducky,' she said archly, fumbling in a drawer of the side table, and handing me what looked like Eeyore's balloon after Piglet had burst it. It was my first introduction to condoms, and I had only the vaguest idea what to do with it. Was it for me or for her? Should it be stuffed up against her dying orchid, or ensheathed on my still flaccid cock? I guessed right.

'Come on, dearie, let yer trousers down,' she demanded peremptorily. I obeyed.

'There's a naughty boy,' she said roguishly, and taking a look at my limp prick, went on in a more authoritative tone of voice: 'Come along, get it up.'

I began to rub it without much conviction.

'Oh well, never mind, just a sec. See whether this'll help.'

She raised her legs, thighs wide apart, hands under the back of her knees. It made no difference, the orchid had totally withered away.

'Come on, get a move on, shove it in. I can't wait all day.'

I felt myself blushing as I stood there, the condom dangling in my hand, and my cock shrinking to vanishing point.

'I... I...'

'For Chrissake, don't yer know what to do?'

'Yes, of course.'

How different it was from that night I'd spent with Hermine von Branden, and how tactfully and delicately she had overcome a similar embarrassment. Where, I wondered was she now?

'Oh shit, I shoulda known. You're a fucking nancy boy, aren't you? I bet you wouldn't be so slow if I was a pretty boy. Now just you bugger off and get one of them fairies as hangs out in the cottage round the corner, and push yer bleeding little dick up his fucking arse, and leave me to get a proper man. I hate faggots.'

Most of these terms, of what I assumed to be abuse, were then new to me, and thus puzzling, though educative. I pulled on my trousers and stumbled out into the street. Sam was waiting for me outside the pub opposite. He waved to me to come over.

'Cor, that was a nice bit o' crumpet,' he enthused. 'What was yours like?'

'Smashing,' I said. 'Let's have a drink on it.'

I thought to myself, if that's his idea of fun, there must be something seriously wrong with me. Aloud I enthused: 'Super; never had it better.'

Sam dug me in the ribs. 'Yeah! I guessed you'd been around a bit and'd know a good thing when you saw it. I bet you got a lot o' crumpet when you was a student in France — and them places where you was studying.'

'Yes, masses,' I lied, and went on to boast of nights with girls from the Folies Bergères.

* * *

Towards the end of our basic training they taught us to ride a motorbike. The course lasted three weeks, and out of our platoon only five of us were chosen to finish it, the rest not having achieved the requisite skill during the first week. Each morning, Sam and Alastair Ross, who were already good riders, and I would run back to the hut after breakfast and fatigues to change out of our denims and into our boots and breeches, and be first at the sheds where the bikes were kept. We each had our own machine for whose cleanliness and maintenance we were responsible, mine a BSA, theirs Nortons. We'd check the oil and the tyre pressure, look to make sure that no nuts or bolts were loose, and then wheel them out on to the parade ground. Mine had a habit of starting at the third kick, and would roar into life to settle down quickly to a sweet, even hum. Soon the others, successful survivors in a tough course, would turn up, a vain lot all of us, for we had taken our ill-cut breeches to a tailor in town and got him to take them in at the knee so tightly that they gripped our thighs, their flared wings standing out stiffly. The army didn't issue us with leathers, but that didn't matter, for our tight clothes hugged our bodies and kept us just as warm.

We mounted and rode past the guard-room, up the hill and out of town along the Roman road that led to Andover. In those petrol-rationed days we had the five-mile straight more or less to ourselves. The cold air streamed like icy jets into our eyes despite our goggles as we rode into our own long shadows cast by the rising sun behind us. The road undulated, and, in those days, was rough enough to force us to grip the tank between our thighs, and brace our feet on the rests till, like jockeys, we stood pivoting on our knees. Then it was left along another straight road, down into Stockbridge and up again towards Salisbury, where three miles short of the town we drew off the road to our right at Figsbury Ring. Here we were to practise cross-country riding, up and down the prehistoric earthworks, and afterwards away over to Battery Hill. Our route back took us across open downland until we struck the road from the Wallops to Tidworth at the improbably named village of Palestine.

The rough ground made our bikes throb and sway dizzily on the slippery grass, while we wrenched the handlebars to stop us, not always successfully, losing our balance. Over the brow of the escarpment we descended a hundred feet or so standing on the footrests, lying backwards over the saddle to remain upright, turning at the bottom, and then, full throttle, up again to the crest, crouching low over the tank, urging our machines on, back to the gentler slope of the wide, curving down. Then, after an hour or so of this, back to Stockbridge, where we drew up outside the portico of the old coaching inn that graces the village street, to stretch our muscles and ease our joints from the rough tightness of our cord breeches, our faces glowing and eyes smarting. I smiled over to Sam, and he grinned back — no need for words. We went inside; a pint of beer, a hunk of bread and cheese, and then out again into the saddle, one quick kick this time, and an eighty-mile-an-hour dash back to barracks.

Motorbiking is a disease: if you catch it young as I did, it's incurable. Bikes, like horses, have characters of their own, and you have to get to know your machine and how to manage it. Never —not for an instant — can you afford to relax or take it for granted. Round every corner danger lurks, be it loose gravel, a careless motorist approaching on the wrong side of the road, a wandering pedestrian, kids playing ball. Given half a chance, your bike will take it into its head to skid and have you off. No other form of transport can give you that sense of freedom and speed a motorbike can. I found it physically and sexually exciting: my bike became my antagonist, my friend and my lover. What thrilled me most was the discovery that I was a very good rider. Having been a dismal failure at all other sports, here at last was something I could do better than all the others except Sam and Alastair.

Part Three: Subversive Patriots

I

Not long before the end of my basic training, Jack Cuttlance had written to tell me he had got a job with a new secret organisation, and he thought I might be suitable for it. He said that he could tell me very little about it in a letter, but he knew that my languages would come in useful if I felt like volunteering. If I was interested, he suggested that we meet to talk about it. I wrote back to say that my course ended in a few days' time, and I would be coming through London on my way to Yorkshire to stay with my father. We fixed to meet at the Salisbury in St Martin's Lane.

The peaceful atmosphere of the Yorkshire dales had helped me make up my mind to accept Jack's invitation to volunteer for the work he had described that evening before I left for Wraysby. I had enough confidence in his judgment to believe that he knew me well enough not to have proposed me for work for which I would be unsuitable or would not like. Although I had not confided in him the full extent of my love for Manfred, and I did not yet think of either of us as gay, I was conscious that Jack had been sympathetic and understanding. If he thought enough of me to recommend me for the Assessment Board, then the rest was up to me.

When I returned to barracks after my leave, I was told to report to the adjutant the next day. He told me I had been called to an interview in London, and that if I were selected, I would be posted immediately. So I packed my kit-bag, said goodbye to Sam, Cpl Wilkinson and my fellow sufferers, caught the train to Waterloo, and in due form reported to an office in a large house in Mayfair.

In the waiting-room, I found myself in the company of a couple of artillery officers, a naval sub-lieutenant, two flight-lieutenants, and an Intelligence Corps major. As the only Other Rank present, I came smartly to attention on finding myself in such august company. I would have stood there like the Pompeiian soldier, faithful unto death, had not the major, seeing my cap badge, told me to stand at ease, and, though he didn't actually say so, inferred that he had no time for such a load of bullshit.

I quickly discovered that we were all linguists, and that if we were selected, we would all be sent to a Students Assessment Board prior to final selection.

As is customary in the services, we were summoned to the interview in alphabetical order, which meant that I was the third or fourth to be called. I put my cap on, smoothed the creases out of my battledress blouse, and, in true Hambledown fashion, came to attention and marched into the interview room. I had anticipated neither its size (it was the ballroom of a large town house) nor the polish on the floor. The ATS corporal who opened the double doors to announce me, shouted my name and I took off — in more ways than one. I had not reckoned as I marched in — left, right, left, right, halt, stand to attention, salute — that the polished studs on the soles of my boots were just about as capable of holding me upright on the polished floor as a pair of skates on an ice rink. As my right arm went up in what I intended to be a smashing salute, my heels shot forward, I lost my balance and crashed to the floor exclaiming loudly 'Oh shit!'

There was a burst of laughter as the ATS corporal rushed to my assistance and, dragging me gasping to my feet, sat me firmly down in the chair intended for my reception. Winded, but happily not irreversibly damaged, I rubbed my bottom in a thoroughly unmilitary fashion, and took stock of the situation. To my great relief I heard a familiar voice ask anxiously, 'Are you okay?' Thank God Jack was on the board, which otherwise consisted of a senior officer from each service, and two civilians.

'Yes thanks,' I said, 'a bit bruised, perhaps.'

'We must do something about this floor,' said the chairman, a full colonel in one of the Guards regiments. 'Alice,' addressing the ATS corporal, 'could you get them to let us have a drugget or something to lay down on the floor. We don't want people breaking their necks.'

Once calm was restored, and we'd settled down to business, the chairman turned to one of the civilians and asked him in French to carry on. He asked me in that language when and where I'd been in France, and when I explained in the course of what turned out to be a chatty conversation about the beauties of the Loire and Périgord, that I had been staying with relations of my great-aunt, he became more interested.

'So you know Mme de Lusignac, do you?'

'Yes.'

'And Mme Loreau too?'

'Yes. I was at school with one of her sons,' I said.

'Did you know Monsieur Bassett?'

'Yes, but not very well. I haven't seen him since he and Mme Loreau came to spend Christmas with my grandparents in 1936.'

The Frenchman turned to the chairman, and said in English: 'His French is good. There's a trace of an accent, of course, but he might be mistaken in the south of France for a Belgian or a *pied noir*. The chairman thanked him and turned to the other civilian, who asked in German where I had learnt the language. We talked about Salzburg and Vienna and the Tessenbergs, but unlike the Frenchman, we did not appear to have any friends in common. The two civilians then left, and it was Jack's turn. He told the board how we had served together in IVAC; a little about the reasons for my having registered as a CO, and why I had volunteered to join the army.

This seemed to go down quite well with the board, who nodded approvingly.

'I expect you are wondering what all this is about,' the chairman said at length. 'I'll tell you. We are looking for linguists, who will be prepared to make contact with resistance movements in occupied Europe. It is a dangerous job, and only those who volunteer freely, and after careful consideration of the risks, will be chosen to undertake it. If you agree to volunteer, you will go before a Students' Assessment Board, and if you pass it, then you will be given special training. We are not asking you to make a decision today, any more than we are making a decision to take you on. Go away for forty-eight hours' leave, and wait till Major Cuttlance contacts you. Then, if we have decided to accept you, tell him your decision.'

Indicating that this was the end of the interview, I stood up and put my cap on preparing to salute. Looking up from his papers, the colonel smiled and said: 'Careful now!' The others laughed while I came smartly to attention, saluted, turned, and stamping instinctively, tit-tupped out of the room, mercifully without further mishap.

Two days later, Jack Cuttlance phoned to tell me that I had been accepted for the Students' Assessment Board, and asked if I wanted to join the Outfit. I said that I did, and he told me to report to a country house in Oxfordshire three days later, and in the meantime to get my officer's kit together. My commission would come through almost at once. He warned me that I would have to undergo another medical, but not to worry as I'd already passed A1 when I joined up. We arranged to meet for a drink in town when I came up for my medical.

'A level head and steady nerves are the first requirements,' he told me when we met. 'An agent's best qualities are not those of conventional serving officers and men. We take some of our agents from outside the armed forces of any country.

'You will be commissioned as a lieutenant. If you are successful you may reach the rank of major: it is unlikely that you will be promoted beyond lieutenant-colonel. You will find that we set little store on rank. You will not be able to tell your family what you are doing: if you go to France, your next-of-kin will get a short notice once a month or so to say that we continue to get good news from you. If you lose contact with us, they will be told that you were very well when we last heard from you.

'You will receive the pay of your rank quarterly in advance into your bank account here at home. Your French is good but not impeccable. You could certainly pass as a Frenchman to a German with good French, but not as a native-born Frenchman to a Frenchman.

'You will be put through a stiff preliminary course of basic military and physical training at our Oxfordshire establishment. As you have already had some basic military training we will probably skip most of that in your case. Your Students Assessment Board will last a week, and, if you pass, you will be sent on a stiff paramilitary course lasting three to five weeks. Here your physical training will continue, and as I told you before, it will include "silent killing" and unarmed combat. They'll also teach you how to use a pistol and sub-machinegun, fieldcraft, map work, elementary morse and raiding tactics.'

I thanked him for telling me this, and said that I hoped I'd get through the courses. 'I wouldn't want you to think that I'd let you down,' I said.

'There's no question of that. If you don't make the grade, don't, for a moment, think you're a failure. Not everyone is suitable for the work and, in any case, there are lots of other jobs in the Outfit you'd be suitable for. I can't stress enough that this is all voluntary;

no one is forcing you to undertake the work, and we are not guaranteeing that you will be accepted, even if you get through to the very end of the courses. But best of luck. I'll probably see you once or twice during your training. Any queries, don't hesitate to ask me.'

* * *

'Gentlemen, you will be given three weeks' intensive instruction in this school of subversive activity,' said the major, a dapper man with the conventional clipped military moustache. There were fourteen of us, and we had arrived at the manor the previous evening. 'There will be lectures and practical exercises in mapping, demolitions, weapon-training, morse, fieldcraft and close combat,' he continued. 'French will be spoken at all meals. You will be worked very hard and your reactions and progress will be carefully noted. Our requirements of physical endurance, patience, technical knowledge and security are high. Not only your lives, but the lives of your comrades will depend on these qualifications. I cannot stress the importance of security enough. No one outside this school knows what goes on here, and nobody must know. All letters written or received will be censored. You may not use the telephone.

'When the course is over, those of you who have passed will be sent to the second course of advanced training. There will be no leave between courses, only after the parachute course, which comes third.

'In conclusion, you'll find the food here is good and plentiful, the canteen is well stocked and the beds are comfortable. That's all. Any questions?'

There was dead silence. Not that there *were* no questions; none of us felt strong enough to ask them.

'My staff and I are always at your disposal for any problems you may have. And now, as you'll probably want to get to know each other before lunch, I'll leave you. Just ring that bell,' he indicated an old-fashioned bell pull by the side of the mantelpiece,' and the mess corporal will get you some drinks. That's all.'

The major smiled, turned and walked smartly out of the room. Temporarily speechless, we gaped at his departing form.

'Well,' someone said, getting up and pulling the bell, 'at least we know what we're in for now.'

'It looks as though the days of Olga Polovski the beautiful spy are over,' said a student who was a good ten years older than the rest of us. 'I can't see myself parachuting and trudging across the Pyrenees at my age. I'm sure to be fired within a week.'

'I don't know,' someone else broke in. 'They'll probably land you by plane. It's a much more comfortable way of travelling. They wouldn't have let you come here if they didn't have a job in mind for you.'

After drinks had been brought, we formed ourselves into small groups, introduced each other by the Christian names we'd been given by HQ — I was to be David — and soon a general buzz of conversation filled the room.

I had been surprised to find Michel Loreau among my fellow students. Neither of us was quite sure whether we should acknowledge to the rest that we already knew each other. I found myself in a small party of three with a pleasant young man called Nigel, and again to my great surprise, my kinsman Charney Bassett. Charney (who was known here as Charles) was the conducting officer whose duties consisted of appraising each student's character and writing a report on him for head office. He studiously avoided giving any sign that he recognised me. He told us that he would accompany us on all the courses, including the parachute training, in which he would take part himself, for the simple reason that he really enjoyed jumping.

'Quite a job,' I said.

'Not really. It's a job kept for those who have been "in the field" and are awaiting their next assignment. It keeps one in good condition, while allowing one's brain to rest.'

'Is it very nerve-racking over there?' asked Nigel.

'You can never relax, if that's what you mean. The actual ops are okay,' replied Charney. 'In fact they're the high spots. It's waiting for ops that becomes a bind. Whether you're in a house, a hotel in town, or in a farm in the depths of the country, every time there's a knock on the door you wonder whether your time is up. You're always thinking of your cover story, altering it to fit new circumstances, and thinking up what you hope are foolproof reasons for being wherever you are.'

'Are there any snap controls on the trains?'

'Yes; but you get quite *blasé* about them because the papers HQ will give you are so perfect. Anyway, you'll hear all about things like that when you get the dope on security.'

We all trooped in to lunch. I was amazed not only by the food, but by the high standard of French at my end of the table. The only person who seemed to regret that French had to be spoken at meals was the camp commandant.

After lunch we started on the course. The first hour was spent learning how to tap out the morse alphabet. Then we went on to map reading, which I found easy, as I had already learnt that at school. Then we were taken outside and shown how to put a detonator into a primer, and how to put the primer into a 'brick' of gun-cotton explosive. After tea we were given an hour's practical demonstration of how to bring down a tree so that it fell exactly in the direction you wanted it to. Each of us had to apply a six-inch 'brick' to a different tree and bring it down ourselves. At the end of this we all felt much better.

A swim in the pool in the grounds rounded off this first afternoon's activities. However, a glance at the notice-board was enough to persuade those of us who might have had ideas of staying up late not to do so, for reveille was at six o'clock, and we were requested to parade in PT kit shortly afterwards.

I found myself in a dormitory for six. On one side of me was a tall young Frenchman, who went by the name of Jean-Paul; next to him was Michel Loreau (here known as Raymond). On the other side of the room were John, a Coldstream regular with fair hair, typical English features and schoolboy French; Gaston, the man in his early forties, who had said that he couldn't see himself trudging over the Pyrenees; and Bill, whose father was English and mother French. Conversation flowed easily in both languages.

As we lay chatting, waiting for 'lights out', Charney Bassett came in to see that all was well. As conducting officer, he had the privilege of a room to himself. His confidence and ease made themselves quickly felt among us newcomers. After a few moments of conversation someone asked him if he could tell us something about his last operation.

'Why?' he asked.

'Well, to hear what it's actually like from someone who's been there seems to me worth more than all the courses.'

'I felt the same when I was doing my training,' Charney replied. 'No doubt if I were to tell you all you'd like to know it would help you a bit, but it would compromise several people, and put the lid on my returning to France.'

'How's that?' I asked.

'If I were to tell you, for example, how Jean Lemaire, the sta-

157

tion-master at Richelieu, and I blew up the line between Chinon and Saumur, for example, one of you might accidentally talk about the incident to a friend in confidence. He, not knowing how vital security is, might innocently tell the same story in his own officers' mess, and the wrong person might overhear it. The enemy would be delighted to learn that the author of the railway damage in Touraine was none other than M. Lemaire of Richelieu. That's why I'm glad to tell you that I've never been to Richelieu or to Chinon or to Saumur, and that there's no such person as M. Lemaire.'

'I see now,' I said.

But what about yourself?' asked Bill. 'How would it stop you returning?'

'Well, the very fact that you know I've been to France is bad enough in itself. If any of you were captured and shown my photograph you might accidentally give a sign of recognition. If then, under torture, you were made to tell them where you'd seen me, the Germans would know that I belonged to this Outfit. What you may not realise is that my cover story claims I have never left France. So, you see, if you could connect me with other people as well, they'd rope them all in and pin me down as a British agent.'

'So the less you know the less they can get out of you,' said John.

'Precisely,' agreed Charney.

'Do many people fail these courses?' asked Michel, who like me showed no sign that he knew Charney Bassett.

'Quite a few. The standard's high because it gives the chaps in France the comfortable feeling that anyone who's passed these courses must be as reliable as they are. But,' he went on, seeing the worried look on some of our faces, 'there's no need to be downhearted. The standards can't be unattainable since an old bloke like me managed to pass them, and if you don't pass them all, there may still be room for you in the Outfit in another capacity!'

He smiled at us and said, 'Goodnight. Sleep well.'

After lights out, I lay awake digesting what I'd heard. Of my five companions, John would probably be given a job in the UK because his French wasn't good enough. Jean-Paul and Nigel would be sure to pass; Gaston might not be able to stand the pace, and Bill might be okay, though he looked a bit undisciplined. As for myself, I had the gravest doubts that I would get through, but I was determined to have a damn good try. Time only would tell.

PT next morning was a good deal tougher than at Hambledown.

Sgt Alan Scott who took us was a sun-tanned Adonis of about twenty-five. He gave us press-ups and bicycling upside-down, and had us swinging our arms about upwards, forwards, sideways, downwards and backwards. After that we had a somewhat unorthodox game of netball, after which most of us were aching from head to foot. As we straggled back to shower, Sgt Scott overtook us easily, covering the hundred yards back to the house on his hands. Those of us who were only just capable of walking the right way up hoped he'd break his neck on the steps which led up to the terrace, but he took them at a run — his body beautiful whichever way you looked at it — swayed gracefully past some potted plants and disappeared from view.

'Exhibitionist,' snorted Bill.

'I think I'll end up in hospital tonight after all-in wrestling this afternoon,' said Gaston.

After breakfast next morning we had weapon training, a lecture on bridge demolition, signalling with an Aldis lamp and French platoon and arms drill, given by Michel, who had done his national service in France before joining the navy, so as to accustom us to the words of command in case any of us, whose cover story claimed that we'd done military service in the French army, should be required to prove it.

After lunch there was a demolition class, during which the 'time pencil' and 'instantaneous fuse' were introduced, as well as the 'pull switch' and the 'press switch'. This was followed by shooting practice, and lastly the all-in wrestling. Sgt Scott, wearing a minute pair of swimming trunks, looked an even more perfect specimen than he had in the early morning. With every movement his muscles seemed to smile as well as ripple. He gently threw us around as if we were paper bags, all the time keeping up a steady patter explaining the art of falling softly or rolling backwards, forwards and sideways. He was like a lithe panther thoroughly enjoying himself, for he never seemed to use more than a fraction of his strength. Nigel and John, who thought they were as fit as Sgt Scott, were rash enough to pit themselves against his vast experience. To their surprise and chagrin, they merely found themselves falling harder and a good many feet farther away from him than before.

We left the 'battle-ground' tired but happy, and together with Sgt Scott, spent a leisurely hour swimming in the pool. Then it was time for dinner.

To my surprise, the first person I noticed on entering the dining room was Jack Cuttlance, and I found myself sitting opposite him at one of the three tables. He made no sign of having known me before, as he said in dreadful French, 'How did you like your first day, David?'

'I think we're all rather stiff, sir,' I replied.

'That'll wear off,' said Jack. 'But you'll be glad to get to bed every day as the course gets more strenuous.'

'I don't suppose Sgt Scott ever gets tired,' said Jean-Paul, somewhat enviously.

'No,' said Jack, 'but Sgt Scott only does one job. By the time you've finished you'll be almost as tireless as Sgt Scott and, we hope, as knowledgeable as all your other instructors.

The following days saw us settling down to an ever-increasing tempo. After a week, we were each put in charge of an exercise, and were marked for the way in which we gave orders to our colleagues and for the speed and efficiency with which we blew up our targets.

By the time the three weeks' course ended, and reports had been sent in, only four out of the original fourteen were turned down. The remaining ten, of which I was one, accompanied by Charney Bassett, left by train for the north-west coast of Scotland.

* * *

After a long and tedious journey, changing at Glasgow, we left the train at a wayside halt near Mallaig. Two 15-cwt trucks met us and carried us at breakneck speed to a country house not far from the sea. Here we were welcomed by an officer of the Black Watch. Six of us were put into one small room with three double-decker bunk beds, and the rest in another even smaller one. When Charney had been allotted the last tiny room to himself, I wondered what they would have done if all fourteen of us had survived the first course. There was hardly enough space as it was to unpack our kit. These cramped conditions, we were told, were because every other large house in the district was crammed with Poles, Czechs, Dutchmen and other Allied soldiers, and with usual British courtesy the best houses had been allotted to them, so that we were left to make the best of a bad job.

It rained incessantly throughout the course, and we had to undertake prodigious exercises every other day, which entailed treks of up to twenty-five miles over mountainous terrain, all done by compass and by following the contours on the map. This was map-reading with a vengeance. We threw so many grenades and fired so many rounds with revolvers and tommy-guns that these became second nature to us. One or two couldn't read maps or master the morse code sufficiently well, but the training staff gave them time and encouragement nevertheless. When the last day of the course came, of the ten of us who had begun it only five remained, and again, much to my surprise I was one of the survivors.

We next went with Charney Bassett to the parachute school at Ringway near Manchester. There were now five of us — Michel, Jean-Paul, myself and two others. Here we were taught how to do rolls to right and left with both hands in our pockets, not to mention backward and forward somersaults. All this was to fit us to land naturally in whatever position we fell with our parachutes. Then we went through the drill of jumping through a hole in the floor of an aircraft, and every day we swung on a giant trapeze to get the feel of landing. Nothing was omitted to prepare us for the real thing. At long last came the five terrifying jumps. If I live for ever I'll never forget them. I didn't find the business of landing all that frightening, for I was so glad to be down on terra firma that I would roll and bounce like a ball, but the idea of leaping through a hole in the aircraft filled me with horror.

II

I had never known Charney Bassett well. He was, after all, of my parents' generation. I had always regarded him as a rather conventional, unimaginative man, who got on well with people, but who never gave anything away and was rather difficult to know. A few years after his wife's death and Hélène Loreau's refusal to marry him, he had sold his farm and rejoined the army. On the outbreak of war he was in France, but was at once recalled to London, where he remained until shortly before the German offensive in May, 1940, and that was the last his English friends saw of him.

Charney's French was impeccable, so he had no difficulty in blending in with the crowds of refugees as they slowly trickled south after the German breakthrough. He made his way slowly, mostly on foot, across the country to Périgord. He knew that Hélène would have remained with her aunt, Madeleine de Lusignac, so he set out to reach Montabourlet by every means in his power.

During the summer of 1939, Périgord seemed unconscious of

the dangers that were threatening France. The countryside had never seemed sweeter or people more relaxed. At Montabourlet, political anxieties seemed remote, and had little or no effect on the local population. One long meal succeeded another; the *paté truffé* was to be found on every table those warm, sunny days along with bottles of Bergerac, Pécharmant and Montbazillac. After all, why not? Périgord is an agricultural region; what else would one expect?

The country rises gently from the low-lying plain of the Garonne in the west to the great highlands of the Massif Central on the east, and through it ancient rivers have cut deep, wooded valleys. It presents a contoured appearance where soft undulations are cut by steep gorges bordered by limestone cliffs honeycombed with caves. As soon as one leaves the densely cultivated valleys of the Dronne, the Lisle, the Vézère and the Dordogne, or, for that matter, the smaller valleys of the Vergne, the Lidoire or the Nizonne, one enters the thickly wooded Périgourdine forest, which covers the innumerable hillsides with a dense green mantle of oak, chestnut and pine. Little towns like Vergt and Villamblard, Cendrieux and Rouffignac, St Astier and Tocane St Apre nestle in ancient clearings among these woodlands. Such is Montabourlet, dominated by the great castle of Jovelles, set upon its massive rock above an insignificant tributary of the Dronne. It was in this outstandingly beautiful region that the French Résistance found ideal conditions to establish itself and flourish.

Four days after war broke out, twelve thousand refugees from Strasbourg arrived in the *département*, and were sent to various towns and villages throughout the region. Madeleine de Lusignac found herself hostess to a dozen snotty-nosed children, whom she set about teaching to speak French instead of the barbarous Alsatian patois in which they were accustomed to communicate with each other.

The German offensive against the Low Countries and France was launched on May 10th, 1940. Almost at once new refugees began to pour into the region, flying in advance of the approaching enemy. On June 16th, the armistice was proposed and signed eight days later. On the day that Marshal Pétain gave the order to French forces to lay down their arms, General de Gaulle made his historic appeal from London: 'France has lost a battle, but France has not lost the war. Nothing has been lost because this is a world war.'

This message of hope and resistance was heard by many in Périgord, among them François de la Beauronne, whose children had switched on Radio London by chance.

'At the time, I was dumbfounded,' he told Charney Bassett later. 'At first I couldn't grasp what had happened, and then I exclaimed to my wife, "We've won the war!" for I knew that if we refused to give up the struggle we must win in the end.'

He and half a dozen friends, who had also heard de Gaulle's broadcast, determined then and there to set up a resistance network in Périgord. The only problem was how, and with what resources.

One of the immediate positive things resistance could aspire to offer was a sense of community. But first it had to achieve it in a country whose atmosphere was one of spiteful recrimination. Resistance rarely expressed nostalgia for the Third Republic; the struggle was not undertaken to protect or preserve ideas and institutions which had proved so lamentably inadequate. Resistance was to be a struggle for a new order, whose nature was ill-defined and perhaps contradictory. In the early days, there was no effective consensus among resisters as to who the enemy was, or who was on whose side, and to begin with, acts of resistance were more or less restricted to gestures of general recalcitrance directed at nothing in particular.

The armistice had established a demarcation line between the so-called free and occupied zones. In the occupied zone, the French administrative services had to conform to the orders of the German military authorities; in the unoccupied zone the administration was undisturbed. Most people in Périgord didn't fully realise the depth of the abyss into which they had fallen. It was only after the *département* of Dordogne had been cut in two that they fully tumbled to what had happened to them. A veritable frontier between the two zones cut the *département* into two unequal parts. This frontier line soon became known in England, for it was the first major obstacle pilots who had baled out over occupied territory had to meet if they wished to escape to neutral Switzerland or Spain. Each pilot carried a silk scarf on which was printed the map of France with the demarcation line superimposed on it, but alas, it wasn't always quite accurate. Many of the villages near the line were garrisoned by German soldiers, approximately a hundred in each village, and in Mme de Lusignac's area there were garrisons at Mareuil, Verteillac, Ribérac and Montpon. Armed guards set up road blocks, and while women were allowed to come and go without papers, men had to show a special white pass. On the whole the German soldiers behaved correctly to begin with, but it was not long before notices appeared on walls stating that for every German soldier that was killed, five French people would be shot.

For people like Mme de Lusignac and M. de la Beauronne the defeat of France was traumatic. But something had to be done, and they refused to pander to the conqueror. Gradually life settled down to something like normality, but an event took place which went totally unnoticed by both the French and German authorities — the arrival in August of Major Maurice Buckmaster from England entrusted with the organisation of escape, sabotage and resistance networks in central France. Charney Bassett was among the handful of British officers who joined him in the course of the next few weeks.

'D'you want to work with the Résistance, or do you want us to try and get you back to England?' Mme de Lusignac asked Charney almost as soon as he had arrived at Jovelles.

'What d'you think?' he had replied. 'Of course I want to stay in France and work with the Résistance. But if I'm to be of any use, I must get in touch with my bosses in London, and to do this, I must be able to pass in and out of the occupied zone as easily as possible. Can you help me?'

Mme de Lusignac assured him that she could. Shortly before the outbreak of war, she and General Fouleix had sold their houses at Le Chesnay and decided to live on her property in the country. The general had died soon after, and she had retired to Jovelles on her own. She was then a vigorous sixty, full of energy, and as imperious as ever. Her former inclination to view Hitler with a mild degree of favour had given way to a bitter loathing, and a determination to see him damned. Like her cousin, M. de la Beauronne, she had heard de Gaulle's broadcast and was resolved to respond to it in any way she could. She did, however, suffer certain disadvantages in being so well-known for her outspokenness, and while she was not ready to put up with any nonsense, whether from German soldiers or Vichy officials, she had to admit that Jovelles was no more than a temporary refuge for Charney, even had he wished to remain longer under her roof.

So after a few days to rest and recover from his trek across France, she suggested that he go to see Gilbert Renault, alias Rémy or Paul Armisch, alias Alembert, an Alsatian refugee who spoke German as well as he spoke French. These two men were rumoured to be in touch with London and with other leading men in the *département* prepared to set up resistance networks.

'But first you must see my cousin, François de la Beauronne. He lives at the Château du Bois, near Sainte-Foy,' she said in a tone that forbade contradiction. 'He'll be able to help you.'

The Outfit, to which Charney belonged, had been set up with the inconspicuous title of 'Section D' soon after Hitler had invaded Austria in 1938, to investigate the possibility of attacking the enemy by means other than the operations of military forces, such as sabotage and propaganda. Charney had been one of its earliest recruits. Immediately following the collapse of France, the chiefs of staff submitted to the War Cabinet a plan to attack Germany by economic means, and the creation of widespread revolt in her conquered territories. It was to these London masters that he was now anxious to report.

The month of September, 1940 saw the introduction of new regulations for crossing the demarcation line. A system of passes was instituted — white ones issued by the Reich, green ones by Vichy, and blue for minor local traffic. All minor roads leading across the line were blocked, either by huge cubes of stone, or by impenetrable barriers of barbed wire, and crossings were confined to certain places only. It was, of course, sometimes possible to cross open fields or thick woodlands, but these were generally patrolled night and day by armed guards. To enable these arrangements to be put in place, the frontier remained completely closed between August 20th and September 5th, 1940.

Soon after Charney arrived at Jovelles, Mme de Lusignac was joined by Hélène Loreau, who had decided to leave her flat in Bordeaux in order to be with her aunt. She had lost contact with her sons, one of whom was serving in the French colonial army, and the other in the French Air Force. Michel had been lucky enough to escape capture after the collapse of armed resistance, and had succeeded in making his way to Jovelles too, where he was hiding out. It was through Charney that he managed a few weeks later to escape through Spain to England, where he joined the Outfit.

As soon as the crossing points were reopened, Charney told Hélène and Mme de Lusignac that he must be off. He cycled to Gabastier, where Mme de Lusignac had arranged for him to meet Alembert. He was received warmly, her introduction having assured the Frenchman of Charney's bona fides.

'Will you permit me to work with you, M. Armisch?' asked Charney.

'But of course,' came the reply.

'To begin with, I want to cross into the occupied zone as soon as I can. I have reason to believe that I may be able to contact an

English colleague near Bordeaux. Mme de Lusignac said you could put me in touch with M. de la Beauronne, who might be able to help me.'

'The Château du Bois is between here and the line. I'll tell you the best way to get there without drawing attention to yourself.'

'Good. I'll go at once.

Madame de la Beauronne received Charney rather coldly at first, fearing that he might be an *agent provocateur*, and kept him talking until her husband arrived.

François de la Beauronne was a man of about forty, balding, with wispy, fair hair brushed across his pate, his aquiline nose surmounting a clipped, military moustache. His hands were roughened by manual work, his well-cut but baggy riding breeches showed him to be a typical gentleman farmer. He greeted Charney warmly after the latter had passed on a message from Mme de Lusignac — a reference to a mutual relation which only a member of the family would have known.

'We were expecting you, but, of course, we didn't know you,' M. de la Beauronne said. 'One has to be very careful.' He went on to tell Charney that he and Alembert had set up their little organisation as long ago as July, very soon after the armistice, and it consisted of about half a dozen close friends. They had established contact with London through Spain, and were asking for a radio, codes, money and arms. Charney told him that his contact near Bordeaux could arrange for him to go to England, and once there, he assured M. de la Beauronne, he would return with the things he needed, as well as a radio operator and as many trained officers as he could manage.

'Could you get me across the line tomorrow?' Charney asked his host.

'Certainly, so long as you get here before curfew. We don't think it would be wise for you to stay here tonight, but Alembert will take care of you if you go back to Gabastier. It's not far; you know his house, and you can go there over the fields the way you came.'

Next day Charney returned to the Château du Bois at the agreed time, and was told that everything was ready.

'We'll leave here on our bicycles with Kiki — he's our farm worker and the local plumber — and stop at La Mothe-Montravel at the house of a friend of mine, which is right up against the demarcation line,' said M. de la Beauronne. 'About five hundred metres beyond it there's a German road block. I'll leave you at my friend's with Kiki, and go on by bike, because I have a permit to cross the line to attend to my vineyard on the other side. Kiki will then take you to the Lidoire, which is the frontier between the two zones. I shall wait for you on the other side at my vineyard, where I've got a small stone hut in which I keep some tools and such like. My land comes down to the Lidoire at the point they'll bring you to. I'll then take you to Dr Puységuin, who's got a car which he's allowed to use for his practice. He'll take care of you from then on.'

Charney duly made contact with his colleagues, returned to England to report and to collect supplies for Alembert's *réseau*, and went back to France, where he remained for nearly a year. By the time he became our conducting officer, he had made no fewer than three separate trips to France, and had established one of the most successful *réseaux* in the south-west.

* * *

Charney came with me to the unobtrusive advanced Lysander base, where they taught me about drops and pick-ups. Although we were both to be parachuted into France, it was essential for me to learn the procedures laid down by the RAF, so that I could organise reception committees and landing strips. On our way down, Charney turned to me and said, 'You've been chosen for the job of my number two for two reasons: first because you passed out of the Training Schools quite well, and second, because I've known you nearly all your life, and because you'll be working in a part of France you know well with people you know and who know you.'

'Oh, who are they?' I asked in some surprise.

'You'll find out soon enough. One of them will almost certainly be Michel Loreau — or Raymond as we must now call him. We were impressed, by the way, that neither of you revealed on the course that you already knew each other, or that either of you knew me. That was a good mark for you both.'

He smiled, and patted me gently on the shoulder. 'But before I ask you to repeat the instructions I have given you to learn, I want you to understand quite clearly that if you think we're asking too much of you, you needn't accept the operation. If you want to cry off at the last moment, no one is going to think any the less of you. Everyone in this Outfit is a volunteer, and every job is of his own choice.'

I smiled at Charney. 'I'm quite happy about it, Charles.'

'Very well, David. But remember, if you get caught, there'll be very little we can do for you. Should you get picked up by the French police you'll be in the unoccupied zone most of the time — the papers you'll be given before you leave England should keep you out of trouble, because they're perfect in every detail. If, however, you should get into *real* difficulties — but only then — you may tell them your English name, and explain that you were a pilot with 605 Squadron, you got away after being captured, and you're trying to get to Spain. If you're lucky, they might turn a blind eye, but don't count on it!'

After I returned from the Lysander base, I was summoned to a house in south London to get my clothes for the trip. They consisted of a badly cut, inconspicuous French suit, a pair of stout walking shoes, a sleeveless woollen sweater, shirts, vests, pants, handkerchiefs and one suit of pyjamas, all of them French. I was also given a French razor, shaving-brush, soap, toothbrush, etc. and ten packets of Gauloises — made in London. Lastly I was given a raincoat, a beret and a pair of corduroy trousers, and a grey leather jacket that looked horribly new. These items troubled me, so I rubbed them on the filthy floor, and walked and stamped on them to make them look old and worn. When I'd mixed some water and dust in the washbasin and rubbed the mixture in wet, they looked so much better that I did the same with my beret.

A station wagon stood outside the front door, and Jack Cuttlance and the colonel who had been chairman of the selection board were waiting to say goodbye. Jack shook me by the hand and patted me on the shoulder affectionately. 'Good luck, old boy. We'll be rooting for you.'

The colonel said a few kind words to me, and handed me an astonishing present, a pair of cuff-links made from four great chunks of gold and two gold anchor chains.

'Just a small present from us all,' he said. 'We like to give all of you some little personal thing before you leave. Something you can use, and to remind you that we are in some sense with you. We're not all strong enough or young enough to go into the field ourselves, are we, Cuttlance?' he said, smiling at Jack. 'They've no English markings, so they might come in useful if you run out of money. You can always hock them!'

I told him that that would be the last thing I'd do. 'You've given me a marvellous present, and I'll keep it as a good-luck token,'

I said.

'Charles and your other colleagues will meet you at the airfield,' Jack said. 'Have a nice trip.'

I climbed into the car. We moved away. They all waved. A light drizzle was falling. It was five o'clock and the rush hour. I stuffed the gold cuff-links into my pocket along with the copy of the cover story I still hadn't learnt by heart.

We picked up Charney and Michel from other houses in London, before setting off for an airfield north of Cambridge. Although the moon was full, it was a grey, cloud-filled sky that threatened cancellation of our trip. The car pulled up outside a small inn near Ely, and Charney told Michel and me to get a drink while he and the escorting officer phoned through to the aerodrome.

'We shan't be long,' said Charney, 'but they may not have the latest forecast yet, so we'll have to wait till it comes through. Get yourselves something to eat, if we're not back in twenty minutes. There'll be a meal at the airfield in any case.'

'What'll you drink, Raymond?' I asked Michel, going to the bar.

'Oh, a pint of mild and bitter, please.' he replied.

I paid for the drinks and came back to the table in the corner. There was no one else in the private bar, and the barman left us to attend to his customers in the public bar. After we had settled ourselves comfortably, Michel turned to me and said: 'So you decided to join up after all. I thought you were a pacifist.'

'I was. I still am, but I came to the conclusion that my position in the ambulance corps was anomalous in the present circumstances.'

He nodded. 'I decided to join the Résistance as soon as I escaped to England. I admit that our people in Carlton House Terrace suggested it first, but once they had, my only thought was to get on with the job as quickly as I could. I wasn't fanatical about it like some men; they put a proposal to me and I accepted it. My taste for adventure, and my vanity — you know, my love of making heroic gestures — balanced each other out. As I see it, my main concern is to survive. By doing what we are, we have a great chance to be true to ourselves, don't you think? I'd no idea what this decision would entail; there may be disappointments, boredom, long periods of dreary inaction in some backwater; maybe some fighting, or rather some guerrilla warfare. This means risking being shot if I'm caught, but I'm prepared to run that risk.'

I nodded my agreement.

'I'm happy to die in my twenties — I've had a radiantly happy life. Until the war, that is,' he added. 'After what the Germans have done to France, I'm more than happy to make any sacrifice, because what I'm sacrificing has been so wonderful. I shall die completely master of myself, I can assure you. I'm doing this, like you are, of my own free will, not because I'm tired of life; just the opposite.

'I had a letter from mother smuggled out of France five months ago. In it she said she rather hoped the English wouldn't invade France, and in a way I understand her. We want to free ourselves by our own efforts. But I've given my word to the Outfit; I've weighed the risks, and whatever doubts I may have had at the outset have now vanished. Because I'm prepared to die, I feel I've conquered life. I savour being alive all the more because I know I may have to give it up at any moment. You may find this hard to understand, David, but in order to be reborn without being a slave to myself, I must free myself from myself. I want to show that doing what I'm doing, I'm no longer just talking or thinking about it. I know I'm going to be frightened, and I shall want to run away, but that's not the point. What counts is to have thought it all out quietly, and to have accepted it calmly, willingly and happily.'

Michel turned away, lost in thought. After a moment, he went on: 'France faces an awful future. It'll be far worse than it is at present. These émigrés — the Free French — will go back animated by motives of revenge against those they now look on as traitors. Before we can re-establish freedom, there's bound to be a period of terror, which will, alas, be unavoidable, because there can be no true freedom while the germs of totalitarianism, and a handful of fanatics for dictatorship, abound.

'If I'd stayed behind in France instead of escaping to England, I'd only have been deported or imprisoned. I'd already decided that I would refuse to submit to the dictates of the Germans and the Vichyites. I'd no intention of becoming their slave, to be marched here and there under their whips, and be massacred by Allied bombs, all the time expected to smile happily at our conquerors. The very idea's absurd.

'I said to myself, when the proposition was first put to me, that if I joined the Outfit, I could go into hiding at Jovelles, but I'd have felt dreadfully guilty if that was all I'd've done, because I'd have been no use to anyone.

'I'm now prepared to sacrifice happiness, comfort, the enjoyment of music and literature in order to defend my rights. I see my supreme duty to be getting on top of life, because life is so precious, and to immerse myself up to the hilt in the fight for freedom. I know I'll be frightened, terribly frightened; I know I'll be disgusted by all the blood and guts, but I'll go through with it just the same, because, quite clearly, I know that I *must.*'

I had never heard Michel talk like this before. My immediate feeling was one of embarrassment. But then, Frenchmen, unlike Englishmen, see nothing odd in expressing their emotions so vehemently. I felt ill at ease, although I understood and sympathised with practically all he'd said, but the thought crossed my mind that I had never analysed my own motives quite so precisely. My reasons for joining up had stemmed from a much less coherent gut feeling that it was the right thing to do in the circumstances in which I found myself, during the last weeks in IVAC. But then, England, unlike France, had not been invaded, and her army had not been so completely defeated.

'It's all very well being an intellectual,' Michel went on, 'but in order to remain one I'll have to get to know how to be a bandit. If I'm at Jovelles with mother and Tante Madeleine, Messieurs de la Déportation will take several months to find me. They're too stupid and dumb. My class is registered in Paris, not the Dordogne, and farmers and farm-workers are exempt. I've cut my medical examination, so there's some hope I may escape detection, because once I land in France I'll be part of the Résistance, unlike you, who are an enemy soldier and protected by the Geneva Convention.'

Just then Charney and the escorting officer came back, and Charney ordered a whisky. Between sips he told us, as though it were scarcely important, that our trip had not so far been cancelled. I was glad, for I was hungry, and Charney had told us about the lavish rations to be had at the airfield.

The sentry on the gate, when we arrived, was huddled under a tree for shelter against the wind and the rain. He knew the escorting captain, and waved us in at once. The mess, a long hut with bare board tables and benches and dirty windows, was misleading, for we ate an enormous meal, after which we were ordered off to the loo to empty ourselves before being trussed up in our parachute clothes and harness.

The hut in which this took place was some distance from the mess. We each had separate cells, and before we were dressed we were searched by a quiet man in civilian clothes, with an old-maidish turn of phrase.

'Oh dearie me, aren't we nicely fitted out now,' he said, running his big hands swiftly through my clothes and tearing a price ticket out of the lining of my beret. He then examined my maps with a magnifying glass he had taken out of his sedate, dark waistcoat. 'Hurry, hurry always finishes last,' he burbled. 'Now then, what have we here?' he found the bag of French money, with which I had been furnished. 'Well, well, young man. You can have a time with all them francs in gay Paree...'

The money was arranged in a white canvas money-belt tied round my middle. There was a great deal of it, hundreds of thousands of francs, and he riffled through the lot to see that no pound or ten-bob notes had inadvertently got into it. I took the money-belt back from him and arranged its bulging bits over my kidneys.

When I had the rest of my clothes on, a young airman came in, and pushed me into my parachutist overalls with a strange coat that buttoned between the legs and zipped everywhere else. The overalls were filled with special pockets, mostly around the legs, holding such hardware as a shovel, a Swiss knife, a small flask of brandy, a .38 automatic, and a tin of emergency rations. Inside my trousers at the back they fitted an enormous rubber mat, inaccurately called a spine pad. Then they strapped me into my parachute harness, which was so designed that I couldn't stand up straight once I was firmly in it. It gave us the swollen appearance of a creature from Mars. At the last moment our escorting officer drifted in, scooped my English belongings — money, note-case, clothing coupons and so on — into a large brown envelope, and asked me to sign for them. In return he handed me two celluloid containers, one filled with white tablets, the other with blue ones, the white for energy, the blue for sleep, or the other way round, I can't now remember, as I never had to use either.

Then in closed cars with the blinds drawn we were driven out on to the tarmac. Our aircraft was warming up, and the crew were having a final check-up of the controls. We got out, and because of the huge bulk of our harness waddled like king penguins to the plane. The noise was terrible; the pilot and another airman came around to shake hands with us, and our escorting officer shouted goodbye in our ears. The airmen then pushed and bustled us under the belly of the plane, and with great difficulty we heaved our enormous bulk up through its navel and into the shed-like interior, where the noise was mercifully less, and where we found several men who fussed around us like ladies' maids getting a debutante ready for her presentation at court.

The interior was spacious. As we were not due over the target area for some six hours, our parachute harness was not hooked up, and we were able to walk about inside. The small rectangular windows were covered with blinds. When we taxied out on the big wet airfield, I lifted a corner, and saw the shining tarmac running past, then the wing-tip gently lowering as the pilot turned in a wide sweep, circling the field and climbing over the long grey mass of Ely cathedral on his course southward.

By the time we reached mid-Channel, the weather had cleared, and it shone silver as we approached the French coast. Before reaching it, we dived sharply down to tree-top level, and crossed the line swerving to confuse the defences. Flak glowed up at us from either side a long distance away. As we flew low over the roads and fields and valleys, I watched every detail of the countryside with a strange sense of detachment. We flew on hour after hour into the heart of France as smoothly as if we were on a peacetime pleasure trip. Around midnight we saw in the distance two huge fires, perhaps the work of earlier bombers. We were offered hot coffee with rum and sandwiches, and then, curling up as best I could, I tried to snatch some sleep before the frightening ordeal of the jump. I was woken by the despatcher, who told us we were getting close to the target, and asked us to sit in our places so that our static lines could be hooked up.

The despatcher is a terrifying figure to the man-about-to-jump. He is the person responsible for seeing that your parachute is correctly attached by its static line to the aeroplane, and that you go out of it smartly when the bomb-aimer decides to drop you. This despatcher was a pleasant-looking youth with a loose, tumbling body. Then the doors over the hole were uncovered, and Charney, who was to jump first, was made to sit on the rim until told to jump.

On the side of the aircraft near the hole there were several little railways for holding the fixed end of the static lines. If we found our objective we would jump through the hole and, when we had fallen a little through the air, our static line would pull the case off the parachute, opening it at the same time. When you thought about it like that, it seemed just as simple as stepping out of a train on to a platform.

Above the hole, there were two small signal lights, one red, the other green. When the plane saw the correct light lay-out and signal letter flashing from the ground, the pilot made a long, careful circle, then, guided by the bomb-aimer, a straight approach up-wind at the lights. When he began this approach, the despatcher shouted 'Running in', and one by one we sat on the edge of the hole. The bomb aimer switched on the red light, and the despatcher shouted 'Action stations'. When my turn came, I put both legs, feet close together, in the hole, my hands at my sides on the edge. I had to remember not to look down at the ground, nor at the light on the side of the plane, but to watch the despatcher's right hand. When the bomb-aimer changed the red light to green, the despatcher crashed down his right hand and screamed 'Go!' They were trained to scream like maniacs, the theory being that the more terrible the despatcher's scream, the easier it was for the jumper to launch himself into space.

After Charney had jumped, the pilot circled again over the dropping zone, and for the next five minutes I was sitting on the edge of the hole looking down at the ground beneath me trying to identify landmarks. Before I was due to go, a container had to be dropped, and suddenly, to my amazement, I heard a loud bang and saw the container dropping to earth. This was the first warning I had that I was about to drop. I knew that if I did not jump like lightning after that, we should probably never see the container again. At the same time the thought flashed through my mind that perhaps they had changed the plan at the last minute, after seeing the ground, and that we were going to make another run — dropping first the containers and packages, then Michel and me. However, I swung my legs into the hole and jumped instinctively. As I went through I heard the despatcher shout something; I wasn't sure whether it was 'Go' or 'Stop', but in either case it was too late. Next moment I was lying on my back in the air watching the fat round belly of the aircraft passing above me, then the soft rustle of the silk as my parachute opened. I saw the rest of the stick floating against the moon. I drifted down over a hill past a wood, and came to earth just short of a hedge. I saw next to mine Michel's parachute crumple and fall past me to the ground. He landed on his back a little higher up the hill, bruising himself badly.

The silence of those few moments after landing was uncanny. I looked around and found myself alone in a small field about a hundred yards from a road and some houses. The moonlight was flooding down, and I could see for miles. The grass was drenched with dew. Of Charney I could see and hear nothing. It seemed impossible to realise that I was in the middle of France, it was so peaceful, the idea of war so remote.

I took off my parachute, and began to fold it in the manner we had been taught on the course, ready to hide it. As I was doing so, I heard someone approaching from the direction of the houses. I stiffened, and felt for my automatic. As the man came nearer, I recognised François de la Beauronne, whom I had last seen at Jovelles five years before. As he drew nearer, he recognised me, and hastening towards me with outstretched hand he said, 'Bienvenu en France. Nous sommes vachement contents de vous voir!'

III

At the end of 1941, there was a great increase in the number of Germans stationed along the demarcation line. This led to a serious incident which took place near Montabourlet. One day, two senior SS officers and their driver turned up on what appeared to be a reconnaissance, but which they tried to pass off as a sightseeing expedition to the Château de Jovelles. They asked for the key to the state rooms, but M. Cousy, Mme de Lusignac's factor, refused to give it to them. They then said that they wished to inspect the caverns in the Forêt de Jovelles.

These man-made caverns, like the state rooms of the château, were at that time filled with art treasures from the north of France, where they had been sent for safety shortly before the outbreak of war. M.Cousy told the SS officers that they had no business to be in the unoccupied zone, and refused to give them any assistance. The Germans took no notice; they drove off towards the caverns, and started to break the chain and padlock with a crowbar. Meanwhile, M. Cousy had summoned help from the village; half a dozen locals turned up and began throwing stones at the SS officers, hitting one of them on the cheek and drawing blood, whereupon his companion drew his revolver and began shooting. Luckily his aim was poor, and no one was hurt. Jumping into their car, they drove off, and there, for the moment, the matter rested. Two weeks later a platoon came to arrest M. Cousy and took him to Angoulême, where he was sentenced to several weeks in prison. But more seriously for Mme de Lusignac and her household, this incident led to an adjustment of the demarcation line bringing Jovelles, but not the neighbouring village of Montabourlet, within the occupied zone.

All this happened while Charney was in England attending our training courses. It had been his intention, when he returned, to make the Château de Jovelles the base for his new operations. Under the circumstances this became, not impossible, but certainly more hazardous, and though we did, in fact, go to Jovelles for a few days, everyone thought it wiser if we found other places farther from the demarcation line in which to lie low. Consequently, Charney made contact once more with François de la Beauronne, whose Ventriloquist *réseau* was operating in the region south of Limoges and north of Périgueux.

This *réseau* controlled a number of factory workers in Périgueux, all trained in elementary sabotage, so it was decided that we should attempt to attack the Bordeaux-Poitiers railway line instead. Several successful attacks were made against the signalling system, but in the course of one of these, Michel and another member of the *réseau* were captured and sent to the prison at Périgueux, later being moved to a concentration camp run by the Vichy authorities at Mauzac, near Lalinde on the Dordogne.

Charney and I, together with François de la Beauronne, planned their escape, and a guard was bribed to let us make copies of the vital keys. At three in the morning a few weeks later, we succeeded in unlocking the door of their hut, and managed to get ten men out before the alarm was raised. One of our men was waiting for them in a truck, and drove them to a hide-out in the woods above Limeuil, where they camped for a week, before splitting up into twos and threes and making for widely separated parts of the region. Michel made for Bordeaux, but unfortunately he was recaptured sometime later, and we heard that he was to be sent to a prison near Angoulême.

One of my jobs had been to train men to become professional rescuers, and I arranged for Kiki and another young man to come with me to remove Michel from the train that would be taking him to Angoulême. One of the prison guards, who was a member of Ventriloquist *réseau*, told me which train he was to be on, so I set our routine plan in motion.

The three of us were waiting on the platform of Bordeaux station when Michel turned up, handcuffed to one gendarme and guarded by a second. They got on to the train, and sat down in their reserved third-class compartment. As usual, the train was packed, and from time to time one of us squeezed through the corridor to make sure that Michel was still there.

The first stop was Angoulême, so nothing could be done till then. Just as the train was entering the outskirts of the town, we moved towards the compartment in which Michel and the two gendarmes were sitting. There were other people in it, of course, but they had nothing to do with us.

Both Kiki and my other companion knew Michel well by sight. Kiki stood in the corridor looking at his watch, and when Michel saw him shake it as if it were out of order, he told one of his guards that he wanted to go to the loo. The gendarme to whom he was handcuffed got up and took him along the corridor, leaving the other to see that their seats were not taken in their absence.

As they made their way to the loo, Kiki followed at a discreet distance, and stood by the gendarme as though he, too, were queuing up for the same purpose.

Having got into this position, Kiki brought out his gun and poked it into the gendarme's stomach, and at the same time told him to walk slowly through the vestibule leading to the next coach. During the negotiation of this rather difficult passage, the gendarme was relieved of his gun. Having got him into the next coach, Kiki, who was still steering him, told him not to get out at Angoulême or to raise an alarm of any kind on pain of death. We eventually let him get out at the next stop but one, Chatellérault, Kiki having got out at the previous one, Poitiers.

Meanwhile, my other companion gave a special knock on the loo door when the coast was clear. Michel came out and was handed a third-class ticket from Bordeaux to Angoulême, which had been correctly punched by passing the guard when his own ticket had been punched, and having the second one punched on his way back down the corridor. My companion also gave Michel a new identity card with his own photograph on it, but in a new name, Jean-Pierre Larthe, which he had to memorise.

When the train stopped at Angoulême, Michel got out, mingled with the crowd, and went out of the station. Meanwhile, I was outside the door of the second gendarme's compartment, watching him carefully. Realising that Michel was supposed to be put off at Angoulême, the gendarme got up to see what was going on. As he barged his way down the corridor towards the loo, he found himself face to face with my automatic, so he was inclined to lend a sympathetic ear to what I had to say to him. Not surprisingly, he returned peacefully to the compartment, where we both sat down side by side like lambs, it having been understood between us that the gendarme would go as far as Chatellérault before he raised the alarm. My other companion followed Michel through the barrier, and gave him a hand in case he was feeling under the weather. It was all too easy, for there, in the station yard, was the good Dr Puységuin waiting for them in his car.

The two gendarmes got out at Chatellérault and I went on to Tours, where I got out, bought a ticket back to Angoulême, where Charney was waiting to meet me, and drove me back to Jovelles to rejoin Michel and the others.

One of my duties was to train local members of the resistance in sabotage techniques, and it fell to me to organise suitable cadres and training. Targets such as bridges and rolling stock were to be selected, and every effort was made to disrupt the enemy's communications whenever the word was given or the need arose.

In the early days, too many sabotage attempts had failed for the lack of a silent time fuse. German patrols had been able to discover bombs laid beneath bridges and culverts when their location was given away by the ticking of the clockwork fuse. It had been essential, therefore, to devise a fuse that was silent, and long enough delayed to give the saboteurs time to get out of the way before the bomb exploded. The Outfit's scientists had come up with a simple device the size and shape of a Cointreau bottle. All one needed was a glass phial containing acid. When the phial was broken, the acid began to eat through a wire which, once severed, set off the firing pin of the bomb. A thick wire would take as long as half an hour for the acid to eat through; a thin one as little as five minutes.

* * *

During the early summer of 1942, our *réseau* received a severe blow in the arrest of François de la Beauronne. One day, while he was repairing a pump in his wine cellar, the gendarmerie turned up demanding to know the whereabouts of the transmitter which we had hidden in the roof of his house.

He had been denounced by one of his neighbours, who had a grudge against him. With the additional help of police direction-finding equipment, they had been led to the district in which the Château du Bois was situated. Luckily, Charney had decided as a precautionary meaure some days previously to move it to a new site, and Mme de Lusignac had agreed to let it be installed temporarily in a turret of the Château de Jovelles, to which access could be gained only by going through her bathroom, the door being cleverly concealed behind a stack of shelves. There was a large element of bluff about this move, for the transmitter was now in the occupied zone, where it was thought the Germans might be less likely to look for it than in the Vichy zone, and also because the locals there were far more hostile to the German authorities than they were in the unoccupied zone.

The despatch of the silent time fuses was held up, partly on account of bad weather during the dropping periods of full moon, and by midsummer Charney thought that it might be expedient for me to return to England to see if things could be speeded up.

Two months later, following the Allied invasion of North Africa, the Germans occupied the whole of France. The enemy garrisons along the old demarcation line were no longer needed, but some were nevertheless maintained at strategic points in the region to protect the main lines of communication.

In those days, there was a railway line which ran from Angoulême to Toulouse through Ribérac and Bergerac. Though much of it was single track, it had strategic importance because it duplicated the main line from Limoges to Toulouse by way of Brive and Gourdon. The headquarters of the garrison covering the northern sector of the Angoulême-Toulouse line was stationed at the Château de Jovelles.

Périgord as a whole was occupied by the SS Totenkopf Division based at Tulle, and it was not long before the majority of the secret Résistance networks had been penetrated and many of their members arrested. But the German troops guarding the railways were drawn from army infantry units, whose officers were not always on good terms with their SS colleagues. In spite of this redeployment, some French arms dumps escaped capture when the Germans occupied the whole country, having been looted by members of the Résistance, who hid the arms away in caves and barns in the forests before the Germans could get their hands on them. It was not long before these arms were distributed to the Armée Secrète throughout the region in order to disperse them as widely as possible.

By this time I had been in the field many months, and it was time I had a break. There had been some important changes in the design of passes and other official documents, as well as to the railway timetables, since the German occupation of the Vichy zone. We knew what a feather it would be in the Outfit's cap, when briefing a new man, to be able to say: 'When you've buried your parachute, walk south five kms to the main road, then follow it due east for another two kms until you come to the station at Coutures.

Spruce yourself up a bit and then catch the 06.12 slow train to Mussidan, where you can change to the 07.45 for Bergerac. You won't have to bother about timetables or ask any awkward questions.'

We knew what a feeling of confidence such precise information could have on a man or woman who was setting out on one of these lonely, nerve-racking ventures, for there was no getting away from the fact that the first few days in occupied France were enough to make anyone jittery.

My replacement was due by Lysander at the next full moon, and I was to return in it and have a couple of weeks' leave before a spell as conducting officer for a new group of trainees. The field we chose for the change-over was near the Dronne, not far from the village of Epéluche. The riverside meadows there were long and broad, and large enough for Halifaxes or Liberators, which needed at least sixteen hundred by eight hundred metres. The field had a good, hard surface, and was flat. The RAF weren't terribly fussy about the unevenness of the ground, but they insisted that there should be no ditches, telegraph poles or trees at either end of the runway. Lysanders only needed a field of eight hundred by four hundred metres, which made landing strips for them much easier to find.

When the position of the field had been sent by code to London, and agreed by the RAF, London told us what BBC message they would send out at 7.30 pm on the night the plane was due to arrive. They also sent us the letter to be flashed up in morse to the pilot as he approached so that he could recognise us. As soon as the pilot saw this letter, he would flash back another, which they also sent us.

We laid out the flare path that evening in the usual way, in the shape of a reversed letter 'L'. Charney posted seven men at intervals of one hundred and fifty metres in a straight line drawn according to the wind direction. Another two men stood at fifty metre intervals, at right angles to the seventh man, at the end from which the wind was blowing. Each man was given an electric bicycle lamp, which he was to shine upwards when the plane was heard approaching. This would tell the pilot that the wind was blowing from the direction of the base line of the inverted 'L' towards the first of the seven lights of the stem of the 'L'. He would then know it was safe to put his wheels down at the first light and run into the wind up to the seventh. When he got there, he would turn round the eighth light — that's to say the middle light of the base line of the 'L' — and come back up to the first light. He would turn there again, and only stop at the first light, when he was facing the wind ready for take-off.

The night before I was due to leave, we received a message to say that a Halifax would be coming instead of a Lysander, and that it would reach us after having dropped its parachutage en route. Soon after midnight we heard it approaching. Charney, who was in number one position, flashed his recognition letter — 'M' — and we saw the pilot flash back a 'Q' in answer. Charney then shone his torch along the flarepath so that the rest of the team could see it. They then lit their own torches, shone them towards Charney to show they'd got the message, and then shone them upwards at the plane, following it as it twisted and turned for its approach and landing.

When the plane landed, the torch-bearers followed it with their lights while it turned round on the field. Only when it stopped beside Charney could they afford to put out their lights and approach the plane.

The Halifax arrived on time; the new recruit got out, a few bundles of supplies were unloaded, and I and a young Frenchman, who was taking back a report to General de Gaulle, got in; the pilot revved up the engines, and the long flight home began. I settled down to sleep in the dark cabin, but it was dreadfully cold, and draughts howled along the floor from front to back, making sleep all but impossible.

The hours dragged by. At last the grey light of dawn began to appear through the right-hand windows — I never could remember whether they were called port or starboard! By about eight o'clock it was full daylight, by which time we were within sight of the English coast. The pilot pointed out Beachy Head to the east and Portsmouth harbour to the west. Suddenly one of the engines began to splutter, and the plane dipped like a wounded pheasant. I looked at the pilot in alarm, thinking what a fine anti-climax it would be to end up in the Channel, within sight of home, after all I had been through in the past few months. The pilot leaned forward to make some adjustment under the dashboard.

'Don't worry,' he said. 'I'll turn her over to reserve. She's enough juice to make Tangmere; it's not more than ten minutes' flight from here, and we've at least half-an-hour's worth in reserve.'

I thought of the Chinese saying: 'He who has ten paces to make and who has done nine of them can only claim to have accomplished half his journey.' Louis, my young French companion, who had been dozing like me when the engine cut out, had gone a pale shade of grey. No doubt I, too, looked equally pallid. We held our breath and hoped that the reserve tank was really full, but the pilot executed a masterly landing. The plane came to a standstill in front of some huts and the second engine died. A great silence filled the machine. We were home.

Presently the door opened and, much relieved, we climbed down on to the tarmac. I stood waiting for the pilot to join us in order to thank him for getting us home safely.

'Phew!' he gasped, wiping the perspiration from his forehead despite the cold morning air. 'I'd just as soon that didn't happen again; we had next to no petrol in the reserve tank, it must have been leaking.'

We made the appropriate remarks of congratulation and relief. Then our attention was distracted by the approach of a small party of British and French officers coming towards us across the airfield, amongst whom I spotted Jack Cuttlance. He came up to me smiling, his arms outstretched in greeting.

'Well done,' he beamed.

I wasn't sure whether he was referring to my achievements, such as they were, or to our scary landing.

'They were biting their nails in the control tower, I can tell you. But you've made it, which is all that matters. Instead of breakfast in the RAF mess, I thought we'd sneak off to a good spot I noticed on the way down in the car.'

I allowed myself to be led off by Jack, only too glad to relax at last.

Beside his car stood a grinning Sam Barker. He came smartly to attention and saluted as we approached. I held out my hand to him, and he grasped it, smiling from ear to ear.

'It's bloody good to see you back, sir.'

I smiled back at him.

'It's damn good to be back, and all the better for seeing your cheery mug again.'

Jack laughed at us both. 'Sam's been my driver for...' he paused, 'how long is it now, Corporal Barker?'

'Just a year, sir.'

'He came to us as a DR soon after you joined the Outfit,' Jack said. 'He's looked after me splendidly ever since.'

I pointed to the two stripes on his battledress sleeve. 'Congratulations, Corporal Barker,' I said, mock seriously.

'Congratulations, Captain Kildwick,' he answered in return.

'Captain?' I queried.

'Yes,' said Jack, 'your promotion came through this week.'

* * *

In the car, Jack said that he would like me to spend a few days with him before I went to see my people. Privately, I was shocked by his appearance. He was still the outstandingly handsome, smart officer I had met when I first joined IVAC, but his face had become lined — almost haggard — and he had lost weight. At first I put this down to the strain of his job, and to the fact that bombing and food rationing were beginning to take their toll on everyone in England. But when we arrived at the little house in St John's Wood I had time to take stock of him properly. Jack shut the door behind Sam, and then turned to me, his arms outstretched. Kissing me on the cheek, he exclaimed, 'I can't tell you how glad I am to see you. You've done extremely well, and I'm very proud of you.'

I felt myself blushing, not quite knowing how to respond to this. I knew I had always been fond of Jack, and that he was fond of me, but it had never occurred to me till now that this fondness might have gone beyond close friendship. Quickly regaining my composure I said, 'You haven't told me how Stanley is.'

I knew at once from his expression that I had committed a faux pas.

'You haven't heard, of course,' he replied. 'He had a relapse a few months ago. They don't give him much longer. He never really got over the accident, and his kidneys were much more badly damaged than they thought at first.'

I stammered out some banal remark, but Jack brushed it aside.

'He's in a hospital at Aylesbury — they thought it better to get him out of London away from the bombing. It isn't too far from the Manor where you went through your first course, so I can get over to see him reasonably often.

I went up to him and put my hands on his shoulders, looking directly into his dark, brown eyes.

'I'm dreadfully sorry. I had no idea. You must be worried to death.'

He smiled wanly. 'I am, and what makes it worse is the fact

that I have to keep it all to myself. If my wife were dying, everyone in the Outfit would be falling over themselves with sympathy, but of course I can tell them absolutely nothing. They wouldn't understand, anyway. If they guessed, I'd be sacked right away.'

For the first time in my life I realised the lengths to which people like Jack and Stanley had to go to conceal their true feelings, and the nature of the love they bore one another.

'But that's outrageous,' I exclaimed impetuously. 'It's intolerable.'

Jack smiled. 'You don't understand, Tony, my dear. But you will one day.'

'I understand perfectly well now,' I retorted, feeling a little nettled. 'If I had shared my life with someone as long as you and Stanley have shared yours, I would feel I had every right to be anxious and depressed.'

Jack shrugged. 'Tony,' he said, as he led me into the library, and sat me down by the fireside beneath Stanley's portrait. 'Tony, my dear, I don't think you realise that the way Stanley and I have lived for the past twenty-five years is totally illegal, and that if it became known, we could be sent to prison for a long stretch. It goes without saying that my career would be ruined if our bosses in the Outfit so much as suspected the truth. That's why I have to be so discreet. But I've always felt I could trust you to be discreet too. You're the only one in the Outfit I can talk to frankly. Of course,' he went on, 'Stanley and I have a good number of friends like ourselves, who know and understand, but most of them are so busy with war work and things like that, I hardly ever see them. Anyway, as you well know, in our racket we have to fall over ourselves to be secure. So many lives are at stake.'

What Jack had just told me turned my thoughts to Manfred. If Jack felt for Stanley what I felt for Manfred, then I understood completely. I had told Jack about our friendship at school, its renewal in Austria and at his home in Germany. From my account it must have been clear to him, even though it wasn't then clear to me, that I was gay but hadn't yet come to terms with it. But his tact and his kindness were such that he had never dotted the i's or crossed the t's for me. It was only now he had unburdened his soul that I realised what a great compliment he had paid me by being so frank and open.

In the course of the next few days I underwent a debriefing at the house in Mayfair where I had had my original interview, and at the end of it I went up to Wraysby for a few days with my father, and then to my mother's in Buckinghamshire.

Before the war, mother had been very abstemious, and had never, so far as I knew, set foot in a pub. To my dismay, I now found that she was, as her neighbours took delight in telling me, the 'life and soul of the party'. The 'party' consisted of a group of hard-drinking people, who congregated nightly in the local to drink themselves into a state of stupefaction. Mother seemed to be their ring-leader, and one by one they told me what a dear old sport she was, and how she could drink the best of them under the table. All that was priggish in me came rushing to the surface. I found myself evening after evening of that dreadful week standing by myself in the bar saying less and less, and feeling more and more wretched and alien. It was as if I were the helpless witness of a rake's progress, and that rake was my own mother, the person I had once idolised above all others, and who had been so often in my thoughts during my absence abroad.

Now she was a complete stranger. Could this blowsy, coarse woman really be the mother I had left behind when I first joined the Outfit? Was it possible for anyone to change so much in such a short time? Perhaps after I'd gone back to my unit, things might settle down, and after the war I could find a niche for myself in this foreign land of which I was a native. But, alas, the damage was permanent; neither the England nor the mother I had known and loved could ever be resurrected. Both had changed beyond any hope of recovery.

During this ghastly week, mother had been critical of everything I said or did. She dismissed my plans for the future as absurd; she wanted to know what I had been doing, and why I hadn't written to her more often. When I refused to tell her, she accused me of arrogance. She knew that I had been decorated and promoted, and couldn't understand why I refused to tell her anything about what I'd been doing or where.

Father, on the other hand, understood completely — at least he understood enough not to pester me with questions I wouldn't and shouldn't answer. Alas, I was only able to spend two nights with him for some reason, which I now forget. At the end of the week with mother, things became so intolerable that I phoned Jack, and asked if I could come and stay with him for the rest of my leave.

'Pretend that I've been called back urgently, otherwise mother will smell a rat,' I said when I phoned him.

He said I could stay at the house in St John's Wood, and that though he might not be able to be with me all the time, I was to look upon it as my own. I thanked him, and in less than an hour a telegram arrived summoning me to return at once to my unit. My mother pretended to be disgusted that my leave should have been cut short.

As soon as I got back to London, I asked Jack if there would be any objection to my phoning the Swedish Embassy to see if Clara Edelstedt had sent me any letters via her uncle. I hardly expected to find a letter from Manfred waiting for me, but at least Clara, if she had written, might have been able to give me news of him.

Jack checked with the Outfit, who said they had no objection provided I showed them any letters I might have been sent, so I phoned to make an appointment, and was told that Count Aldqvist could see me the next day. When I turned up, he welcomed me warmly and said that Clara had written to me via the diplomatic bag several weeks ago, but as he didn't know how to get in touch with me, he had kept the letter safely until I came to fetch it. I opened the envelope in front of the Count to show him there was nothing illicit about it, and asked if I might read it in his presence, and then give it to him to read if he wished. I explained that I had given my army superiors an undertaking to show them the letter, and assured him, laughingly, that I had no wish to cause a diplomatic incident.

Clara wrote that 'our friend' had found Russia unlike anything he'd ever seen before. He called it a 'country veiled in secrecy' and all that he'd heard about it concerned the oppression of the people was true. He had never been told about the poor — the really poor. It was, he said, as if the people were enclosed behind a wall. But until they invaded, he had never grasped the reality of it. Peasant houses with straw roofs no better than dog kennels; the people themselves were dirty and ragged; the roads either feet deep in sand or, when it rained, morasses of mud. The towns were almost as bad as the villages, and yet the land itself was incredibly rich. 'As far as the eye can see,' he wrote, 'were wheat and cornfields without end. The workers' paradise is nothing but a heap of hunger and misery, murder and mass imprisonment, slavery and torture.'

He had spent his first Christmas in the Kursk salient. Day after day, and night after night, they had had to sit out in the open air in temperatures of minus thirty to forty degrees centigrade with a rain of artillery and small arms fire pouring down on them. They had no real billets, and officers, NCOs and men stood thirty together in a room three by five metres, without windows and no heat other than that of each others' bodies. On Christmas Eve they had managed to decorate a tree — a branch of willow — and they put two candles, two apples, two stars, four red-spotted mushrooms, a little bell and some tinsel on it, all of which had arrived some days earlier in one of the men's Christmas parcels. They had stood round it singing 'Stille Nacht, heilige Nacht' and 'Tannenbaum, Oh Tannenbaum, wie treu sind deine Blätter' and other carols.

The Russians attacked on Christmas Day in the worst snowstorm of the winter, and they had had to retreat thirty kilometres.

'We dragged ourselves along wordlessly, in knee-deep snow. Our men were too weak to carry much, and often ammunition boxes had to be left behind because no one could carry them. At every place we stopped, someone dropped dead in the snow. My feet were completely knocked out with frostbite; we only had what we could carry; everything had been lost or destroyed in the retreat. Our socks were soaked through and rotten; so were our boots, and our shirts and underclothes were black, for we'd not been able to change them for weeks. And all the time there was this ear-splitting racket of shells and the scream of rockets. It was a never-ending inferno. Some mornings it was so foggy you couldn't see more than twenty metres in any direction, and people lost their way. When men loomed up out of the mist, you didn't know whether they were friends or foes, and there was much hand-to-hand fighting.'

In June 1942, Manfred's regiment was advancing again, when he was wounded. He said it was like the first days of the war in Poland: the same wheatfields and the same hidden mines. They'd advanced about twenty kilometres that morning, and had reached the heights just south of Lugansk. There was a sudden explosion near him — no whining of the shell, just the muffled cough of a mortar shell, he wrote. 'I was on my face in a split second, and then there was a second explosion, and I was conscious of a roaring in my head as if my ear-drums had burst. I wondered what had happened to me, and felt my skull, which seemed all right, then my chest, and I could move the upper part of my body. I felt my legs and found my breeches were ripped to pieces, and blood was flowing from my knee. After three years at the front and four campaigns, I could have wept with anger. I'd got a splinter of shrapnel in my leg, and my first thought was that I was going to lose it altogether, or if not, that it would become as stiff as a board for ever.

Well, they've saved the leg, but it's stiff I'm afraid. They evacuated me to the casualty clearing station and eventually to this hospital in Warsaw. I tell you,' he concluded, 'when I got there, and was washed and put in a clean bed with fresh linen and attentive nurses all round me, I felt as if I had been reborn.'

I returned from the embassy with mixed feelings. I was thankful that Manfred was alive, and at least his wound would mean that he was no longer fit for front-line service. Where he might be now, I could not even guess, except that I knew he would not be on the Russian front. I wrote a hurried note to Clara to thank her for her letter, and asked her to let 'our friend' know that I was fit and well, I was thinking of him, and hoped it would not now be too long before we could meet again. At the same time, I asked her to convey my best wishes to his mother and father.

IV

The time had now come for me to return to France. I was to be dropped by Halifax together with supplies for our *réseau*. I hoped that my fear of dropping would be less this time, for by now I had made more than half a dozen successful drops, without any mishap beyond a few bruises. Sitting on the edge of the hole, faced with the inevitability of the jump, I thought that death was only painful to those who watch it, and that dying must be like jumping, but my mind took a resolution over my body stronger than any human instinct. My body no longer concerned me: I actually didn't mind whether my parachute opened or not as I pushed myself out into space, and I derived a strange pleasure from this physical unconcern, this victory of mind over body.

But on the way down, this feeling receded and my body began to take over again. I was so engrossed in what I was doing that I forgot to watch the ground until a soft thud brought me back to it. I found myself sitting in a marshy field and under my head lay the soft, friendly soil of France. In the distance I caught sight of the black Halifax silhouetted against the sky. Just as she flew over a line of trees, she waggled her wings in a last friendly goodbye.

It was cold and dead silent. I got to my feet and began folding my parachute. Things had to be done quickly and silently. I cocked my gun and left it on 'safety'. A few seconds later I heard good, southern French voices and I got up and waved to a black figure who was running towards me.

The operation had gone well. We had arrived at about one o'clock in the morning. The moon was high in the sky, and though we had missed the dropping zone the first time, because it had been moved about a kilometre from where we had been told it would be, we flew off again in the direction of Brantôme. Then we had turned once more and come in again directly above the waiting maquisards, losing height and throttling back the engines. We had come in so low that we could see those on the ground instinctively ducking, thinking we were going to land on top of them. As we came in a third time, our crew lit a sign under the fuselage which spelt out the word 'Compris! Understood!', and immediately there had been the great flourish of parachutes, attached to each of which were the tubular containers full of arms and sabotage gear.

'Wonderful pilot you had,' Michel declared, as he ran up to me. 'This is the best parachutage I've seen: thirty-two parachutes all in one go.'

Michel had grown up to be an extremely handsome man. He had dark hair, small, strong teeth and a fair, sun-tanned complexion. He was about five foot nine tall, and very broad-shouldered. I embraced him with a kiss on each cheek in the French manner.

'Why did we take so long to contact you?' I asked.

'I don't know. I think you must've been a little off course, or they hadn't given you quite the right location of the dropping zone. But come now, you must be cold and hungry, and you're soaked. I'll take you to the farm while the others see to the collection of the material and containers.'

'Did they tell you about container seven?' I asked. 'It's a special one. There are things in it I've got to see to myself.'

'I'll make sure Jean-Luc looks after it for you,' Michel replied, and going over to a young man who appeared to be in charge of loading operations, said to him, 'Mon ami, David, veut que tu garde recipient sept pour lui. Il y a quelque chose de spécial dedans.'

'C'est ici, Raymond, veux-tu que je le prenne aux Faurieux, ou que nous le deballions maintenant?'

Michel turned to me and asked if I wanted it unpacked immediately.

'Yes, please if you don't mind. The things I want out of it are quite small. They're among the arms the others are to have. I expect you've been told about them.'

'No; what are they?'

'Silent fuses,' I replied. 'Just get him to open the container and I'll take them out at once.'

'Okay. And then we'd better get going.'

We went to the maquisards, who were loading the containers on to a cart. I quickly extracted the two small packages, while Michel looked on as I extricated them along with my backpack, in which I'd taken the precaution to put a few clean clothes.

'I'm ready,' I said as soon as I'd collected my things. 'Let's be off. Where are we going?'

'To Jovelles, of course. Mother and Tante Madeleine are waiting up. They thought you'd be hungry, so they've got a meal for you.'

'But they told me in London that Jovelles had been taken over as a German HQ.'

'It has! That's one of the reasons you'll be safe!'

'I don't get it. How can we be safe in the same house as the German HQ?'

'You'll see. There is a way in they haven't discovered yet. You'll be quite safe. They know I'm a member of the family. They've been told I'm an epileptic and am on a short visit from hospital. I don't show my face too often, of course. I've brought a couple of horses for us. It's about ten miles from here to Jovelles through the woods; it'll be quicker on horseback than on a bike.'

By now the maquisards had emptied all the containers, which they had taken to a nearby barn and then dumped in the river. After hurried farewells, they vanished in different directions, leaving Michel and me alone. He led me up a track from the riverside and into the woods, where we found the horses tethered to a tree. Giving Michel my backpack, I took the two packages of fuses, put them into the saddlebag we had asked him to provide, and set off. About a mile from Jovelles we stopped at a farmhouse and dismounted. Michel went up to the door and knocked loudly. There was a pause, then a light appeared in the window and the sound of a door being unbolted.

'Nous sommes arrivés,' said Henri in a low voice. 'Prenez les chevaux, s'il vous plaît.'

The farmer came out and took the horses' bridles, and led them into his barn.

'We'll walk the rest of the way.' Michel said as he unbuckled the saddlebag, while I hefted my pack on to my back.

It was good to be once more in familiar country, for I soon

recognised my whereabouts from earlier visits. Michel led the way to a small wood, where before the war I had once gathered mushrooms. It lay in a small declivity — you could hardly call it a valley — through which the little river Euche made its way behind the great outcrop of rock on which the château was built.

Turning to me, Michel whispered, 'Take my hand. The next bit's a bit tricky.'

He led me up a steep, narrow path hardly a foot wide, to a small ledge just beneath the apse of the castle chapel, which reared up above our heads for what, from that angle, seemed an enormous height. Stretching up, Michel was able to find a handhold, and telling me to wait where I was, he climbed up and disappeared through a small opening in the living rock. From where I stood I could only just make it out, for it was almost completely hidden by long fronds of creeper. On our left, on the steep slope running down to the stream below, there were thick evergreens, which ensured it was quite invisible from a distance of more than a few yards. A second or two later, Michel looked out and whispered, 'I'm letting a rope down. You won't be able to see the foot and hand-holds in the dark.'

In next to no time I had climbed up and through the opening. 'This is the family vault,' Michel explained, once I'd got inside. 'There's a staircase from here into the chapel above, and from there you can get into our part of the château without being seen. The Germans are in the other wing.'

The château was built above a labyrinth of natural caves which, apart from the small opening through which we had climbed, were only accessible from inside. The Germans did not even suspect their existence.

'What makes this such a splendid hiding place,' Michel explained, 'is that even if by some mischance they did discover the vault, they would be unlikely to find any of the other caves, as they are entered from inside the château itself.'

I told him that I remembered exploring these caves when I stayed here before the war. Switching on his torch, Michel led the way through a door in the corner of the vault to a spiral stairway and a twisting passage in the rock. This sloped gradually upwards, and from it there were other passages leading off to left and right. At last we reached another staircase and climbed up till we came to a second door. Michel knocked on it softly two or three times, and I could hear the sound of furniture being moved. After a short pause,

I heard the key turn and the door opened, revealing a brightly lit room and Hélène, Michel's mother, standing there, her arms outstretched in greeting, as we stepped out of the dark passage. She threw her arms round Michel and embraced him tenderly, and turning to me she said, 'Welcome back to Jovelles, Tony. I'm so glad to see you.'

'Don't forget that I'm David here,' I said grinning. 'It's good to be back.'

* * *

The Château de Jovelles was a medieval castle, to which a large wing had been added in the time of Louis XIV, when the Seigneurs du Buisson were at the height of their influence and wealth. They had built their small Versailles along the crest of the cliff, upon which the stronghold of their medieval ancestors had been set for defensive purposes. Two large wings, each as long as the main block but only two storeys high, were built at right angles to enclose a large *cour d'honneur*. The fourth side of the courtyard was enclosed by a high stone wall, pierced by an ornamental gateway in the style of a Roman triumphal arch, in which was set a pair of solid, wooden gates. This gave the courtyard the enclosed feeling of a college quadrangle. The wing on the west side comprised the stables and coach houses; the one opposite was divided into two or three small dwellings where the *gardien* and a few old retainers lived. The Germans had commandeered the stable wing for their officers' mess and administration offices, together with a suite of rooms on the ground floor at the western end of the central block farthest from that part of the house still occupied by Mme de Lusignac and Hélène Loreau.

The imposing state rooms, which took up two floors of the central block, had been sealed off and taken over for the storage of those art treasures too delicate to be stored in the man-made caves in the surrounding woods. This arrangement ensured that the part of the château occupied by the Germans was completely separated from the rooms, in which the family still lived. This part of the château was entered by a separate door outside the *cour d'honneur* from a small courtyard in front of the chapel, which was situated at the extreme eastern end of the building. Thus it was that the secret way Michel and I had got in was completely hidden by the thick woodland that grew on the steep slope beneath the chapel and fortress, not only from the Germans, whose quarters overlooked the *cour d'honneur,* but also from the locals, who could not approach any nearer than the opposite bank of the Euche. Apart from the physical exertion required to climb in and out through the opening in the cliff face beneath the chapel vault, it was possible to come and go more or less as one pleased.

Inside the château, the place of concealment was even better. The spiral staircase, up which Michel had led me from the vault, led to Mme de Lusignac's bathroom. The door to this staircase had been completely hidden by a stack of shelves, on which she kept her scents and toiletries and a large collection of china figurines. This stack of shelves was firmly attached to the door itself, so that when it was shut, they duplicated a second stack on the other side of the bathtub, which stood out at right angles from the wall into the middle of the room. To the casual observer, the bathroom had only one door — the one from Mme de Lusignac's bedroom, to reach which one had to go through a small ante-room at the top of the main staircase. The spiral staircase from the vault did not, however, end at the bathroom level, but led up to a sizeable room in one of the pepperpot towers, from which there was a door giving on to the leads. Since, however, this part of the roof was surrounded by a high parapet, and cut off from that part of the château occupied by the Germans, one was completely safe from observation except from the air. In this hide-out our transmitter had been housed for many months, and I used it now as my base.

I had only been at Jovelles a few days when I found myself one evening alone with Mme de Lusignac. The conversation came round to the incident in which M. Cousy, her *régisseur,* had been involved with the SS.

'At least there are a few gentlemen left in the German army,' she remarked. Major von Schrade (she pronounced the name to rhyme with 'parade') could not have been more considerate. He has saved us several times from those beastly SS thugs.'

'I was at school with a von Schrade,' I said. 'How old would you think he is?'

'About your age, I should say. Perhaps a little older. He has been severely wounded, which makes him look older than he may really be. He told me he was sent here because he is no longer fit for front-line service. If he were not a boche, I think I could get to like him very much. He speaks no French, but his English is very good. He always talks English to Hélène and me. It is a pity you cannot meet him.'

'D'you happen to know what his first name is?' I asked.

'I'm not sure. Martin or Max, I think.'

'Could it be Manfred?'

'Possibly. I really have no idea.'

I could feel my heart beating at the unlikely possibility that this charming German officer might be Manfred. Not wishing to press Mme de Lusignac on the point, I determined to catch a glimpse of him if I could. On fine days I could walk up and down on the leads without being seen, and there was one corner where a gap in the parapet gave me an excellent view into the *cour d'honneur*, and which, incidentally, could have been a superb vantage point for a sniper. From here I could see the comings and goings of the German soldiers in complete safety, and sooner or later, I was sure, I would see their commanding officer.

Because of the distance between my vantage point and the *cour d'honneur*, however, I was afraid I might not be able to see him clearly enough to recognise him for certain. Since we had last seen each other he might have changed as I had too. He might have grown a moustache, or the effects of his wounds might have left their mark on his features. I had to be sure before making any move that might place me, not to mention my Résistance colleagues, at risk. Even when I was sure, I had to find out, if I could, what his attitude towards me might be. The shock of seeing me here in France would be considerable, for he had every reason to believe that I was still an ambulance driver in England.

I decided that I would tell Hélène and Mme de Lusignac of my suspicions. I suggested that they make a point of inviting him to their part of the château on some plausible pretext, and that Hélène, whose English was better than her aunt's, should bring the conversation round to where he had learnt the language. I suggested she should casually mention that her son had spent some time at an English public school, and in this way mention Templars and me. Depending on his reaction to this, we would then decide what our next step should be.

No opportunity arose for a week or two, but I had observed the major on perhaps four or five occasions. Each time he had walked into the house without turning in my direction. Certainly he seemed to be about the same height and build as Manfred, but his wounded leg caused him to limp so badly that I could not be completely sure. At last Hélène told me that she'd had a chance to talk to him. He had admitted that he was at Templars for a couple of terms in 1936, but there had been no plausible reason to mention my name, and there the matter rested.

This, however, was enough to confirm my suspicion that Major von Schrade was none other than Manfred. The next decision I had to make was whether to let him know I was in France., and if so, how. Obviously there was a tremendous risk if I did, for not only would it be his duty to arrest me as an enemy soldier, but he would also be obliged to hand me over to the SS. If Hélène and Mme de Lusignac were to be in any way involved in my self-disclosure, they would be at risk for associating with me, even if I succeeded in hiding the fact from him that they had been harbouring me. At best they risked being sent to a concentration camp, at worst they would be shot.

I was under no illusions that Manfred could afford me the least protection in such circumstances. Before making any move, therefore, I had by one means or another to find out more about his attitude towards me, to the war, to the Nazis, and, above all, to the Résistance. This was bound to take time, and the only people who could possibly find answers to these questions were Hélène and her aunt.

There were further difficulties: how much longer was Manfred likely to be at Jovelles? Members of the occupation forces were moved frequently, mainly to avoid the danger of fraternisation. Already he had been many months in this posting. He might be moved at any time, and be replaced by who knew what kind of man. I had told Hélène we had been close friends at school, and how I had visited him at his home in Germany shortly before the war. I told her, too, that he had sent news of himself to me through a mutual friend in Sweden, and though our mutual friend might have passed on a message to him from me, I could not be sure that he ever received it.

I explained that, though, like the vast majority of young Germans, he had been a member of the Hitler Jugend, he was never a very fervent Nazi, even if he had regarded Hitler at that time as the saviour of his nation. Much had happened since, and though I could not be certain, I thought it quite likely that his attitude had changed now that a German victory seemed less probable than it did in 1939 and 1940.

I suggested a number of topics upon which she could sound him out. Was he, for example, strongly pro-Nazi, just lukewarm, or merely doing his duty as was required of him as an army officer?

What was his attitude towards the British as a whole? Did he seem to be a man who thought for himself, or did he appear to be one not to reason why? Could she somehow bring my name up in conversation and tell him in a roundabout way that I had enlisted in the army? Could she gain an impression of what his reaction to this news might be, and did he still think of me as a friend?

In the end, Hélène was able to bring me answers to some, but not all these questions, and it was not until well into the autumn that I'd heard enough to judge the risk of revealing my identity worth taking. At the same time I had to safeguard, so far as possible, my hide-out and my links with the Résistance.

During this period of waiting, I had, of course, kept Charney informed of what was happening, and we discussed the problem at length. At first he was wholly opposed to my seeking a meeting with Manfred, but gradually he came round to the view that positive use might be made out of my acquaintance with him.

For some time, our *réseau* had been growing impatient at the lack of action. Strict orders had come from London urging restraint until the time for concerted action was ripe. This would be immediately before the invasion and during its earliest, critical phase. The Normandy landings were still some months in the future. Charney suggested, therefore, that it would not be hard for a group of our men to 'kidnap' Manfred, and take him to a safe house where I could confront him. This would serve the double purpose of boosting morale, and give me the chance of talking to him. The safe house we chose would be surrounded by maquisards, and Manfred and I would talk to each other in private, after which we would then decide what our next move should be.

The very fact of kidnapping a German officer entailed grave risks of reprisals, but it had been done before, and had occasionally resulted in a quid pro quo, the Germans turning a blind eye to certain activities of which they would otherwise not have approved, in return for the safety of the captured officer. On balance, therefore, it was thought to be a risk worth taking, especially if it turned out that my former friendship with Manfred could secure some positive benefits, though at the time, we had no idea what these might be.

In the event, the plan worked much more easily than we had anticipated. Manfred's chauffeur-batman was having an affair with a local girl, who was a member of the Résistance. It was arranged that his staff car was to sustain a puncture, and that she should 'detain' the driver while it was being mended. As soon as the car arrived, and had been taken into the garage to have the wheel changed, the mayor of Montabourlet, who was a member of our *réseau*, and was known to Manfred, turned up and invited him to wait in his house until the car was ready. Suspecting nothing, Manfred went into the house, which was close by, but once inside, the doors were locked, and though he didn't realise it at once, he was a prisoner. Two maquisards then came, blindfolded and handcuffed him, took him to a waiting car and drove him to the safe house. This was only a few hundred yards from the mayor's house, but he was driven by a very circuitous route, which took about twenty minutes. When they arrived at the house, Manfred was led into a room handcuffed to a chair in front of a roaring fire, with his back to the door. I, meanwhile, was in another room, and once they had left him alone, the maquisards came to tell me that he was now ready to be 'interviewed'.

I had insisted that no one should be present when I confronted him, and that the kidnappers should remain within earshot in another room, should things go wrong and I need their help. Otherwise they were to wait until I told them to return Manfred to his car and his driver unharmed.

V

My heart was beating fast as I entered the room, locking the door behind me. They had placed Manfred on a wooden chair, his wrists secured behind his back. As I came in, he shifted his position, but made no attempt to turn round. The first thing to catch my eye was his right hand, which had been manacled so as to lie above his left. All that remained of it were the thumb and index finger, the top joints of the other three fingers having been shot away. My immediate reaction was one of impotent fury. I thought I would choke with anger. Manfred's were the most beautiful hands I had ever seen, and now they would never be able to play Bach or Mozart, Beethoven or Schubert. If some thug broke into Jovelles and slashed a painting or broke a vase, there would be a craftsman somewhere capable of repairing it so that people would hardly know it had ever been damaged. But no one could mend this infinitely more precious treasure, and restore the perfection of this man's damaged body. I could feel no anger for the Russian gunner who had fired the missile that had torn through his body, but only helpless rage at the obscenity of the act of war that had done this to him. I was utterly consumed by frustrated rage. My instinctive desire was to run and put my arms around him, to console him, to lavish upon him all the pent-up love I cherished for him; to curse and blaspheme at the fate that had so cruelly mutilated the most beautiful man I had ever known.

I almost felt pain in my own hand and leg, as if I, too, had been wounded; as if the one body and one soul we had felt ourselves to be that night on the mountain, had been ravaged. It was as if our single entity had been disfigured.

Now, in this French farmhouse, with the war dividing us, I dimly began to understand what he had meant when he asked me if I truly loved him. Nothing that had occurred in Austria or at Jeven had caused me to doubt my feelings for him, or to think we had done anything of which to be ashamed. The war and the consciousness of ever-present death made us wish to consummate our love regardless of what the world might have thought or the law condemn. Our new occupation, soldiering, the physical and emotional climate in which we found ourselves, our friendships, all had become of supreme importance because we felt they might not last: the past had vanished, the future was unceratin. As I stood there looking down at Manfred, blindfolded and manacled, his chin resting on his chest, I was utterly overcome by my love for him.

Stifling these emotions as best I could, I stood there watching him. How would he react when I disclosed myself to him? Would he regard me as his enemy? How could I be sure that the wounds to his hands had not been inflicted by one of the bombs I and my fellow maquisards had set? What, indeed, was the difference between the Russians inflicting wounds and us? Were we not all part of the same hostile machine? What were the psychological effects of his wounds? How could I ever make amends to him for the pain and suffering he must have endured, perhaps at my expense?

I lent towards him, and touched him lightly on the shoulder to give him an idea of where I was.

'Bin ich immer noch dein Freund bis in alle Ewigkeit, Manfred?' I asked softly.

He reacted as if my touch had been a strong electric shock. Instinctively, he tried to move his manacled wrists, and his head jerked sideways. After what seemed an age, he said in a low voice in English:

'Is that really you, Tony? Or am I dreaming?'

He paused an instant and then said: 'Ja, du bist immer mein

ganzes Herz.'

I quickly unlocked the handcuffs, whipped off the blindfold, and coming round to face him, we stood, arms outstretched in friendly greeting. He had aged a great deal. A scar marked his right cheek, and I noticed with what difficulty he had stood up after I had released him. But his eyes and his smile were as beautiful — even more beautiful — than I remembered. After the initial shock of seeing me, he opened his arms wide and we threw ourselves into a warm embrace, kissing and hugging each other passionately. This was much more than the avowal I had hoped for. Tears came to my eyes and I was grinning at the same time. I covered his wounded hand with my own, looking around the simple, dirty, ill-furnished room — anywhere but directly at him.

When the first tumult of our meeting was over we began to talk. I had not known what I would say to him, or if I should find him responsive to my questions. I was still very unsure how far I should go in explaining how and why I was here in France, and not driving an ambulance in Italy or Burma. But he seemed to have no wish for explanations. Of course, he guessed that I must have something to do with the Résistance. His conversations with Hélène and Mme de Lusignac had made it clear to him, even if he affected not to know, that as patriotic Frenchwomen they, too, must be sympathetic with the Résistance, to say the least. He, of course, was well aware of my connection with the Loreau family, so the mention of my name in conversation had in some measure brought me to the forefront of his consciousness.

I drew up a chair and sat down by him in front of the fire. I told him that we had as much time as we liked, but that he would be returned unharmed to his car and his chauffeur as soon as we had finished. I said he had made such a good impression on Hélène and Mme de Lusignac that I had felt justified in taking this risk of kidnapping him. He told me they had not even hinted that I was in France, even though they'd made it plain that they knew me well.

'We are going to lose the war,' he said at length. 'All that anyone like me can do is to behave in as civilised a manner as possible so that afterwards people will realise that not all Germans are monsters.'

I told him that I knew from Clara that he had been wounded. He told me he had taken part in the Polish, Norwegian and French campaigns in '39 and '40, and then been sent to a training regiment in eastern Germany where they had prepared for the invasion of

Russia.

'My car was hit, and I was lucky to escape alive,' he said. 'I was sent first to Warsaw and then to Germany to convalesce, but my wounds were too severe to allow me to go back to my old regiment, so I was posted to light duties guarding lines of communication. The duties I had there were not very different from those I have here. At first they sent me back to Russia, but when we began to retreat, I was stationed in eastern Poland.'

I enquired after his parents and sister. I said that Clara had told me they were well in '42, but I'd had no news from her since. He said he had heard that I was still in England at about the same time, so dear Clara had been faithful to us both. Hélène, when my name had cropped up in conversation, had pretended to know nothing of my whereabouts. He looked away, a pained expression clouding his face.

Embarrassed, we chatted at first about trivialities, as often happens when two people who have not seen each other for a long time. We had so much to say to each other we didn't know where to begin. I got a bottle of Scotch out of the briefcase I had brought with me and poured out two large tots. He sipped his pensively for a while, and then said: 'I used to look at things through emotional eyes; now I look at things with the eyes of reason, sometimes with other eyes, but I try to create a synthesis between the rational and emotional aspects of my life. It hasn't been easy.

'I felt that the first two years of the war were a kind of religious experience. Such uncertainties as I had had, uncertainties concerning my worth, my true nature, my sexual orientation, the rightness of the German cause, were swept away overnight. The enormous successes we had in Poland, and then in France and Russia, made me think that perhaps Hans had been right after all, and that I and my parents, and most of my army friends, had been wrong about Hitler. The demands of life had suddenly become clear and unequivocal — loyalty, courage and other military virtues became predominant. In 1940, at the height of the emotional upsurge that marked our enormous successes, I began to believe that perhaps, after all, we Germans were superior to all other races. I think we were all caught up in the elemental necessity of protecting the nation. It was a feeling I couldn't explain, but it was a time of overpowering certainty and joy.'

'In a perverse way,' I said, 'we felt like that after Dunkirk. We, too, were caught up in an elemental need to protect our country.

Irrational as it was, I don't think any of us for one moment thought that we could be defeated. It wasn't just Churchill's inspired speeches, it was a gut feeling, a gut reaction to the circumstances that was totally illogical and against all reason. That's what Hitler failed to understand — and many of the French, too, for that matter.'

'The French certainly didn't understand it,' he said. 'I was in Paris in June 1940, and most of the French people I met then were totally convinced that England would soon be defeated.' He paused and took a sip of whisky. 'But when things began to go wrong for us — after Stalingrad — I realised the implications of what Hitler had done; the irrationality of everything he stood for. I felt as if we were passengers on a train heading for a collision. But that wasn't the only reason I began to see the light. It was something far, far worse and much more personal. It concerned my parents and my sister, Helga. They've all been shot.'

I put my hand on his arm. He turned, and I saw the same bitter expression come into his eyes.

'Only tell me if you want to,' I said.

He shook my hand free. 'I've not had the chance to tell anyone the truth till now,' he said. 'It was all to do with Hans Streiter. He has been not only my evil genius but also my family's.'

He drained his glass. I took it and refilled it, and taking it from me, he stared into the fire and began in a toneless voice: 'Hans's mother and uncle were not well off, and to help them, Hans became a gym instructor for several months while attending his university course, where he met someone who recruited him into the Sicherheitsdienst. He was entrusted with the study of the French press, and in particular with articles published in France by German refugees.

'In June 1940, Hans was sent to France to investigate the activities of anti-Nazi Germans and Austrians, Jews, freemasons, communists, homosexuals and all enemies of Nazism. He didn't have to work through his nominal chief, though he usually did so. When he needed help from the army, he simply went to General von Stülpnagel and told him what he wanted. At one moment he would be laying down the law to an elderly general, the next supervising personally the round-up of unfortunate Jews and so-called undesirables. On one occasion he was responsible for herding several thousand Jewish children and their parents into a sports stadium while they awaited shipment to the east for what, in Germany, we call "resettlement". They stayed there several days without food and with only one water hydrant between them and not more than five latrines. They stayed there while Hans discussed in a leisurely manner with the Vichy authorities what was to be done with the children. After they'd been there six days, the mothers were taken away, leaving them behind, to start the journey to Poland. The Vichy authorities held that the children should be spared and sent to French orphanages, but Hans took his duties more seriously. The children must be exterminated. There was a snag, however. There was no transport for them. They were useless because they couldn't work for the Reich like their parents. He soon solved this little problem, and they were shipped off, a couple of hundred at a time, in cattle trucks on a journey which took three days, without food or water.

'Oh, Hans enjoyed his work, make no mistake,' said Manfred bitterly. 'When he was stationed at Kiel the summer before the war, when you met him at Jeven, he made a lot of acquaintances who were useful to him later. I have to admit that he is hard-working, capable — too capable, in fact — and well-disciplined, but though I had strong suspicions while we were at Haase, I didn't quite realise till too late that besides being a sadist, he is a sex maniac. At Kiel, it was rumoured he had started a chain of brothels to augment his income, and it has been heard he has done the same in France. Here they are ostensibly for the benefit of sex-starved soldiers, but you can bet he has more devious reasons for doing this than military welfare.

'He was supposed to be engaged to my sister, Helga. She, poor girl, was nothing but a silly, romantic child. She was never a philosophical Nazi like Hans was. She adored him because he seemed to her to be so simple and honest and brave. He seemed to see everything in black and white, and he was deaf to any question that did not admit to a clear-cut solution. He was handsome, she admired him and his certainties. He appeared to be such a man of the world. He is an excellent horseman, a first-class fencer — one of the best in Germany — he also has a distinguished appreciation of art, and, as you know yourself, he is a talented musician as well.

'At first he gave my parents the impression of being a man of discretion and integrity, but he was perpetually chasing women. One night in Kiel he got drunk and raped a girl. To keep her quiet he threatened to denounce her as an enemy of the state. He spent a lot of time in night clubs, going the rounds with a few friends to orgies that lasted all night. The brutality he had shown at school became worse as he grew older, but this was a quality that served him well in the Party. He was fairly skilful at hiding it when it suited him, appearing disciplined and respectable, but the strain of concealing his sexual exploits from his superiors manifested itself in ferocious outbursts of temper.

'D'you remember my telling you an incident when we were at the Gymnasium together about a boy who was caught stealing money?' he asked.

'Yes. I even remember the boy's name — it was Felix, wasn't it?'

'That's right. You remember that the affair ended in the expulsion not only of Felix, but also of Hans and Kurt von Bahlenburg? Well, they threatened then to get their own back on me for reporting it, and, by God, they have. Hans began his revenge by attacking me through Helga and my parents. He knew that my father and mother greatly admired England and all things English, and that they had sent me to an English school. Hans put it about in Party circles that they were spies. He saw how friendly you and I were, and by dropping a hint here and a hint there, in 1942, he manoeuvred things to the point where father and mother were arrested and sent to a concentration camp. He couldn't harm me directly because I was safely in the army, but he did the next best thing by attacking me through my family.'

'Did he marry Helga? What had she to say to all this?'

'That was the worst of all. You could see how infatuated she was with him when you stayed with us in '39, couldn't you? Well, as far as Hans was concerned, she meant nothing to him. Nothing whatever. All he wanted of her was a tool to attack me with. Not long after war broke out, while I was in Poland, Hans came to Jeven, ostensibly to make arrangements for the wedding. One night he went into Hamburg with Helga to a restaurant where they were to meet Kurt, who was to be Hans's best man, and another SS bastard. After a lavish dinner, no expense spared, the three of them took Helga back to Kurt's digs where they gang-raped her. When they'd finished, they phoned SS headquarters and told them to come and take her away, as they had "evidence" she was a British spy. These thugs duly arrived, took her out and shot her.'

Once again I put my hand on his shoulder to comfort him. 'That's not the end of it,' he said softly. 'You can't begin to understand the depths to which the SS has sunk.'

Manfred reminded me that under the terms of the armistice signed with France in June 1940, the Germans had the right to exercise the functions of an occupying power. The French government agreed to facilitate the regulations relative to the exercise of these rights, and to conform to those issued by the German military authorities. In all the administrative measures it was called upon to take, the military administrators would, as a matter of principle, use the channels of the French authorities. This explains why the German authorities gave such a warm welcome to Frenchmen who agreed to collaborate with them.

'When the SS and Gestapo interfere, this risks ruining everything,' Manfred went on. 'Hans was the chief SS officer of the anti-Jewish section in Bordeaux. He is a fanatical Jew-hater. He practically goes into a trance every time the word "Jew" is mentioned,' he added with a wry smile. 'When the antisemitic measures were brought in in France, he watched the trials of the victims with the utmost relish, and gave vent to vehement protests whenever anyone tried to show the least compassion.

'Hans installed himself in a large house in Bordeaux with an entourage of thugs. He has helped French antisemites with advice and money to set up an institute to "study the Jewish question". In this way, having become tools of the Gestapo, these Frenchmen became the most active suppliers of forced labour.

'Vichy promulgated a "Statut des Juifs" which defined anyone with at least one Jewish grandparent as Jewish. Hans asked for a number of inspectors to be transferred from the Prefecture of Police, thus conforming with the wishes of the military authorities that the French should, themselves, carry out orders required by us.

'Throughout 1940 and 1941,' Manfred continued, 'the Gestapo remained in the background, working in the shadows. But in the course of '41, the standard of military surveillance slackened, and the Gestapo began to carry out house to house searches and arrests. In effect, they became responsible for the security of the rear areas. Last summer, Kurt von Bahlenburg was sent to Limoges with full police powers, and made responsible for seeing that the French chiefs of police act in accord with the local military commander. In Périgord and Limousin, this means with my colonel. The French police, of course, were placed under the "tutelage" of the German police and SS in the occupied zone, after the whole country was occupied, everywhere in France.'

'So Kurt joined the SS as well, did he?' I remarked.

'Oh yes. He and Hans are birds of a feather. After Kurt was expelled from the Haase Gymnasium, he gravitated to Hamburg, where he studied engineering. He was short of cash, but once he'd joined the Sicherheitsdienst in 1935 his financial worries came to an end. He was posted to Heydrich's staff, and became one of his most devoted collaborators. I ran into him when he was chief of police and SS in a town in southern Poland. It was after I'd been wounded and had been posted to communications guard duties. Kurt and I left Poland at about the same time, and we were both sent to France. I seem to be haunted by him and Hans,' he sighed. 'Kurt was promoted to the rank of Standartenführer, that's colonel, when he came to France. Not bad for a twenty-seven-year-old. He has the reputation of being a patient, kindly sort of fellow, quite good to his subordinates and all that. I suppose by the standard of those wild beasts he is. His duties here are to organise the "emigration" of Jews and other undesirables. I'm sure he does his duty with the utmost relish and efficiency.'

Manfred fell silent, lost in thought. I didn't wish to break in on his reveries, for I felt certain that he was glad to have someone he could trust, to whom he could talk freely.

After a long silence, he began again: 'Tony, I don't quite know how to tell you what happened next. I saw something in Poland, which has haunted me ever since, and which will continue to haunt me for as long as I live. It was something so horrible that I still can't believe that Germans, people like myself, could do such things. But I desperately want to tell you, so that you may understand how I now feel about my country, about the war, and about the future of Europe.'

He sighed deeply, lent forward and stirred the logs on the fire with his good foot.

'One day, when I was in Poland,' he began again, 'I was ordered to take a detachment of men to a railway siding in a forest, where I was told we were to meet a train. I was to post my men on the perimeter of the goods yard to make sure that no one without authority came near. I imagined that we were to guard the arrival of an ammunition train or some new, secret weapon, so I thought little about it. It was all in the day's work, dull but necessary.

'The train duly arrived. It was long past midnight. I can't remember how many wagons it consisted of — perhaps twenty or thirty, it was a very long train. As it drew into the goods yard, SS men and militia squads, about four to six men in each squad, opened the sliding doors of the first half-dozen wagons. Each of them was filled to the point of suffocation with men, women and children destined for the nearby camp, which we had been told was a munitions dump. As the poor wretches spilled out of the wagons on to the ground, the SS men prodded them with bayonets to herd them into some kind of order.'

Breaking down, Manfred began to cry, hard choking sobs. I put my arm round him and stroked his head, trying to comfort him. After a moment, he pulled himself together, and continued in a flat, toneless voice:

'An old woman with snow-white hair was standing not far from me, holding a tiny baby in her arms,' he went on at last. 'She was singing a soft lullaby to it and tickling it under the chin. The child was cooing with delight. The parents were looking on with tears in their eyes. The father was holding the hand of a boy not more than eight or nine years old, and speaking to him softly; the boy was fighting back tears. To distract him, the father pointed up to the full moon above the line of pine trees that divided the railway yard from the camp, stroked his son's head, and seemed to be explaining something to him. Perhaps he was telling the child that the craters were not really the man in the moon.

'Just at that moment Kurt von Bahlenburg appeared, and came up to me. He told me that my men could be stood down, but he wanted me to come with him, as he had something he wanted to show me. I handed the detachment over to my sergeant and followed Kurt. He led me through the gate and into the camp. It was the first time I'd been inside, so I had no idea what to expect. We walked down a long tree-lined drive between rows of huts till we came to an open space. There I saw an enormous mound of earth some forty metres long and more than two metres high. Standing near it was a group of prisoners from the train. They were by no means all Jews. I could tell because some of the men were blond and wearing pink triangles on their sleeves instead of the yellow star of David. Kurt pointed these men out to me saying: "Those are the worst of the lot. Filthy perverts. Germany can do without scum like that." There were also people with gross deformities — hunchbacks, twisted limbs, club feet — and others who were quite clearly mental cases. These were the most pitiable of all, for they looked blankly through glazed eyes with vacant expressions on their faces, uncomprehending.'

Manfred stopped and shifted in his chair, hanging his head trying to stifle his sobs. 'Kurt went up to one of the SS men standing by the mound and gave him an order,' he went on in the same toneless voice. 'This man shouted to a comrade, who counted off about twenty people from the group of prisoners, and told them to go behind the mound of earth. Kurt and I followed them at a short distance. The earth had been dug from a long pit, and he led me to a point where we could see the whole length of it. The family I had seen getting off the train was among the group that had been selected, together with two young men wearing pink triangles. The mother was holding the hand of a little girl. She was about eleven, dressed in a frilly white frock, white socks and black sandals. As they shuffled past us towards the pit, the child stumbled and cut her knee on a sharp stone. One of the pink triangle men bent down and picked her up, kissed her and, taking a handkerchief out of his pocket, tied it round the wound, then handed the child back to her mother. The mother smiled her thanks: they had no common language.

'People were wedged together in the pit, lying on top of each other so that their heads were visible in the bright light of the floodlamps. Nearly all had blood running over their shoulders and heads, which showed that they were still alive. The pit was already two-thirds full. I guess it held at least a thousand people. I looked for the men who did the shooting. There were three of them, and they were sitting on the edge of the pit, their feet dangling into it, smoking cigarettes, tommy-guns on their knees. They might have been a gang of workmen on a building site taking a break between shifts.'

Manfred stopped again, seemingly lost in thought. The strain of telling this ghastly story contorted his face with pain. I took his glass, filled it up again with whisky, and handed it back to him. He took it without looking up.

'The prisoners went down some steps cut into the wall of the pit and clambered over the heads of those who were lying there to the place to which the SS guards directed them,' he continued. 'They lay down in front of the dead and dying. The old lady went on stroking and tickling her grandchild, and the father spoke to his son in a low voice, while the two pink triangle men tried to comfort the little girl and her mother. Then I heard a series of shots, and saw the bodies twitching, blood running from their necks. The little baby began to cry, and one of the SS men took his rifle by the barrel, went down into the pit and beat its brains out with the butt.

'The next batch of victims was already approaching. They, too, went down into the pit, lined themselves against the previous lot and were shot. They included an old, terribly thin woman who seemed to be paralysed, for she had to be carried by two men, both wearing pink triangles, one of whom was almost as old and thin as she was.

'Kurt forced me to watch this for three hours. It was his way of getting his own back for my having had him expelled from school.'

The silence in the room was broken only by the ticking of a large grandfather clock, and the crackling of the logs on the fire. Manfred sat with his head sunk on his chest, his whole frame shaken convulsively by agonising, tearless sobs. I took his mutilated right hand in mine and brought it to my lips, and with my other hand I kept stroking his head, murmuring to him as one would to a child distraught by pain. Without looking up he said in a barely audible whisper: 'I feel so utterly, utterly ashamed and humiliated for Germany's sake.'

I squeezed his hand, and went on stroking him gently. I was too moved to say anything. He just sat there, sobbing, while I supported him in my arms, comforting him as best I could. Gradually his sobbing ceased, and he pulled himself together. Lifting his head, he turned towards me, his lips trembling, trying to speak.

'No more, Manfred,' I whispered, 'No more. I understand. I'm most desperately sorry. I still love you, and I always will. Du bist immer mein ganzes Herz. I shall love you to my dying day.' I kneeled down beside his chair, took his head in my hands and kissed him fiercely on the lips.

I don't know how long we stayed like that, hugging each other, afraid to let go, both of us drained of all ability to speak, holding each other like two frightened children hiding from a storm. By and by I drew myself away, and went to pour him another Scotch. I handed him the glass which he took and drained in one gulp. He gave the glass back to me, and tried to smile.

'You were right, Tony, to abandon your pacifism in order to fight us,' he said softly. 'But we are not all monsters, though far too many of us have supped for too long with the devil.'

VI

When he was calmer, he went on to say that it was patently clear to him and to those who thought like him, that Germany had lost the war, and that Hitler must be removed if peace was to be made with the Allies. This had to be done by the army, for it was the only active force in Germany not actually created by the Nazis, or fully infiltrated by them.

He said he could count on the understanding, support and sympathy of none but those who he was certain shared his views. He mentioned his cousins, Berthold and Peter, and above all, his former commanding officer, Claus von Stauffenberg.

'Hitler is not only the arch-enemy of Germany,' he said, 'he is the arch-enemy of mankind. Whatever sins I may have committed in this life, I believe that God will forgive me for everything I have done in the fight against Hitler. God promised Abraham that he would spare Sodom if ten just men could be found there; I hope he will spare and not destroy Germany because of what we have done. None of us in the resistance can complain of our lot. All of us who joined it, as I did, knew what we were doing. The moral worth of a man is certain only if he is prepared to sacrifice his life for his convictions, and we are utterly convinced that Hitler and the Party are wicked.

'There's a world of difference between what we have to do and what the French Résistance fighters are doing,' he added. 'They are patriots, who are fighting to rid their country of an invader. They've the support not only of the local population but of the Allies. We are traitors. The Allies don't trust us, because they're afraid that a Germany rescued from the Nazis by the army will eventually arise and start another war.'

He took a log from the basket and threw it on the fire.

'Their call for unconditional surrender has played into the hands of Goebbels and stiffened the resolve of ordinary people. The Allies have offered us no hope. Why can't your people grasp the fact that the Nazis, and all they stand for, are as much our enemies as yours?'

'Not all of us think like that,' I replied. 'I think the Allied leaders are waiting to see signs that the masses have lost faith in Hitler before taking action to support you.'

'But don't they realise that the mass bombing of German cities has only strengthened the will of the masses to stick it out. It was the same with you in England in 1940. We have been offered no hope. The only hope the masses have is still in Hitler. What other hope do they have?'

'But do the masses really still believe in him?' I asked. 'The last time the German nation had the chance to express any opinion on the matter was ten years ago, and even then Hitler got less than half the votes.'

'Oh come, Tony! You know as well as I do that no British government this century has been elected by more than half the popular vote. Ever since the Anschluss, Hitler has been regarded in Germany as a saviour endowed with God's grace and the kind of luck that sticks. Since then, those of us who have dared to oppose him have been forced to keep our views entirely to ourselves, or to express them in whispers.'

'But isn't there anyone you can trust?'

'Yes; I can trust men like General Beck, for example, and Field Marshal von Witzleben. They would go to almost any lengths to get rid of this monster and his vile gang.'

'But to succeed, they've got to stage a coup d'état. How else can they get rid of them?'

'That's true, but I don't think, Tony, that you quite realise the impossible position Hitler has put us in. On the day he made himself head of state, every man in uniform, from field marshal to private soldier, was required to swear an oath to render unconditional obedience to him personally, and that he would be prepared, as a brave soldier, to stake his life at any time to his oath. You don't appreciate what this means to those of us who have been brought up to hold Christian values. Both as officers and Christians our oath is inviolate.'

'But in *Mein Kampf*, Hitler himself said that if a government uses the instruments of power in its hands to lead the people to ruin, then rebellion is not only right, but the duty of every individual citizen.'

Manfred looked away and shrugged his shoulders: 'I know, but that doesn't make any difference.'

He went on to tell me that Claus von Stauffenberg had made up his mind to kill Hitler. But he made it clear that the very nobility of spirit in most, if not all, of these highly placed officers and civilians, their idealism and their Christian background, lessened their effectiveness as conspirators. They approached their dreadful task as idealists seeking to restore the lost honour of their country, not as realists seeking the most practical way of overthrowing a tyrant. The older among them, he told me, had been staunchly against assassinating Hitler. The younger ones, like himself, realised from the start that Hitler had to be killed. But their influence in resistance circles was not very great. Hitler, in any case, was not very easy to kill. He was becoming less and less accessible to either bullet, bomb or poison.

'There are signs, however, that the older generation are coming round to the view that the only way to dispose of Hitler is to kill him,' he concluded.

I sympathised strongly with Manfred's dilemma. I could see he was suffering the same crisis of conscience that I had suffered before I finally decided to join up.

'I think we've got to look at it this way.' I said. 'After this war is over, the nations of Europe must come to their senses, and cease their ancient civil war. The greatest thinkers, the greatest scientists, the greatest painters and, above all, the greatest musicians have all been Europeans. The leaders of the new Europe will be men and women of our generation — survivors of this beastly carnage. It is our generation that will have to see that a third war doesn't break out. Our loyalty — yours *and* mine — is now the same; it is to Europe rather than to Britain or Germany. In twenty or thirty years' time it will be as anachronistic to be a German or British chauvinist as it is absurd today to be a Schleswig or Yorkshire chauvinist. Of course we love our country and its customs, but our allegiance must be to something larger than the narrow piece of land from which we have sprung. We are all Europeans, and it is to Europe that we should devote our lives, but so long as Hitler, Mussolini, Stalin, Churchill and Roosevelt live, I'm afraid this will be difficult to achieve.'

Manfred thought for a moment, and then said; 'What you've just said eases my conscience. People like Mme Loreau and Mme de Lusignac and the French resistance fighters are not morally and physically inhibited like we are. In their situation the immediate appeal for action is self-evident; we, on the other hand, have had to search our consciences before deciding whether we were right to take action against the acknowledged leader of our country.

'I can say to you, Tony,' he continued, 'what I could never say to most of my friends at home, even to those I know share my feelings about the way in which things are going. Hitler is not only leading our country to destruction — that would be a matter of politics or military strategy — but he is a kind of devil, an anti-Christ, and the only way to get rid of him is to kill him. I don't know how this can be done, but if anyone can make the attempt it will be someone like Claus.'

'But even if someone does succeed in killing him,' I said, 'what about the others — Goering, Goebbels, Himmler and the rest? How will you get rid of them? Will there be enough of you to form an alternative government the people would accept? It was different in Italy. Most Italians were against the war from the start, and a lot were openly hostile to the regime.'

'I know. And their army didn't have to swear an oath of loyalty to Mussolini; their loyalty was to the king. We have no one — no one but that fiendish psychopath. The worst thing about Nazism is that it requires us to use Nazi methods to destroy it. Claus realises that Hitler must be assassinated, but our older friends simply cannot bring themselves even to think of such a thing. For them, Hitler has to be arrested and brought to trial. For them, it's a matter of honour and their oath.'

'We, too, have had to swear an oath to the king and his lawful successors. It is unlikely, but not inconceivable, that in the aftermath of this war Britain might have a communist government headed by some demagogue. He would be the king's lawful successor. We're all in the same boat so long as loyalty to the nation state is demanded of us. Your friends would be doing a service not just to Germany and Europe, but to mankind as a whole in ridding the world of Hitler. That's easy for me to say as an Englishman, but your consciences can be clear if you think in European terms. The last war was supposed to end all war. It didn't for a host of reasons, but mainly because the majority of our parents' generation couldn't think as Europeans, least of all us British. Men and women like us belong to the one class of society where nationality has to a large extent become irrelevant. We belong to a European aristocracy, but we are only a tiny minority, for the whole trend of politics this century has been against us. And d'you know why? Not because we oppressed the proletariat, but because we allowed our feelings of national patriotism to come before our European patriotism. As a class, we deserved to lose our power. It is now up to us, not as aristocrats, but as members of our generation, to see that we don't make the same mistakes again.'

Manfred told me of the many setbacks the German resistance had suffered. Hitler was always shuffling his generals and other important officers. There was a grave difficulty finding anyone brave enough to undertake what amounted to a suicide, or near-suicide mission, who, at the same time, had access to Hitler's person. Then there was the lack of any kind of support or encouragement from the Allies, which might help to maintain morale, and convince the doubters that the removal of Hitler would lead to a more favourable peace than could be expected while he remained in power.

Manfred said that Hitler was terrified of assassination. This was why he seldom moved by a set route or a set time. For long periods he lived almost inaccessibly in the Chancellery or at Berchtesgaden, or in his closely guarded headquarters — the Wolfschanze — behind the eastern front. None of the key resistance people had regular, direct access to Hitler, so they were reduced to trying to find chinks in his security measures, and inserting a would-be assassin into one or other of them. It seemed a hopeless task.

'Apart from all this,' Manfred said with a sigh, 'we have not been able to find a reliable time fuse for a bomb that doesn't make a sound. You can't leave an alarm-clock ticking away under a table, and expect no one to notice it.'

He got up and limped painfully back and forth across the room, his face drawn, his expression one of hopeless resignation. I felt deeply sorry for him, and watched him silently for a few moments before I spoke again.

'Manfred, what would you say if I were able to supply you with a completely silent time fuse? Could you get it to someone who could use it effectively?'

He stopped in his tracks and turned towards me. 'Does such a fuse exist, then?'

'Yes it does. And what's more, I know how I can get hold of one.'

His face lit up with excitement. 'I'm certain I can find someone who would be prepared to try and use it.'

'I need only get you one fuse. Your people won't have any difficulty copying it. The trouble is, how do I get it to you? I would have to give my bosses in England a good reason why I needed more than I've got already. I could, I suppose, arrange for your people to capture one, but what guarantee would we have that it came to you?'

'None.'

'I'm prepared to try, but could you give me an undertaking that the aircraft bringing it was not attacked? I would have to make out a good case to my superiors for asking for some to be sent, and I'm by no means sure they would take my unsupported word that they were intended for bombs to blow up Hitler.'

He laughed. 'Of course not.'

'Let me think about it. I'll let you know what I come up with as soon as I can. Either I've got to convince them at home to let me have one of the fuses we have here already, or it's got to be done in a round-about way through Sweden or Switzerland.'

'I know. I'll think about it too and give you all the help I can. It won't be easy. The SS and Gestapo already suspect me of being too friendly with the French. I'm high on their list of suspects; they're just waiting for me to put a foot wrong, and I'll be posted elsewhere. I'm going to have the devil of a job explaining away this afternoon's little escapade, believe me!'

'I'm afraid that's up to you. I don't suppose your driver is too keen to have his affair with this girl exposed, so if I take you back at once to your car, maybe you can bluff your way out of any difficult questions that may be asked.'

We had been together much longer than I had expected, but Manfred would be able to explain it away as being due to the obstructive French *garagiste*'s failure to find tyres of the right size to replace the ones that had been damaged. Charney, when it appeared that my meeting with Manfred would exceed the time we had planned for it, had taken the opportunity to slash the three good tyres while the original puncture was being mended.

The safe house was close to the garage where the staff car was being repaired, and to avoid any suspicion on the part of the driver, and of any maquisards who might be watching, I told Manfred to leave the house as if nothing had happened, return to his car, and hope that it was ready. After that, it was entirely up to him. I said that I would communicate with him through Hélène, and would contact my people in London as soon as I could.

VII

Before I could take any further action, I had to consult my superiors both in France and in England. I thought that what Manfred had told me was of such importance that I could not trust reporting it by our usual method of communication. Although I could trust Manfred implicitly, I knew that many, if not all our messages were being intercepted by the Germans, and I did not know how successful they might have been in breaking our codes. I knew that Manfred was in the confidence of Claus von Stauffenberg, who, he had told me, was then stationed in Paris on General Stülpnagel's staff. I considered the existence of a plot to assassinate Hitler to be a matter of such enormous interest that it was my duty to confide at once in Charney, and together we would have to decide what best to do. If we could convince the Outfit to let us have some silent time fuses, I was prepared to guarantee that Manfred would do his best to see they reached those members of the German resistance best able to make use of them. I could not guarantee that Manfred could hand them personally to Stauffenberg or Stülpnagel, but I was sure he would do all he could. The risk, in other words, of trusting him, seemed to us to be one worth taking.

In view of the highly dangerous position into which we were plunging Manfred, Charney sent a brief message to London asking that I be flown back to report a matter of extreme urgency. It was all the more urgent because Hélène told me that Manfred had just told her he had heard that Stauffenberg was likely to be posted to Berlin quite soon. Although Hélène did not know the significance of this message, she dutifully passed it on to me the same day.

Manfred had told me he would be prepared to shut his eyes and look the other way if a plane was sent to take one of us back to London, provided we let him know when it might arrive so that he could order his men to be in another part of the district. This information was passed on to London, but I had not seen fit to tell Manfred that we had a comparatively safe landing strip at Epéluche, which we had used on several occasions already because it was so far from that part of the *département* in which his men were stationed. I had thanked him, and told him I hoped to procure some more fuses within three weeks of our meeting, knowing that another supply was due in any case with the next parachutage during the full moon period.

Charney's message had been couched in such terms as to rouse the curiosity of our bosses in London, and they agreed at once to recall me for a consultation. The message was longer than we would have liked, but it was written in such a way that we believed the German interceptors, assuming they were reading our ciphers, would not understand the reason for my recall. Three days later we got an order summoning me back to London, and warning us to prepare the Epéluche landing strip for the arrival of a Lysander in two days' time if the weather permitted.

The night of my departure was overcast but dry. We assembled at the safe house at St Paul-Lizonne about ten o'clock, and at about one, I went down with Charney to the landing strip. We heard the plane circling to the south and west of us ready to make an approach from the direction of Aubeterre. Everyone stood his ground, and he landed safely and came to rest opposite Charney. I hurried forwards towards the plane.

'Safe journey, David,' Charney shouted.

'I'll be back as soon as possible,' I shouted back. 'Probably next week.'

The pilot had opened the door of the plane and I clambered in. He revved up his engine and we took off again at once. This time, the flight was uneventful and we landed six hours later among the green fields of Sussex.

Once again Jack Cuttlance had come to meet me. He and Sam Barker greeted me warmly and whisked me off to Jack's house in St John's Wood. On the drive to town, Jack told me that my message had been received with a degree of suspicion by our boss, and it had taken some persuading to convince him it was worthwhile to recall me. For my part, I'd had doubts about the amount of faith I could repose in Manfred's ability to get the silent fuses into the hands of those who might be able to use them effectively. With Hans and Kurt breathing down his neck, I didn't imagine it would be easy for him to hide his friendship with Stauffenberg from the Gestapo, and I could only hope he could find a good excuse for a meeting with him in Paris, On the other hand, Manfred's account of the terrible things he had seen in Poland totally convinced me of his determination to do all in his power to rid Germany of Hitler.

Although I was now ready to tell Jack rather more about the nature of my feelings for Manfred than I had done on my last trip to England, I did not think, at this stage, that I should say any more than I had then. That, I reckoned, was enough to persuade my lords and masters that I could trust him, and that I had been dealing with a man I knew very well. But if that were not enough, there was something else I could tell them, which would, I hope, put their doubts to rest. Manfred had told me that another distant relative of his, Fabian von Schlabrendorff, had come to England in '38 to do some research for a biography of his great-grandfather, Baron Stockmar, the friend of Queen Victoria and Prince Albert. He had wished to examine the royal archives at Windsor, and had asked Winston Churchill, to whom he had been given an introduction, to get permission for him to do so. During this visit, he had told Churchill that he and his friends were waiting for an opportunity to stage a coup against Hitler, to arrest him and to have him declared insane.

Fabian's had been a private visit, and had not been noticed by the press, so it was known only to very few people indeed. If my bosses still had doubts about Manfred's bona fides, this conversation, which was known only to Fabian and the Prime Minister, could be confirmed by Churchill himself.

Although I was not sanguine enough to believe that anything I might say about my conversation with Manfred would have the slightest effect on the Allied demand for unconditional surrender, I was firmly of the opinion that it was my duty to report what Manfred had said on the subject. The decision whether or not to provide the fuses to be used in an attempt on the life of Hitler was something that Jack and I both believed would appeal to our bosses' and the Prime Minister's maverick sense.

To my surprise and gratification, the account of my conversation with Manfred was well received, for I was quite prepared to be hauled over the coals for such an unconventional operation, which risked not only my own cover, but that of my colleagues as well.

I reported that the German army and its officer corps were largely free from Gestapo surveillance and penetration, and that the elimination of Hitler by a systematic and coordinated method could be accomplished only by members of the armed forces, and in particular of the Wehrmacht. Besides Hitler's most loyal henchmen, a few senior army officers were almost the only others with access to his person. Among the latter only a handful were willing to make an assassination attempt provided a suitable opportunity could be arranged.

I went on to point out that an army officer's decision to break his oath, and to act against Hitler, the supreme commander, would totally isolate him from his comrades and his class. Such a decision could not be expected of many, but I was convinced that Manfred von Schrade would be among them. Manfred had told me that he considered his oath invalid since the man to whom it had been sworn had broken his oath of office time and time again.

My debriefing lasted nearly all day, but at the end of it, I was assured that I had done right to come back to report in detail what I had learned, and my boss did not hesitate to authorise me to return with five silent fuses for Manfred's use.

'We will get them to you, together with a supply of plastic explosive, by the day after tomorrow,' the colonel said, 'and Major Cuttlance will make arrangements for you to return to France at the earliest opportunity thereafter. From what you have told us, Major von Schrade may be posted away at any moment, so it is essential that the stuff reaches him as soon as possible. Good luck.'

* * *

I had not told either of my parents I was back in England, and when Jack invited me to stay at his cottage for the few days before my return to France, I accepted at once. On the drive out of London, I took the first opportunity I had had since my arrival to enquire after Stanley.

'No better, I'm afraid,' he sighed. 'The doctor told me they don't expect him to last much longer — a matter of weeks rather than months.' I expressed my sympathy, and we went on to talk of other things, as he seemed reluctant to say more in front of Sam Barker.

That night I walked in the garden with Jack. We talked shop. He argued that practically all the men in the Outfit, despite their superficial cynicism, had high ideals. There was no other motive, he asserted, to warrant the running of such risks as all of us, in our different ways, were prepared to do. There would certainly be no fame, or reward, or money to be gained.

I agreed, but added that I thought Manfred and Michel, Hélène and Mme de Lusignac, in their different ways were likewise motivated by high ideals. I agreed that to defy torture one needed such ideals, and only with their help would it be possible to do so. These alone would give one enough strength of mind and purpose to resist the pain as martyrs, throughout the ages, have defied the rack and the thumbscrew. Manfred had said that somehow Germany's good name had to be won back cost what it might. And when I had asked him what the chances of overthrowing Hitler might be, he had said that he didn't know, and that it didn't make any difference. 'I've only got one head to lose,' he'd said. 'I know of no better cause than this for which to risk it.'

'I agree,' Jack said, 'because then you would have really known yourself though it cost you your life to do so. I think it was de Musset who says somewhere that the man who has never suffered cannot truly know himself.'

I thought to myself that we poor ignorant mortals are always consumed by that Greek curiosity to know ourselves, and we depend entirely on the estimation of our friends to hold that only mirror in front of our eyes.

Two days later, after an early and rather silent dinner, Sam Barker reported with the staff-car to take Jack and me to the airfield. We didn't talk much on the way; perhaps we both had presentiments of the future; perhaps he was thinking about Stanley as I was thinking about Manfred; or perhaps it was just the normal burden of anticipation, and the screwing up of one's nerves to face the coming unknown.

We arrived at the field, and Sam jumped out of the car to open the door for us to get out. He came smartly to attention and saluted me, even though I was dressed in my French civilian clothes.

'Good luck, sir,' he said, his faced wreathed in a broad smile. 'We'll look forward to seeing you again soon, won't we sir?' turning to Jack.

'We certainly will, corporal,' he said, and turning to me patted me affectionately on the shoulder. 'Tell them to let me know when you arrive. Good luck and bon voyage.'

'Remember me to Stanley,' I said. 'I hope things turn out better than you fear. And thanks for putting me up, it was a great break.'

I turned and went straight to the dressing shed, where I was helped into all the cumbersome flying kit and parachute harness. The RAF crew of the Halifax clustered round, joking and talking flippancies to keep my spirits up. The navigator whispered in my ear: 'Poor sod, I pity you having to sit with all that stuff on for five hours.' A last look at maps and the final words of encouragement and advice from Jack, and we went outside to the plane.

The four engines of the machine were roaring in the slipstream. I was to be the only passenger in the plane that night, and indeed the only human cargo in all these other Halifaxes leaving with us. I must have looked as lonely as I felt, knowing that when I jumped out into the moonlight over France, I would be going back through the gates of a prison. The aircrew would be eating their breakfast back in the safety of England by dawn, while for me the future stretched away uncertainly with all its dangers and surprises.

I gave a last handshake to Jack and to Sam Barker, and clambered up into the fuselage of the plane. The door clanged behind me with an air of finality. It was as if I had died to the familiar world of England, but I was eager for the new adventure that lay ahead. I made myself as comfortable as I could in all my kit, and stretched myself out in the dark interior of the bomber. Jack had seemed upset to witness my departure, I thought, and I could not have stood the strain myself much longer. I imagined him now driving back to London in silence, wondering whether we would ever meet again.

The door leading into the pilot's cabin was open, and as we flew deeper over enemy territory the moon stared in through the windows of the cockpit, illuminating everything like daylight. From time to time the pilot would climb and then dive down steeply to confuse the flak. It was too noisy to talk, and I found the journey much more unnerving than last time. I think I had lost what little courage I possessed, which on that occasion had come from ignorance of what was in store for me. I began to reflect on the work I was doing, and on the people I was doing it with. The colonel, at my debriefing, had hinted that he thought my trust in Manfred was probably misplaced, and that the chances of any attempt on Hitler's life being successful were exceedingly slight. If my mission failed, everyone would say 'I told you so.'

But my mission was not just to take some fuses to Manfred. I had received orders to take back to Charney and our *réseau* for action in support of the coming invasion. Though my French was good, I didn't look like a Frenchman, and Jack, I knew, thought I was foolhardy to have volunteered to go back, although he had never done or said anything to discourage me. Had he, I wondered, guessed the nature and depth of my love for Manfred? With hindsight, I'm sure he had, for I am now aware that he knew me better than I knew myself.

But there was another reason, which drove me on. At the outset of the war my pacifism had been sincere, but what influenced my present thinking almost more than anything else was the knowledge that I had been born and bred in a country that had offered me the right to obey my conscience at a time of great national danger, when the help of every able-bodied man and woman was desperately needed for the defence of the country. Such a society just had to be defended and preserved, cost what it might. I compared my dilemma with Manfred's. Both of us had been nurtured in a tradition where murder and the betrayal of one's solemnly given word were condemned; but he was prepared to betray his oath and kill to rid his country and the world of a devil. This was an infinitely more serious decision than the one I'd to take when I joined the army.

There was another aspect to it too: I felt it was important to show that privileged people from the class of society to which Manfred and I belonged did not lack the necessary courage and endurance. But I was certain that real courage had little to do with nationality, class and politics. Just as in France, Jews and communists, priests and aristocrats were all fighting together in the underground war, so in Germany I now knew there were people from all classes, and priests from all faiths, who were struggling to find ways of overthrowing Hitler. But above all, I felt that more than ever before it was our privileged class that was on trial before mankind, for it was men of our class who had led Europe into the last war, and who had failed to prevent the present one.

If Manfred and I were to die, we would die as volunteers for the cause in which we both believed with ever-increasing conviction, for the ideas of Nazi philosophy were more diabolic than anything yet known in European history. The Nazis were not just the enemies of my country as the French had been at Waterloo, they were the destroyers of everything European and Christian, and the embodiment of the very forces of evil. God knows, Britain and British society was not perfect, but I now regarded the war as more of a crusade than the Crusades themselves ever were. Manfred and Michel and I were fighting not against ignorant vandals, who knew not the value of what they destroyed, but against conscious, calculating nihilists, who struck at all culture and religion, precisely because they knew that cathedrals and schools are the nerve centres of that great spirit which they were aiming completely and for ever to destroy. Men and women who were now resisting this evil in Europe with their lives would be martyrs in every sense of that word. But very few at home, least of all the politicians, seemed to understand this.

But what if I survived? I was not one of those who believed that if I got through the war it was God's intention to spare me for some special purpose. If I survived it would be a matter of sheer luck, and if Manfred survived it would be a miracle. If I died, I would die happy in the knowledge of his love, and that together we had contributed our mite towards the salvation of our civilisation.

There was yet another side to the work I was doing. Underground war often breeds a race of professional mercenaries, who love war and can only live in an atmosphere of violence. To lead armed bands of hungry, desperate men, each eager for revenge against his own political enemies, was a nightmare that sometimes haunted me. Up to now, I had undertaken with Charney Bassett and my friends in the Armée Secrète precise and definite tasks with which I was in complete agreement, and none less than my present mission. But to take on a general mission of indefinite scope might be a very different matter, for I had carried over from my pacifist days the unalterable belief that ends do not justify means. I had not yet spilt human blood, and if I had to, then I would do so impersonally and in obedience to orders, and not in cold blood or as the tool of the Outfit or my political masters in London. It was far better to lead an ordinary life in an extraordinary manner, and to serve an ideal amid the humdrum surroundings of everyday life.

But the bloom of our youth — Manfred's and mine — had gone, and the hard path of duty faced us both. Certain people like Manfred are intended as beacons to the world, reminding us of the external existence of those ideals which call men out against all reason and self-interest. If there ever comes a time when the race of such as he die out or fall asleep, then humanity will sink into perpetual despair. In war one witnesses the phenomenon of ordinary men and women raised up to the heights of sublime heroism and self-sacrifice. The only happy man is he who serves some ideal other than his own self-interest. All ambitious men who have purely personal objectives will never be satisfied but will only realise more and more the futility of their ambitions. While in contrast, the man who seeks sacrifice and service feels more deeply within himself that glow of true happiness. There was so much in my small world to love that it would take for ever to complete, and yet at the end of it all, to die for one's fellow men would be the greatest blessing of all. Those who fall in war are thereby privileged to make that supreme act of self-sacrifice. They are the truly fortunate, for those who return to the humdrum world have the harder task to bear, being haunted by the memory of those who have paid the sacrifice.

I lay in the dark thinking of Manfred asleep in France, oblivious of the danger I was now facing. Yet I did not grudge him the warmth of his bed, but only hoped that if my mission was successful, he and his friends would be able to complete it, and rid the world of bloody Hitler and his gang. I thought, too, of Jack, who had risked his life in the last war for Stanley, who was now on his deathbed. I knew that Jack wished me well, and I thought how strange it would be if I could look into the future and see what it held for all three of us, lying there in the darkness of the fuselage. And then again the spirit faltered, and I wished I were returning home.

I had been told that I would be landing near Le Bugue, and because of the terrain thereabouts, I would have to jump from a greater height than usual. In the course of the flight a strong wind had got up, and almost at once I lost sight of the reception committee's lights. When at last I touched down in a field, and my parachute was billowing on the ground beside me, I realised that I hadn't any idea where I was. During my descent, I had seen in the distance a river, which I took to be the Vézère or the Dordogne, and a railway line running along its southern bank. When I had buried my parachute and taken stock of the situation, I decided to make for the railway line and the nearest station, where I would discover how far I was from Jovelles.

I had landed in a country of small, twisting valleys and deep forest, which made it extremely difficult to keep going in one direction for more than a few hundred yards at a time. After walking for about two hours, it began to get light and at last I found myself in a station yard where a train was waiting in a siding with its engine getting up steam. I thought, mistakenly as it turned out, that I was at Lalinde or Le Bugue, but as the train seemed to be pointing in the general direction I wanted to take, I got on board, locked myself in the loo and went to sleep.

Many hours later I woke to find the train standing outside a station in the middle of wooded countryside. Almost at once it began to move, and not long after stopped at Negrondes, even farther from my destination than when I had landed, but not more than thirty miles from Jovelles. It was a Sunday, and there was not a soul to be seen in the village. The church seemed a good place to hide, and I took part in no fewer than four services that day, before slipping out quietly after dark.

I arrived on foot the following morning, got into the château by the secret entry beneath the chapel and climbed up to the pepperpot tower where I found Charney and Jacques anxiously waiting for me. Their welcome was warm and betrayed their relief at my delayed arrival.

* * *

Only Charney Bassett and three trusted maquisards had known anything about my meeting with Manfred and brief return to England. I had asked while I was in London how the fuses were to be given to Manfred, and had suggested a second meeting with him for this purpose. This had not been well received. I was told that I had already taken a very serious risk in meeting him at all, and it was pointed out to me, not without reason, that the SS would almost certainly have got to hear of his mysterious three-hour disappearance. With this I had to agree, for Manfred himself had told me that the SS, in the shape of Hans and Kurt, were breathing down his neck, waiting for an excuse to denounce him.

On the other hand, the German army was a fraternity, and one of the features of the military resistance to Hitler, he had told me, was that any particular anti-Nazi army officer could talk to another pro-Nazi officer with considerable frankness in the almost certain knowledge that he would not be betrayed. I only hoped that the officers under his command were such as these. However, I pointed out to my superiors that Manfred had been very discreet; he had confessed that I was the first person to whom he had felt able to unburden himself frankly in the certain knowledge that what he had told me would never reach the ears of the Gestapo.

I was asked what reason I had for believing that Manfred, or one of his fellow army conspirators, would go to the length of killing Hitler. I had replied that I knew Manfred and his family very well, and that although assassination was a long way beyond obedience to the sixth commandment, he and those Germans who thought like him owed no loyalty to a tyrant. Hitler's opponents had the right and the duty to follow the dictates of their own consciences. Their duty to their country was to rescue it from utter collapse, and so save millions of lives. Resistance was self-help and had nothing to do with Allied war aims and plans. Murder was indeed an ignoble word, but the assassination of Hitler could be equated with duty.

'I am lucky in one sense,' Manfred had said to me, 'in that I can see only one point of view where the Nazis are concerned. I have been brought up to believe in the value of principles and ideals, and in the individuality of the human being. The Nazis constitute the sort of mass movement which I distrust automatically. I loathe their cant and their hysteria. Hitler's dictatorship has been an assault on society and on religion, and has been designed deliberately to surrender the citizen to the state.'

In the end I had convinced my superiors of Manfred's sincerity, and they had agreed to my proposal to supply him with silent fuses for an attempt on Hitler's life. But they had categorically forbidden me to hand them to him personally. I was instructed to give Charney a letter on my return to France, in which he was deputed to supply the fuses by whatever means he thought fit. So, on my return to Jovelles, we began to plan how this should be done.

It was, of course, quite out of the question for Charney or Michel, or any member of our *réseau* to make personal contact with Manfred. In fact, the only people who could, and whom we could trust, were Hélène and Mme de Lusignac. Neither of these ladies knew of my meeting with Manfred; all they *did* know was that he had been at school with me, but this was enough. Furthermore, Hélène and her aunt had to meet him from time to time to discuss problems connected with his troops, who were occupying part of their château. Charney, however, was reluctant to place Hélène and her aunt at risk, for should the SS get to know that Manfred had received the fuses from them, they would certainly be arrested and shot. On the other hand, Manfred would be expecting either to receive them from me, or, if I were not able to hand them to him, then to receive some sign that I had failed to get permission to let him have them. From his point of view, this news would be most likely to come from Hélène Loreau or Mme de Lusignac, with whom he had already established a relationship.

Nearly three weeks had elapsed since our meeting, and time was running out. Manfred had told me he expected to be moved at any time, so it was vital to get the fuses to him without delay. In the end, it was agreed that I should leave Jovelles at once and Charney would make up a packet of three fuses, including in it explicit instructions on how to use them, and give this to Hélène. She was to hand the package personally and privately to Manfred at the earliest opportunity.

Two days after I had left Jovelles, I heard that this part of my mission had been successfully accomplished, and that Manfred had told Hélène he had been posted to Paris, and would be leaving as soon as his relief had arrived. We sat back to await events.

VIII

The winter of 1943-44 was a period of frustration and waiting. The Armée Secrète continued to receive periodical parachutages of weapons and explosives, but our men became restive, and we found it difficult to keep up their spirits and prevent them going off to attack the occupying forces on their own. But January 1944 marked the beginning of a campaign against the German communication system in preparation for the coming invasion.

The lines from Bergerac to Sarlat and from Cahors to Périgueux crossed at Le Buisson and were within the field of my new *réseau*'s operations. We attacked them practically every day at one point or another. Late in March, we were told to attack a train of petrol tankers parked in the railway sidings at Le Buisson.

Michel and I set out from our safe house in the woods above Cadouin late one afternoon on our bicycles. Michel was in an ebullient mood, and rushed down the hill towards Le Buisson without touching his brakes, whistling and singing all the way. I couldn't help being cheered by his high spirits. It was a lovely spring day, but there were clouds piling up in the west, and there would be a storm that night. All the better: a good rainstorm would be perfect for what we had to do. There was a small bistro at the far side of the town, where I knew we could eat and pass the time till the other members of the detachment joined us later in the evening. Anyway, you ate well *chez* M. Barbier.

Michel was still singing away:

'Sur la route qui va, qui va
Et qui ne finit pas...'

'What are you going to do after the war?' I asked casually.

'A lawyer, I hope. What are you going to do?'

'I don't know. I've not decided. I'll probably finish my degree at...'

The words died on my lips as though my throat had sucked them back into my lungs. There was a German soldier in the wood on our left. He was only a yard inside the bushes. He didn't seem to be paying any attention to us. We cycled on for two or three yards, breasting a long slope, then both of us saw what lay about three hundred yards ahead by the level crossing — several German lorries waiting to cross the railway line, and a Gestapo man examining the papers of a civilian, who had been riding his bicycle not far ahead of us.

'We must turn back,' we both said simultaneously.

We swung round as quickly as we could and pedalled off furiously in the direction we had come. As we turned, one of the Germans spotted us and yelled: 'Terroristen!'

We had put five or six hundred yards between us and our pursuers. We threw our bicycles over a small cliff into a stream, and ran on for another half mile or so. Then we stopped to regain our breath. Not far from where we were was a small cliff in which I could see the entrance to a tiny cave. We dashed inside and sat down weak with exhaustion, to take stock of our situation.

It was still light, but the sun had set and the light was fading fast. We were not due to meet the other members of our detachment for another four or five hours. They would go to M. Barbier's bistro to wait for us there, for they had precise instructions not to attack the petrol tankers until Michel and I arrived. We came to the conclusion that the Germans would call the search off after dark, and in the meantime search for us in the direction of Cadouin, rather than in the direction of Le Buisson, which had been our destination. We reckoned we had probably thrown them off our scent, but that they would resume the search when they had summoned up reinforcements.

I thought that the last thing they would expect us to do would be return to the place where they had so nearly caught us. After dark it would be almost impossible to recognise us, for they had only caught a fleeting glimpse of us. So we decided to split up. Michel would go to Le Buisson from the direction of Fontenelle, and I would make a longer detour and approach it from the direction of the road to Alles. We would meet at the railway workshop about two o'clock, after I had contacted our comrades at Barbier's bistro, which I reckoned I could reach in about an hour and a half, provided I avoided our pursuers.

Our plan worked perfectly. We got to the workshop and were let in by the watchman who was expecting us, and rapidly posted ourselves at strategic points around it and around the sidings. The petrol train was standing some way out of the station near the workshop. It was not difficult to approach the last three tankers since they were hidden from the road by the workshop and some other wagons. It was a simple matter to dash out, plant the explosive between two tankers, set the fuse and escape before they blew up, setting, we hoped, all the other tankers on fire.

Michel volunteered for this dangerous job, while the rest of us kept watch. It was now nearly three o'clock in the morning. There were no signs of the Germans. I came to the conclusion, wrongly as it turned out, that they had all gone after us in the direction of Cadouin and Siorac, but just as Michel had fixed the explosive and set the time fuses, a patrol came to make a snap inspection of the sidings. They saw him as he ran back towards the workshop and opened fire, killing him instantly. While the battle was raging, the two tankers blew up setting all the others alight. By now a much larger enemy force could be heard approaching, and I ordered our men to retreat as fast as they could. Luckily we were able to take Michel's body with us, though it severely hindered our progress, and we hid it in the cellar of Barbier's bistro until it was possible to bury him with full military honours a few days later.

Although I was sad to have lost a friend and comrade in Michel

Loreau, his death did not affect me profoundly. Ever since Hawkspur days a barrier had grown up between us, and I felt that he had been keeping me at arm's length. This I found perfectly understandable, especially as there was a paramount need to avoid any sort of emotional entanglement in the face of the work we were doing. Though I had been much attracted to him at school, I looked back on my adolescent infatuation for him with some embarrassment. My great love for Manfred had shown me how different these attachments were, for now I had matured and was able to distinguish between adolescent calf-love and true adoration.

As ill luck would have it, one of the railwaymen, who came from Montabourlet, had recognised Michel. Under torture he told his SS captors that he was the son of Mme Loreau and the nephew of Mme de Lusignac. His interrogator was none other than Kurt von Bahlenburg, and it was not long before a force of SS under his command came to Jovelles, and demanded to search Mme de Lusignac's part of the château. Manfred's protests were brusquely swept aside, for Kurt, with the rank of Oberführer, the equivalent of a brigadier in the army, was much senior to him. The SS burst into the house and ransacked it.

Before they reached Mme de Lusignac's bathroom, from which the secret stairway led up to the turret in which Charney was hiding, she, with great presence of mind, undressed, locked the door and got into her bath in the mistaken belief that, confronted with a naked old lady, the SS men would desist from making too close an inspection of the bathroom. Her faith in the chivalry of men like Kurt was sadly misplaced, for, ignoring her protests, they battered down the door, stormed inside and seized her, naked and wet as she was, beat her up, and shot her. They then started to break down the shelves that concealed the hidden door, found it and stormed into the turret, dragged Charney out and shot him in the courtyard in front of Hélène, while Manfred was forced to look on helplessly. They bundled Hélène into a truck and took her off to prison, leaving instructions for Manfred to have his men garrison the whole building and dispose of the bodies.

Although she was tortured under interrogation, Hélène survived, and was freed by the maquis some weeks later. Very soon after this incident, Manfred was transferred to the Reserve Army in Berlin — to the staff of Claus von Stauffenberg.

The day after Mme de Lusignac and Charney Bassett were shot, Hans Streiter sent Kurt von Bahlenburg with another SS unit to make a more thorough search for maquisards at Montabourlet and in the surrounding villages. The news of the raid on Jovelles gave warning to those with most to fear to hide in the woods, so when the SS arrived with fixed bayonets, they found only women and children together with a few old men. They arrested the mayor, who denied all knowledge of the 'terrorists', but Kurt, who conducted the interrogation, did not believe him. All the same he let him go, confident he would lead him and his SS men to the maquisards' hide-out. That night, the SS seized all the cars they could find, breaking down garage and barn doors, and beating up the owners if they protested. They broke into several houses, ousting the occupants from their beds, and demanding rooms for themselves.

The next day, a workman scything grass on the roadside between La Rochebeaucourt and Montabourlet was shot dead, and his brother-in-law and another young man were arrested and beaten up in an attempt to make them reveal the whereabouts of the maquisards. They both died of their injuries without revealing anything. About midday, the SS occupied the whole of the Château de Jovelles, posting guards in the courtyard and on all the approach roads. As the peasants began walking home from their fields for the midday meal, the SS opened fire on them, killing more than a dozen men and women. They then set fire to the château, though owing to a lucky change in the direction of the wind, only a comparatively small part of it was destroyed, but not before the bulk of the art treasures housed in it had been reduced to cinders.

After the skirmish at Le Buisson I dashed out of the railway sidings and made for the woods, and took the road south leading to Montferrand. A few miles farther on I came to a pond by the roadside. Taking advantage of the cover surrounding it, I stripped down to the skin and cleaned myself with soap, a scrubbing-brush, and water fetched from the pool in my water-bottle. When I had got the mud and dirt off my clothes I spread them out and scrubbed myself all over. Then I put them on wet, ate some chocolate, and drank the water from the pool strained through my handkerchief into my hand. When I had shaved, the sun had risen warm above the trees, and I felt a new man. Two hours later I arrived at Montferrand, where I was welcomed by one of the maquisards from my *réseau*. Here I holed up for a week until I was able to make contact with our wireless operator, who told me that he had no news from Charney, and feared that he might have been killed or captured — the full story of the massacre at Montabourlet and Jovelles did not reach this part of Périgord until later. I told him about Michel's death and the successful attack at Le Buisson, and asked him to report it to London as soon as possible.

* * *

After the attack on the petrol train at Le Buisson and the deaths of Michel and Charney, I began to fear that my own luck was running out. It had been made clear when we joined the Outfit that we would not be expected to continue serving in France against our will, and that no one would think any the worse of us if we decided we'd had enough. By the early summer of 1944, I had had two spells of service in France, and spent more than eighteen months with the maquis. With the approaching invasion, the resistance groups we had built up all across France were beginning to fulfil their purpose with stepped-up attacks on German lines of communication. The Armée Secrète was now supplied with French officers, and the time had come for the French to compass their own deliverance with less help from us. So I applied for home leave, and a transfer to a job in England. The Outfit was still training men and women for sabotage work in occupied Europe, and after two weeks' leave, I was posted to the Manor as a conducting officer.

I had spent the first week of my leave with my mother. It was not a success. I was nervy and irritable; suffering, no doubt, from a severe reaction to the tension of the past months in France. She, of course, had no idea why I should be in this mood, for she assumed that I had been no farther from home than, perhaps, the north of Scotland, where she knew I had been in the early stages of my army career. When people asked where I had been, I let it be assumed that it was in the highlands or islands.

I had planned to spend the second week of my leave with my father in Yorkshire, but the day before I was due to go there, we had a telegram telling us that he and my stepmother had been killed in an air raid.

My father's death came as a bitter blow, for I was becoming very fond of him, and was looking forward to the benefit of his sound advice and help in the difficult period of adjustment to civilian life, which we knew could not now be much longer delayed. After the funeral, I returned to duty at the Manor, and almost at once, Jack Cuttlance asked me if I would like to be billeted with him. Stanley had died during my last tour of duty in France, and

Jack had moved into the Manor rather than continue living alone in the cottage. As we were now working together, our lords and masters saw no objection to our moving in together, for this relieved the pressure on accommodation in the Manor itself.

These were difficult weeks of adaptation to the drab and dreary life of wartime Britain. Both Jack and I were depressed by our respective losses, but in addition, I was worrying all the time about Manfred. The attack on Jovelles, and his posting immediately afterwards, were sinister, for I could not doubt that Hans or Kurt were in some way responsible for it.

Less than two months after my return, I awoke one morning to hear the BBC broadcast the news of Claus von Stauffenberg's unsuccessful attempt on Hitler's life.

'There is nobody in Germany who does not learn with a feeling of deep gratitude that the Führer has escaped uninjured the attempt on his life,' began the official Nazi announcement quoted in the *Times* on July 21st, 1944. 'The enemy thought to attain by a murderous attempt what he cannot do by honest arms. As on several occasions before in the course of the last few years, the German nation can thank Providence for preserving the Führer so that he may accomplish his great task with which he has been charged by Fate. The attempt which has failed must be a warning to every German to redouble his war effort.'

Hitler's broadcast to the German nation that evening was quoted in full.

'Suddenly, at a moment when the German army is engaged in a bitter struggle,' he screamed, 'a small group emerged in Germany, just as in Italy, in the belief that they could repeat the 1918 stab in the back. But this time they have made a bad mistake.' He threatened the ruthless extermination of this 'miniature group of criminal elements'; he demanded to know how it were possible that, out of the millions of brave men sacrificing their lives at the front, 'at home a small, filthy, ambitious, self-seeking group could seek to sow the seeds of despair', and more in this vein.

Gradually, as the days went by, more news trickled out of Germany. The English papers reported on July 22nd that Claus had placed the bomb, which had failed to kill Hitler, and that he had been summarily shot the next day. 'Nothing is known about the future plans which the conspirators had in mind — whether to fight on under more prudent and abler generalship or whether to approach the Allies for armistice terms,' Reuter reported. The Nazis said that Claus was the 'instrument of a small ambitious clique whose connection with an enemy Power was established a few hours after the attempt, when documents and other incriminating evidence was discovered. An interrogation of the principals of the plot shortly before they were shot further corroborates this evidence.'

This made depressing reading indeed. A *Times* leading article stated: 'It need hardly be said that the rivals for Hitler's power are no friends of the Allies. Generals who set themselves up as pretenders claiming to supplant the Nazis do so as champions not of liberty but of militarism, which they believe they are better able to further, or to rescue, than the upstart politicians of the Party.'

I was quite sure that the *Times* leader writer had completely misunderstood the idealism that animated the conspirators, for I was certain that what Manfred had told me at Montabourlet was far nearer the truth than this biased English view.

Two days later, the *Times* quoted a vitriolic attack on the conspirators by Robert Ley, the leader of the German Labour Front: 'I have received detailed information on how the attempt was made,' he said in a speech to munitions workers. 'A mine of the heaviest type, imported from Britain, was hidden. The Jews of Moscow ordered it, and German counts and noblemen threw it. Swine, blue-blooded swine, fools and idiots, criminals and murderers, reactionaries that is what they are. Criminals paid by the Jews.'

Next came the news that General Stülpnagel had been seriously injured by a 'terrorist attack' while travelling in eastern France. The announcement went on to call him a 'prominent Nazi Jew-baiter, who signed an order in 1942 stating that all Jews over the age of six must wear the six-pointed star of David bearing the word "Juif" on it.'

These reports did not square with what I knew to be the truth, but when Goebbels screamed that the attempt was committed with 'explosives made in Britain' and that 'the culprit, Claus von Stauffenberg, was entangled with the British aristocracy', I knew that Manfred's fate was sealed, and that he must have been tortured, for who else knew how the fuses had reached the conspirators?

All this depressed me profoundly. I began to feel responsible for Manfred's fate. I could not hope that he had escaped arrest, but the names of only the most prominent conspirators were reported. I did not have long to wait before I knew the worst.

Soon after I returned to England, I phoned Count Aldqvist at the Swedish Embassy to ask if Clara had a letter for me. I had written to her on my brief return earlier in the year to thank her for her letter, to tell her that I had met 'our friend' and that he had recovered from his wounds. I realised this would puzzle her, for she would have had no means of knowing how or where Manfred and I had met. I now wrote to tell her that I was back in England should she have any more news to send me. After several months, her uncle phoned to tell me that he had a letter for me, and invited me to lunch at the embassy. Under the agreement we had made, I insisted that he opened any letter to me from Clara, and that he read it to satisfy himself that it contained nothing subversive. His invitation to lunch surprised me, for our previous meetings had been purely formal, and had lasted no longer than it took to hand over and read the letters. I went, therefore, with a sense of foreboding, afraid that Clara had sent me bad news.

Her letter was very short, but she enclosed one addressed to me from Manfred. How he had managed to get it to the Swedish embassy in Berlin was a mystery for it had been written after his arrest and imprisonment, and must have been smuggled out. It was not very long.

'They have spared no effort to make us look contemptible traitors,' he wrote. 'They tortured us and tried to make us confess. Nazis and Christians share one thing only: both want to possess the whole being, body and soul. We have chosen the right path in our search for the preservation and renewal of all that is best in Germany and the German people. I believe that the Christian ethic will eventually emerge triumphant, and that one day right and justice will prevail. But, dear Tony, they will only prevail if England and America treat Germany with fairness and compassion when this war is over. If the Allies, including Russia, impose upon us a vindictive treaty like the one imposed on us in 1919, the year you and I were born, there will be another war between us in twenty years' time. German guilt does exist: it is a reality. It cannot be shovelled off on to the Nazis. We have all been guilty of failure to understand, of wilful blindness, of servile, misguided obedience, of petty compromises, of exaggerated caution and of shirking logical conclusions. But we have been punished enough.

'When you receive this, Tony, I shall be dead. We did what we did to prove to the world, and to future generations, that we dared to take a decisive step and to hazard our lives upon it. Unfortunately it was a step that failed to achieve what we had set out to do, but compared to this step, nothing else matters.

'I still love you, and thank you from the bottom of my heart for what you were able to do to help our cause. I thank you for your understanding and for your friendship. Du bist schon immer mein liebster Freund bis in alle Ewigkeit.'

Manfred was brought to trial in August along with the other conspirators. He had been imprisoned in solitary confinement and in chains. His cell door was left open, and the light left on all day and all night. He was given only a third of the normal rations, and as winter set in he suffered intensely from the cold. He was forced to scrub the prison floor on the express orders of Obersturmbann-führer Hans Streiter, and supplied with a toothbrush for the purpose. Instructions were given to the warders to kick him whenever they found he had left part of the floor unscrubbed.

In a perverse concession to the notion that justice should be seen to have been done, Hitler ordered that the trial of the leading conspirators should be filmed. Early in February 1945, Manfred was taken to the Plotzensee prison in Berlin, where he was confronted by Kurt von Bahlenburg, who had been appointed by Hans Streiter to be his gaoler until the death sentence was carried out. On the day of his execution, Kurt dismissed the executioner, telling him that he would be personally responsible for Manfred's death. Two warders took him to the prison yard, stood him on a block of wood, placed a wire noose round his neck, and attached it to a meat hook slung from a bracket fixed to the prison wall. Hans then dismissed the guards and the executioner, while Kurt set up a movie camera on a tripod to record the proceedings. When he was ready, Hans went up to Manfred, spat in his face, and kicked the block away from under his feet. It had been a few inches too low, so that instead of dropping to an instant death, he was slowly strangled as the wire cut through his neck.

Epilogue

After I heard of Manfred's frightful death, I continued as if nothing had happened. I attended lectures, wrote reports, went on drinking with my colleagues and the men on the training course. I read the papers, discussed the war news, and tried to pretend that my life hadn't changed. At first I was rather proud of my self-control — in any case, I knew no one except Jack who might begin to understand what Manfred's loss meant to me. But the core of my agony was loneliness. The pain might pass — would pass in time, but meanwhile the desolation remained.

Manfred took to visiting me in dreams, calling out to me as he slowly strangled to death, and I would find myself trying to reach him across the bleak concrete of the prison yard; but the harder I struggled towards him, the more tightly unseen hands held me back. If I could only touch him; if I could lift his tortured body and untie the wiry noose; if I could only hold him in my arms and comfort him; and I would wake up with the perspiration soaking me, and the sound of my own voice crying out in tormented frustration. After a while to regain my composure, I would fall again into a fitful sleep, and see him in all his resplendent beauty as I had known him in Austria. As he came towards me, his arms outstretched and smiling in welcome, his whole form dissolved into a twisted, writhing, shapeless plasma. His eyes and mouth were open, and his tongue was hanging out; unable to scream out in his pain, he yet somehow conveyed to me those words of love and gratitude with which he had ended his letter.

And I? I saw myself bow down in shame before him, and heard myself whispering: 'It is I who owe you so much. It is I who am in your debt because of your fortitude and your sacrifice.'

Once I dreamt that death embraced us both, and that I, too, had died on the meat hook with him, and I woke weeping inconsolably.

But I had to struggle on as if nothing had happened. It was this that hurt most, for it seemed to me to be a denial of the most beautiful experience of my life. For the sake of my dignity and self-respect, I had to act out the part of a carefree returned warrior, set upon making a proper start in life, after my long-postponed beginning in 1938.

Englishmen, particularly public-school Englishmen, don't cry. It wasn't done — still isn't. Today when your lover dies, usually from AIDS, you hide your grief as best you can. 'He'll get over it,' friends say to one another; or 'There's always another guy.' They may be right for all I know. So what? That's how it is today, but not then. Then, dear God, it was the utter devastation and aloneness, the permanent blank, where once there had been laughter and hope, even when we had met in the improbable and dangerous circumstances of wartime France. Hope of future love and laughter. But now half of me had died, and what was left just ached, but went on behaving as if nothing had happened.

The only person who remotely understood was Jack, for he, too, had suffered the loss of his lifelong friend. But when we found ourselves alone together in the cottage after a hard day's work at the Manor, we talked only of insignificant matters, for both of us wanted to avoid any allusion to our losses, to the past or the future. The continual restraint in what we said, our constant and careful avoidance of everything that might lead to a mention of their names, brought before me with still greater poignancy what we were both feeling.

But unmitigated grief is as impossible as unmitigated happiness. It was easier for me than for Jack, for I had my job to do, and my future to think about, whereas his job, as the war neared its end, became more and more routine, and when eventually it did end, he would have enough money on which to retire, or, if he wished, he could pick up the broken threads of his business, and re-establish it. Life would not stand still for either of us; we had to go on living. Hard as it was to emerge from that secluded realm of contemplation in which we had been living till now, the cares of everyday life demanded our attention, and against our will we gave ourselves up to them. At first we had wanted nothing so much as to be left alone, but this solitude tortured and exhausted us, though it was just what we needed. As soon as either of us interrupted it, we would pretend to be busily engaged in something very important, but in reality, all we wanted was for the one who had intruded to leave us in peace.

* * *

The war ended at last. The Outfit offered those of us who were still young and who had no careers to return to, jobs, if not for life, for at least the foreseeable future. Jack, who was by now in his mid forties, decided after all to try and rescue what remained of his business, but I had to think of how to occupy the next fifty years of my life. There was no further need for me to continue lodging in his house, but I was strangely disinclined to leave. Where should I go? Ever since the disastrous leave after my first tour of duty in France, I could not bear the thought of returning to live with my mother, for our relationship had been irredeemably shattered. My father's unexpected death had derprived me of the support I was now going to need as I set out on a lifetime's career. The only person I could turn to for sympathy and understanding was Jack.

'Why do you feel you should go back and live with her?' he asked when I spoke of my dilemma.

'If I don't, I'll have to find somewhere else — possibly buy a place and live on my own.'

'What's wrong with staying on here?'

Jack said this as if it were a plain statement of the obvious. I looked at him and said, 'That's very kind of you, but why should I put you to the trouble of having me around all the time?'

'You won't be around all the time if you're job-hunting.'

Not taking him seriously, I said, 'Well it's very good of you; I'll think about it.'

Six weeks after I was demobbed, I accepted his invitation to stay at his cottage until it was time for me to return to Cambridge to take up my studies once more.

During those final months of the war, when I was fulfilling my duties as a conducting officer, I had tried to recapture the enthusiasm I had experienced when first I joined the Outfit, and for a few days — a week or two, perhaps — I thought I had exorcised the devils of sorrow and sex. I swore to myself that I would get drunk as often as possible, and stupefy myself into impotency.

This programme did not go unnoticed by Jack for long. My drunken bouts increased in number and degree, until one day, when I returned to the cottage very drunk, he said, apropos of nothing: 'You're not one of those young men who suffer from guilt, are you? Did you regard your relationship with Manfred and mine with Stanley as immoral?'

Taken aback by the bluntness of his remark, I sobered up instantly, blushed and made some flippant, irrelevant remark, and left it at that. That had been many months ago, and I had not given his question another thought. But I had thought much about his invitation to go and live with him.

It was a cold Friday evening, and I had lit the fire when I got back from the Manor. Jack was due down from London for the weekend, and I had cooked a meal, awaiting his return. My mind was on the report I would have to write about my wartime missions to France for inclusion in the Outfit's war diary. It was my last military assignment, though I was still on my three-month long demob leave. With my gratuity and the money my father had left me, I had enough to return to Cambridge to take my interrupted degree. I would then go to an agricultural college to learn farming, a career I then favoured as being the complete antithesis of what I had been doing during the war. Over supper, I must have seemed preoccupied, and so did Jack, for he, too, was silent, lost in his own thoughts.

Later that evening, when we had cleared the dishes and washed up, I found myself sitting on a low stool in front of the fire by Jack's big, leather wingchair, looking into the flames, watching the sparks fly up the broad, open chimney. We were listening to a concert on the radio, when Jack lent forward and began to stroke my hair. It was the first time anyone had done that since Manfred when we met in France. I lent back till my cheek brushed against his leg, feeling the warmth of it strike through.

I was under no illusion now. I was certain that he loved me, and that I loved him in return. Not as I had loved Manfred; I could never love anyone as I had loved him, but as a friend, a tender father-like lover. I understood, too, that though Jack certainly loved me, and had done for longer than I realised, it was not as he had loved Stanley. That love, like mine for Manfred, could never be recreated. And yet, our love was in no sense a second-best. It was just different from those other loves, but none the less genuine.

Why, I asked myself, should I slink through life furtively afraid and burdened with a sense of guilt and sin? I had been brought up to believe that a relationship such as mine with Manfred should not include the physical. True, we had had scant opportunity to consummate our love, but I could see nothing wrong in what we had done. If both of us wanted a physical relationship — and we certainly did — then yes, our love should encompass it. What we had done, we had done because we were born to use all the fragments of our lives, spiritual, emotional and physical. Circumstances alone had prevented Manfred and me living the rest of our lives together as Jack and Stanley had lived theirs.

While he stroked my hair, I poured all these thoughts out in a torrent of half-articulated words, thankful, at last, to be able to unburden myself.

'I need hardly tell you, I'm sure that Stanley and I never considered our relationship as anything other than natural and moral for us,' Jack said to reassure me. I turned to look at him, and he smiled down at me: 'That's why I have never made any sexual approach to you, my dear. I could see that you weren't ready for it. It's only now that I feel free to speak so openly to you. I also happen to believe in God, and that makes me uneasy to have sex with someone much younger than myself. My moral scruples would prevent me corrupting (if that's the right word) someone who was too young to know for sure what he was. But I'm not even sure that having sex with someone much younger than oneself, provided it is undertaken willingly and without coercion, is corruption.

'I knew that you weren't ready to have sex with me when we were in Northumberland in IVAC, though we had plenty of opportunity, and I found you extremely attractive!'

I turned to him and smiled: 'Jack, I love you,' I said. 'Not as I loved Manfred, but I love you and want to share your life.'

He bent down and kissed me. 'Tony, I love you so much. I love you perhaps too much.'

'Why too much?' I asked.

'Why too much? Well, what d'you think? What d'you feel in your heart of hearts?'

'I'm sure you love me as I love you.'

He was silent a while. 'I'm glad,' he said, taking my hand and kissing it.

I felt happy and deeply moved. He pressed my hand and let it go. 'Love? What is love?' he mused. 'Love hinders death,' he went on. 'Love is life. Anything at all that I understand I understand only because I love. Everything exists; everything is only because I love. All is bound up in love alone. Love is God, and to die means that a tiny particle of love will return to the universal and eternal source.'

We got up. I put the guard in front of the fire, and together we went to his room.

FINIS

Gay Men's Press books can be ordered from any bookshop in the UK, North America and Australia, and from specialised book-shops elsewhere.

If you prefer to order by mail, please send cheque or postal order payable to *Book Works* for the full retail price plus £2.00 post-age and packing to:

Book Works (Dept. B), PO Box 3821, London N5 1UY
phone/fax: (0171) 609 3427

For payment by Access/Eurocard/Mastercard/American Express/ Visa, please give number, expiry date and signature.

Name and address in block letters please:

Name
_____

Address
_____

_____

_____